TOTAL
SYSTEMS

EDITED BY

ALAN D. MEACHAM and VAN B. THOMPSON

Enoch J. Haga and Maurice F. Ronayne, Coordinating Editors

© 1962 American Data Processing, Inc.
All rights reserved.
Library of Congress Catalog Number: 62-14778
First Edition

Second Printing 1963
Third Printing 1964
Fourth Printing 1965

PUBLISHED BY AMERICAN DATA PROCESSING, INC.
4TH FLOOR BOOK BLDG. • DETROIT, MICHIGAN 48226

Printed in U.S.A.

Contents

THE CONCEPT OF TOTAL SYSTEMS

PLANNING TOTAL SYSTEMS

IMPLEMENTING TOTAL SYSTEMS

CASE HISTORIES

Preface

WITH THIS BOOK American Data Processing, Inc., launches one of its most ambitious editorial projects: the Data Processing Library Series. It is the intention of the Editors of the Series to provide a library of basic reference books, each covering in detail an important data processing subject. All of these books are directed primarily to management personnel in organizations employing or considering electronic data processing systems. The Series should thus be of use, also, to the serious academic researcher into this most dynamic field.

That the field of electronic data processing is dynamic is attested to by the choice of TOTAL SYSTEMS as the first book in the Library Series, and by its contents. There are few subjects that excite the interest of knowledgeable management personnel in business and government to a greater degree than the idea of a totally automated, fully responsive, truly all-encompassing information system embodying the collection, storage and processing of data and the reporting of significant information on an as-needed basis. With the possible exception of some operational military systems, which are not considered in this book, we do not believe any organization exists anywhere which has achieved this ultimate systems goal. But one, a few, or many may do so at any time. If they do, they will undoubtedly follow some of the approaches outlined in this volume.

In setting out to collect the most authoritative opinion available about the total systems idea, the Editors sought out well known systems experts and asked for their recommendations. The lists of authorities thus compiled bore a striking but not surprising resemblance to one another. Those who are at the forefront of total systems development know their peers. They are not misled by the vast and somewhat appalling array of recently published material dealing casually or directly with total systems but saying nothing.

There are no parrots among the authors who have contributed to this book. Each has something original to offer, gained through experience and hard work. We are pleased to be able to present the writings of so many of the top level researchers in total systems development.

Much of the credit should be given to the two Coordinating Editors of TOTAL SYSTEMS, Enoch J. Haga and Maurice F. Ronayne. Mr. Haga is Senior Publications Engineer at Lockheed Missile and Space Company, Sunnyvale, California; Editor of the *SABE Data Processor,* official publication of the Society for Automation in Business Education; and Contributing Editor for the *Journal of Business Education.* His position with SABE, begun while he was Assistant Professor of Business at Stanislaus State College, California, is particularly significant in that it has given him access to much of the current academic research extant in total systems.

Maurice F. Ronayne is Digital Computer Systems Analyst with the Division of Management Assistance, U. S. Federal Power Commission, Washington, D.C. He is vice president of the Washington, D.C. chapter of the Systems and Procedures Association. Of especial interest is his recently completed project as Editor of *An Annotated Bibliography for the Systems Professional,* part of which is included in this book.

In addition to supplying articles of their own, both Coordinating Editors also made use of their knowledge of persons engaged in advanced systems studies and solicited and edited a number of the manuscripts which form the contents of TOTAL SYSTEMS. They reported a common reaction among data processing systems authorities which was also found to be universal among the authorities contacted by the Editors of this book: a desire to see publication of a realistic treatment of total systems ideas and experience.

Such a treatment is given in this book, which begins, as all definitive works must, with discussions of varying points of view about the basic concept of total systems. The authors of these first 10 articles bring into this discussion backgrounds in consulting, business, government, the military, and universities. We are again indebted to the Systems and Procedures Association for permission to include William B. Worthington's article, "Total Command, Management, and Administrative Systems," which had appeared in the proceedings of their eleventh International Systems Meeting titled *Ideas for Management*.

TOTAL SYSTEMS continues with six articles dealing directly with the planning effort required in any total systems project. Again, the authors bring varied and significant experience into their discussion. Next is a series of four articles dealing with aspects of the implementation of total systems — a most difficult subject, since so little real experience exists.

The next section of the book is a most important one. In it are case histories of five companies engaged in the quest for a total system. One is a medium sized insurance company that decided to ease into electronic data processing by replacing its punched card system with a small card input/output computer, and found itself forced into an integration of many of its procedures. Another is a manufacturer whose mathematics research group is involved in the study — and application — of automatic control over the entire manufacturing process. A third is a giant transportation company which has consistently pioneered in the use of computers and communications systems to guide and correlate its far flung operations. A fourth is a missile manufacturer now setting up integrated procedures for its widely separated divisions and their computer centers. The other is a chemical firm which has used the marketing activity as its avenue toward total systems.

The approaches of these five companies are radically different. From them may come answers to the problems still standing in the way of our systems people in their attempts to do a comprehensive job. It is our hope that this will be the case.

The Publishers

By Douglas J. Axsmith
McKinsey & Company, Inc.

A Management Look at Data Processing: Promise, Problem, and Profit

AFTER MORE THAN 10 YEARS of management experience with electronic data processing, the early enthusiastic promise of the new technology has only in small part been realized. As a matter of fact, attempts to apply new data processing approaches have in many cases generated unforeseen difficulties. As a result, in company after company the advantages that were anticipated have only recently begun to be achieved.

That such is the case should not be surprising, for on reflection it was unrealistic to expect management to be able to anticipate the difficulty of re-defining business problems in the terms required to take fullest advantage of the capabilities of the new data processing technology. At this point, substantial progress has been made not only in thus defining these fundamental problems, but also in identifying the enormous number of substantial and often subjective subordinate decisions that are required to use data processing effectively as a management decision making tool.

The growing awareness of these problems on the part of management defines on the one hand the realistic limits of what should be expected from data processing. On the other hand, it substantially expands the horizons of its capability.

Looking ahead, the challenge to management lies in extracting more and more from this increasingly potent management problem solving tool and the related information system techniques. For, while what we have learned is valid, there is much more to be learned in applying the computer to the increasing number of variables and accelerating rate of change with which every business will have to deal in this dynamic decade.

Technology, concepts and practices are developing with great speed and on many fronts to match the pace of developments in the business environment. Some of the changes have significance chiefly for the scientists who design equipment. Many concern the growing corps of specialists who design and operate complex data processing systems. But most, in some measure, affect the general business executive, whose responsibility it is to see that his company is served profitably and well by the new technology of information handling.

TRANSITIONAL STAGE FOR COMPUTER

The computer today is in a time of transition from initial acceptance to intensive exploitation by business. It would be difficult indeed to find a large corporation that neither has nor uses at least one electronic computer. It is becoming increasingly hard to find medium size and smaller corporations that do not have modest installations of their own or do not occasionally use computer service bureaus.

Those executives who adopted a wait-and-see attitude have, for the most part, liked what they have seen. Those who first thought of the computer as an expensive toy now think of it as a powerful tool. Those who called electronic data processing a fad now acknowledge it as a fact of corporate life. The computer has been accepted, but its acceptance is yet to be followed by full realization of its potential.

This is also a time of transition from the single, self-contained computer to complex electronic systems of which a computer is only one part.

In early installations, a single computer received information from a human operator, processed it and produced output that then had to be carried away by the operator. Today, however, more and more linkages are developing which make it possible to collect a wide variety of data from many points, to produce output in many forms and in many places, and to join individual computers with others to form extremely powerful and versatile systems.

A third transition is in the kind of data being processed. From early preoccupation with accounting data and record keeping, systems designers are now turning their attention to a far broader range of management information needed for effective decision making.

Finally, there is a transition in the expectations of management. Initially, most computers were installed on the strength of anticipated clerical cost reductions. There is now a shift to the broader concept of profit improvement.

This shift in no way signals a relaxation of requirements for adequate return on the substantial investment in a complex data processing system. It is simply a recognition that the return will increasingly come, not from reductions in the clerical payroll, but from better decision making and control throughout the organization.

How an executive reacts in a time of transition depends largely on his ability to distill the most important developments of the past and to discern the principal changes that lie ahead. In the case of electronic data processing, a backward look of 10 years covers its entire history, and a look 10 years ahead encompasses as much of the future as seems relevant to the types of decisions that must be made today.

THE FIRST 10 YEARS

The overwhelming characteristic of the first decade is growth. Not until April, 1951, had business data ever been fed into a computer. Not until three years later had a corporation installed a large scale unit. But from 1954, growth has occurred at an explosive rate. During the three years 1955-57, 200 large scale computers and more than 800 medium scale machines were put to use in business. Now, five years later, some 8,000 installations of various sizes are on record and the number continues to grow.

Many things have contributed to this phenomenal growth. The equipment itself has been vastly improved. And the men who design and manage computer systems have learned much from the mistakes and successes of the past 10 years.

ADVANCES IN DATA PROCESSING TECHNOLOGY

From the early 1950's, new designs in computer hardware have followed one another rapidly.

Most of the technological advances have had the effect of increasing the speed and storage capacity of computers and of substantially reducing the cost per unit of work performed. New memory devices, such as ferrite magnetic cores, have enormously increased the speed with which information can be handled within the computer.

These and other devices make it possible to go almost directly to particular addresses for particular information instead of having to plow sequentially through magnetic tape, one character at a time.

Today, highly reliable transistorized logic and arithmetical elements for computers are common, and the trend toward modular design of computers permits users to adjust a given system to their needs.

Input and output devices have also changed and improved. Input bottlenecks were broken by high speed sensing of tapes and cards. Input costs were lowered by semi-automatic collection and transfer of information from sources to computers. Magnetic ink and document reading machines, in some very important applications, did away with much key punching work.

On the output side, printing speeds increased by a factor of six to one. New methods of printing evolved. The charactron tube, for instance, assembles a whole page at a time for instantaneous photographing and later printing. Graphs and engineering drawings can now be produced directly by the computer.

Meanwhile, computer software (the codes or programs through which computers work) was going through a similar evolution. As companies programmed more engineering problems and accounting procedures to computers, they began to realize that certain formulas, accounting routines and other business processes appeared repeatedly. Rather than reprogram them many times, these companies began setting the special subprograms or subsystems aside so they could easily be reached and tossed into a larger program as needed. They began to build up libraries of such common routines.

An obvious next step, to avoid repeating work that had been done long ago, was to borrow and adapt existing subsystems from another library. This, of course, required that the material in different libraries be in the same language or be easily translatable from one company's language to another's. This was not often easy or possible, since every machine used a code of its own. But a number of cooperative libraries did gradually build up.

Equipment producers themselves assembled large libraries because they found that extensive preprogrammed subsystems were an important sales tool.

COMMON LANGUAGE SOUGHT

To make programming easier and less expensive, manufacturers also tackled the job of coding routines in English. This way, instead of writing programs in English and then coding them into machine language, programmers could give the computer instructions in English that it would recognize as commands to assemble designated routines in specified sequences. Each manufacturer's language was highly stylized and understood only by his own computer, but inevitably these various manufacturers' programs developed striking similarities.

Then the U. S. government, the world's biggest computer customer, stepped into the picture as referee. Because its hundreds of computer systems encompass so many computers of so many different types, the government has a constant giant-sized programming headache. Especially in the defense area, where it is obviously important to have computers that can transfer information back and forth between themselves, the government's need for common computer language was acute.

In May, 1959, under department of defense auspices, a number of manufacturers and users of computers met to try to achieve a common language that would make computer programs interchangeable between various types of installations. The expanding product of these efforts is COBOL (COmmon Business-Oriented Language), which, while following precise and formal rules in order to

be intelligible to the computer, looks and reads very much like English.

The ultimate savings from common language systems will be very great. This is because it costs several dollars to program and code each new instruction in a computer system, and even programs as simple as most payrolls involve tens of thousands of instructions. COBOL, plus adequate subsystems libraries, will make it possible to program complex systems that, under old techniques, would have been prohibitively expensive.

CONCENTRATION ON ACCOUNTING DATA

Some who scanned the horizons during the past 10 years saw computers revolutionizing the practice of management. But initially those who sold the machines and those who put them to work saw them primarily as a means of reducing the clerical work force.

The early uses of electronic data processing were largely an extension of tabulating systems already in use. The machines were programmed to handle routine, repetitive data processing tasks. Their own costs were to be justified by displacement of clerical personnel and reduction in the cost of accounting paper work.

These were not, of course, the only applications, but were the predominant ones. In its 1958 study of business electronics, The Controllership Foundation compiled extensive data on business uses of the computer. More than 12 times as much space was required for its listing of payroll applications as for applications in operations analysis, simulation and linear programming combined.

EARLY EXPLORATION OF ADVANCED SYSTEMS

During the 10 years just ended and especially during the last few, there have been pioneering explorations beyond handling of conventional accounting data.

Advances in computer technology and operations research techniques have reinforced each other. Much of the mathematics that applies to business problems involves far too many calculations to be handled economically by a tabulating machine or by hand. The computer made some very powerful mathematical approaches practical.

One well known development was linear

programming, which has produced guides for gasoline blending in petroleum refineries, analyses for physical distribution management and assistance on facilities planning and production scheduling problems.

At the same time the computer was making applied mathematics possible, mathematics was itself multiplying the value of the computer. For example, early computer based inventory control systems were little more than the simple accumulation of large quantities of individual transactions. With the addition of some mathematically developed decision rules, however, it became possible to process individual pieces of data in such a way as to produce inventory control guides far superior to the ordinary exercise of judgment.

Another development of far-reaching significance has been the emergence of integrated data processing. Many computers had been loaded with one task after another, each developed and processed very largely without reference to another. The result inevitably was lost time and duplication of effort.

In recent years, however, substantial efforts have been devoted to integrating the various data processing tasks into what ideally would be a single, unified system of data processing. Accomplishments in this area are relatively meager, but they have been sufficient to demonstrate the feasibility and value of much greater progress in this direction.

CHANGING ORGANIZATION FOR DATA PROCESSING

When computers first began to appear in industrial corporations, they were almost invariably placed under the care of the company's chief financial officer. The decision, although practically automatic, was usually sound. The computer was perceived as an ultra high speed development of the conventional tabulating machine. Its principal application was thought of as more rapid processing of the same data that had been prepared in the past.

There was another reason for locating computers in the financial officer's area, and that was his leading role in the feasibility study that typically preceded the installation. This study was, in most cases, chiefly concerned with drawing a comparison between the heavy expenses of the new equipment and the clerical cost reductions that it could be expected to produce. This kind of financial analysis is, of course, properly a function of the financial officer, and most of the cost elements and savings were within his own field of responsibility.

But the initial placement of the computer has not always turned out to be a permanent home. The range of computer applications has far exceeded the limits of the accounting system. The management of a computer service within a corporation has extended far beyond the technical problems of converting older methods to computers or of providing machine time for various parts of the corporation that have their own programs. And the attention of management has begun to shift from computers themselves to the integrated systems that computers make possible.

This growth of the management-information systems concept has extended the organizational impact of electronic data processing from the machine room to the board room.

In companies with extensive computer experience, several shifts in organization have typically occurred. Almost without exception, responsibility for computer-based services has risen in importance within the financial officer's organization. The establishment of a separate computer department has been only the first step. Usually the increasingly technical services required to take advantage of the rapidly growing potential in EDP have soon led to the creation of a key position near the top of the financial organization structure.

Lately, some corporations have decided that the task of designing and operating business information systems is one that deserves a top level place outside the financial organization structure. And so there is emerging a new kind of corporate staff concerned exclusively with systems and analytical methods for decision making. Management services is a name frequently used to describe this new function.

GROWING MANAGEMENT SOPHISTICATION

Good things are often oversold and sometimes solid accomplishment is dimmed by unreasonable expectations. This has certainly been the case in the first 10 years of business data processing. The earliest installations were expected to yield savings that would pay for the equipment within a period of months. The conversion of manual or tabulating methods to electronic techniques was expected to be swift and painless, for only the simplest procedures like payroll accounting were involved. The fruit turned out to be not quite ready for plucking.

A number of companies began to discover that even a simple payroll application was much more difficult than anticipated. Those who had spoken most proudly (and sometimes loudly) of the savings and efficiencies their new installations were expected to accomplish, suddenly lapsed into silence.

For the first several years, tales of trouble were quite as common and as well founded as reports of success. But these years of trial contributed greatly to management sophistication and produced a wealth of insights that will certainly accelerate exploitation of computer potential in the future. Some major lessons learned include:

1. *Finding the profit-producing applications.* The difficulties and disappointments were, almost without exception, not attributable to any limitations in hardware capability. Rather, they resulted from misuse of hardware; that is, failure to identify and cash in on the more dynamic, profit making applications.

   For example, many executives have learned that the major potential value of the computer lies in its management use, not in its replacement of clerical labor. Little benefit has been gained from merely substituting the computer for punched card equipment or other less complex office machines.

   Those who have profited most have focused on the design of applications that help to improve management decision making and control of operations.

2. *Hammering out clearly stated objectives.* In the first decade of experience with electronic data processing, managers have learned that it is not enough that technicians and executives seem to understand each other. What is required is a statement of the electronic data processing program's objectives in the form of specific operational or economic goals. Moreover, these objectives must be documented if they are not to be blurred by time or distorted by individual interpretation. Implicit in this sort of goal setting is the requirement that an audit be made periodically to determine whether the specific objectives are in fact being achieved.

3. *Recognizing the magnitude of the undertaking.* The effort and cost involved in carrying out most computer applications were typically underestimated — often quite badly.

   Managers learned, for example, that computers themselves represent only one element of the overall data processing system. Initially, the costs and systems design effort associated with data collection and data transmission were sometimes treated almost as incidentals.

   It came as a shock that creating source data and transmitting them to the processing point could be substantially more costly than the computer itself. One large electronics company found that the cost of developing and maintaining its nationwide data collection, data communication system would equal the yearly rental of three large scale computers — roughly $900,000.

   While these unpleasant facts were coming to light, the discrepancies between estimates and actuality did more to undermine management's faith in electronic data processing than did anything else. Now, experience-wise executives and systems designers are much more realistic in scheduling completion dates and estimating conversion costs.

4. *Choosing the right people.* Finally, management learned that in one important respect data processing is exactly like any other business function. The single most important determinant of success is the capacity of men who manage it.

DATA PROCESSING IN THE YEARS AHEAD

The main lines of development in data processing seem clearly indicated by events of the past 10 years. There is a sufficient time lag between technical developments and commercial application to permit rather confident forecasting of equipment advances over the next few years. And the changes in the general patterns of business usage seem now to be indicated by early but unmistakable signs.

EQUIPMENT OF THE FUTURE

There will be continued rapid advances in the design and manufacture of electronic data processing equipment, encompassing an ever widening array of both general and special purpose devices concerned with every aspect of data handling. Large computers will become larger, faster, more expensive, and more efficient per unit of work handled. Those who see only these developments will be impressed with the inevitability of super-centers for data processing. But small computers will become better and more efficient, and those who are philosophically attached to decentralization will take comfort in these developments.

Some of the most dramatic technical advances will occur in devices for getting information to and from the computer itself. The result will be the development of huge intracompany communications networks, of which some early forerunners already exist. Lockheed recently began the operation of a multimillion-dollar, 100,000-mile, nationwide communications network, which ties together its widespread locations. Sylvania's early 20,000 mile communications system was a prototype of such a network. North American Aviation pioneered in the interconnection of computers with microwave lengths when it leased from Pacific Telephone and Telegraph Company a microwave system that linked two large scale computers in California.

Frederick R. Kappel, president of American Telephone and Telegraph Company, believes that by 1970 at least half the communications volume carried by the Bell System's associated companies' leased lines will be in the form of business machine communication. Donald Powers, chairman and chief executive officer of General Telephone and Electronics Corporation, expects that within a decade business data communications in the U. S. will exceed all other communications.

FURTHER GROWTH OF INSTALLATIONS

Over the next 10 years, computer installations will change in several dimensions. First, more and more companies will employ electronic data processing of some type. It is perhaps conservative to estimate that the number of such companies will double over the next five years.

Installations will not only grow in number, but individually they will grow in size and complexity. Large scale computers will supplement or supplant medium scale computers. Single computer systems will expand into multiple computer systems. Computers themselves will be linked to more and more peripheral equipment.

Finally, corporate installations will assume much greater diversity. In the beginning, one payroll installation looked rather like another. But these systems similarities will tend to disappear. No two businesses have the same information content or the same information need. The great variety of control units and special purpose devices, and the trend toward modular design, both seem to be leading to a unique configuration for each complex data processing system.

RISING LEVEL OF APPLICATIONS

Whether these new and more complex installations make more money than they cost, and solve more problems than they create, will depend on the way they are used. The search for fruitful applications can be expected to develop along four main lines.

1. *Accounting data processing:* Although accounting data processing was the mainstay of early computer installations, the potential in this field is by no means exhausted. There are opportunities to bring other accounting tasks into the accounting fold. There are perhaps far larger opportunities to integrate separate accounting tasks so that more useful things are done with a single piece of information.

2. *Process Control:* Computers, usually highly specialized, are now used to position machine tools and to control certain industrial processes. These uses will grow substantially in number and importance as sensing and actuating devices become more generally available, and particularly as technicians and managers are able to establish decision rules to guide the computers.

3. *Decision models:* Mathematical formu-

lations for solving difficult one time problems and for simulating complex events will be much more frequently employed by managers. Several such models already exist, particularly in production and physical distribution operations. These will multiply and to them will be added models for making decisions on marketing, finance, facilities and other strategic questions.

4. *Management data processing:* By far the most extensive and important advances will take place in the development of integrated management information systems for decision making and control.

Such business intelligence systems will go far beyond the limits of classical accounting information to process and analyze a broad range of data — nonfinancial and financial — that are needed by top management to run the business. The ultimate achievement would be a system that not only encompassed all information handling requirements, but processed each piece of information instantaneously.

The ultimate is certain to prove attainable, of course, for every advance will undoubtedly reveal still greater opportunities. There will, however, be giant strides forward in providing up-to-the-minute information for better control of marketing, production and distribution, and in providing incisive analysis for longer term tactical and strategic decisions.

As computerized accounting and finance systems are tied in more closely with simulation and mathematical models, management judgment will become increasingly fact founded across the whole spectrum of corporate decisions.

"At the bottom of the decision spectrum, practically no judgment is needed: Certain basic facts produce certain specific answers. As we move up the spectrum, more and more human judgment is injected into the decisions.

"There is one common thread, however, that runs through the entire spectrum and that is the need for good,

accurate, timely information. Nor is the information at the top independent of that below.

"Just as the finished product of an assembly line is a reflection of the characteristics and interrelationships of the parts, materials and skills that went into its design and manufacture, so do the decisions of top management reflect the interrelationships and characteristics of the routine operations of the business.

"In a truly integrated management information system, the basic data inputs will be combined, changed in form, merged, consolidated and analyzed so that the information needs of every level of management are met in a timely, accurate and useful fashion, with minimal duplication of input data. The interrelationships of the various functions and operations will be so accurately reflected that every decision in the spectrum will optimize over-all company goals rather than those of any particular part or function."*

IMPACT ON MANAGEMENT

Some of the effects that new data processing systems will exert on management will be primarily continuations of changes already begun. Others will be largely or wholly new.

Organizational changes that can be foreseen will stem mainly from the broadening objectives of data processing. The computer based management information system of the future will be designed primarily to meet the needs of operating management.

Clearly, it must encompass a vast body of operating data as well as data generated by the accounting system. It must provide information for planning or decision making and not merely for record keeping. It must embrace external economic information and competitive intelligence as well as internal corporate data.

Whoever has the responsibility for the design and operation of management data processing systems must have the understanding and capability, and the status within the

*AMA Management Report Number 41, Some Organizational Effects of Integrated Information Systems, Charles Stein, Jr.

organization, that will enable him to develop and to apply a fundamental top management viewpoint to a swiftly moving, highly developed technology. We can anticipate, therefore, a growth in stature of top analytical and planning executives, reflecting their larger contribution to corporate welfare.

Along with the growth of computerized systems will come a growth in the staffs that manipulate and interpret the information flowing through a company. Because an integrated system involves constant interactions between many sections of the business, these design and study staffs will contain people with experience and understanding of many departments and phases of the business. They will be hard to find, hard to train, and sometimes hard to keep.

There are spirited arguments today about the long-term effect of advanced data processing systems on corporate centralization or decentralization. New computer system capabilities will permit certain kinds of decisions, now widely diffused, to be made more efficiently at a single point. It will be possible to make a larger quantity of information available for decision making further down in large organization structures.

Specialists have a way of thinking exclusively in terms of their own specialties. It is not surprising that computer technologists see the shape of organizations determined largely by information technology. But this does not appear to be likely, at least in the foreseeable future.

In the years ahead, general patterns of centralization or decentralization will be matters not of technical necessity, but of management decision. In fact, management's freedom to implement either philosophy will be considerably enhanced.

New data processing systems will, however, profoundly affect the content of managerial jobs, as some decision making responsibilities are redistributed. If machine tools can be better loaded by computer than by judgment, then production scheduling decisions of this sort will no longer be a regular part of the manager's job. If the distribution of product and logistics of supply can be better managed electronically than by present methods, then the jobs of men who now perform these functions will be materially changed.

But decisions of this sort are not the whole of management. Almost certainly, for every problem that the computer solves, 10 more will arise to plague the men who run industrial corporations.

Finally, one far reaching impact of management data processing involves the time span of executive decisions. Two things will happen. First, there will be increased responsiveness to internal and external change. Top executives will be aware of changes more quickly and will be in a position to react far more rapidly. Secondly, they will be able to look further into the future. Their ability to forecast more accurately and to explore alternatives with greater precision will permit longer planning and decision making.

TOP MANAGEMENT RESPONSIBILITY TODAY

In this time of transition, an executive can take six precautionary measures to be sure his company neither lags nor moves in the wrong direction.

1. He can make sure that every major move is taken against a broad and sound concept of corporate information needs. Only with an over-all plan can he be sure he is moving in the right direction. And only with an over-all plan can he protect himself against the delays and inefficiencies of piecemeal progress.

2. He can insist on planned flexibility, even though flexibility may become more difficult as it becomes more essential.

   A data processing system is the adaption of technical capabilities to the information needs of the corporation. Technical capabilities change constantly and so do information needs. The needs change as the corporation molds itself to its own environment. New organization structure, new product lines, new competitive situations, new relationships with government, new markets both domestic and international, all present different information needs.

   But the growing complexity of electronic systems and the integration of many different data processing activities tend to introduce serious rigidities. The executive's insistence on flexibility is his insurance that what was meant to be a support does not turn out to be a restraint.

3. He can insist on equipment and systems uniquely tailored to his own corporation's needs. The most effective systems are likely to be those developed by a partnership of executives and technicians. The role of the executive in this partnership is to make sure what is designed is not a technical triumph alone, but a commercial success in his own company.

4. He can focus attention on the large and growing potential in management data processing as contrasted with accounting data processing. Because he himself is the man who will use it, he can force a concentration on information for executive decision.

5. He can anticipate the organizational impact of advanced data processing systems. Systems now in being and yet to come will alter working relationships and job content. Unanticipated, these changes can be corrosive. Anticipated, they can add to executive capacity.

6. Finally, he can give his principal attention to the new managerial skills and decision making patterns made possible by management data processing. The potential of the machine can be exploited only by the system in which it operates. The potential of the system can be exploited only by changes in executive behavior. The planned change of executive behavior is uniquely a responsibility of top management.

Managers and technicians have learned in the last 10 years the basic lessons of electronic data processing. They have learned from the mistakes that invariably accompany innovation. They have learned from the computer's successes as well.

The promise of electronic data processing is now achievable. Its problems can be handled. What electronic data processing contributes to profits in the future depends on the skill with which management applies the lessons of the past. The contribution can be great. The responsibility is clear.

By J. W. Haslett
Shell Oil Company

Total Systems – A Concept of Procedural Relationships in Information Processing

LIKE THE PHRASE "operations research," the words "total systems" are applied without too much discrimination to a concept which is scarcely new, but whose practice and accomplishment are for the first time finding general support and recognition among those who have to do with managerial record keeping.

For as long as mercantile operations have existed, record keeping of one sort or another has attended all business transactions. In modern times the word "paperwork" has come to represent the output of the vast clerical group which comprises a major segment of the labor force and is occupied with recording information so that business and industry may operate in a systematic way.

With the advent of electronic business machine systems the word "paperwork" was supplanted by the phrase "data processing," to distinguish between manual information handling and machine manipulation.

More recently the words "integrate" and "total" have become adjuncts to the systems analyst's vocabulary. By inexact definition, their usage with other special methods words such as "data" and "systems" has broadened their scope of meaning to comprehend all company administrative operations rather than those confined to segments of a company.

Thus, integrated data processing and total systems convey the idea that the area of interest takes in the recording work of all departments of the company, with particular reference to the relationships among similar or similarly used information.

To many top executives the concept of total systems is new; to the student of advanced management principles and practices only the phraseology is novel.

The philosophy of a total systems approach has long been understood by seasoned methods analysts. But the concept could not be realized in actuality until the numerous basic company practices were systematized and standardized, numerical coding systems established and made uniform, and the entire organization's recording processes recast into a logically related mold.

With these preliminaries attended to, the comprehensive approach became practical, and in today's highly competitive climate, imperative, since a reduction in the cost of doing business is a determinant of industrial survival.

Conceptually, the relationships and particularly the similarities within an information system are the matters with which methods and procedures specialists are now contending. These relationships, and how they should be handled are the major concerns of total systems.

OBJECTIVES

The first consideration in describing the total systems concept is, of course, its objectives. They can be simply stated:

To organize administrative work flows from the viewpoint of the company as a whole without regard for barriers of organizational segments.

To develop an information system whereby source data are recorded once and thereafter perpetuated in various summary forms to meet departmental operating and financial needs without repetitive processing.

Although these two aims can be accomplished to a limited extent by manual methods, automated data processing has proven a more feasible technique in the total integration of clerical and accounting work.

As to the first objective, the company-wide

viewpoint requires that purely departmental considerations be subordinated to the interest of the organization as a whole. Thus, changes which may not be economically or otherwise justified in a single department may prove desirable at the corporate level. To obtain balanced over-all operations, each separate departmental activity must be judged in the context of its relationships with all of the others.

A high degree of administrative talent obviously comes into play in the exercise of this judgment. As in the balancing of the purely physical operations, the balancing of the paperwork and data processing which reflect and control them requires a mature analysis of departmental work flows in terms of their interrelationships. Only after such analysis can a total system be put together.

As to the second objective, its aims are as broad as the needs of all levels of management from the president to the operating supervisor of the smallest organizational unit. In a large, decentralized company, the information requirements of the intervening levels ordinarily account for the bulk of data handling.

Both objectives have interdependent components which, when separated for purposes of analysis, clearly indicate the course of action which should be taken to accomplish the goals of total systems in a company. The components are: organization structure; groups of procedures and sub-procedures, including forms; electronic and other processing and communication equipment; employees; and the data originated, summarized and otherwise processed. How well these resources and techniques are integrated into a single system, or originating and processing network, determines the degree of totality of total systems in a business or industrial enterprise.

Also inherent in the total concept is the principle of an electronic data bank, or pool of information, from which reports of many types can be drawn. Historically, under manual methods of paperwork processing, identical numerical and other information were copied and recopied ad infinitum to fulfill the reporting requirements of many departments within a company.

It later became clear, when business computers came into use, that costly recopying of the same numbers was an obsolete way of doing things. So the data bank idea came about.

So much for the explanation of the fundamentals separately. Taken collectively, they form a network for information gathering, communicating and processing which reaches into nearly every department and office of a company.

INFORMATION NETWORK

The basic input of the network consists of the individual transactions which occur in the course of business. These are composed of the introduction and change of status of many types of physical units; raw materials, finished products, supplies, employees, dollars receivable and payable and other items.

At the point of the transaction, the recording is prepared in such form as to provide both the action paper and a notation in a mechanical or electronic memory medium which may be automatically carried forward for future use.

The next point to which the data are carried forward depends upon how the company is organized. If it has a centralized data processing system, the data are transmitted to that point from the office originating the transaction, after any local reports have been drawn off. If the company has an intermediate processing level, the data are communicated first to the intermediate office, where summary reports are prepared, then from that point to the main data center where final consolidations, analyses and forecasts are developed.

Usually there is a feedback of data downward in different form from the top and intermediate offices. Sometimes there is horizontal communication of data at the middle level. Simply stated, that is the form of a management information network which is a significant end product of a total systems effort.

But the path toward developing such a network is a complex affair. Not only must each type of original transaction be followed through its primary and other processing at all levels, but it must also be identified with related transactions and their processing at all levels.

Before the advent of the total systems concept, most methods studies were confined to a single procedure and its sub-procedures within a single department or organizational level of a company. While this approach usually yielded benefits in time, money and staff, it fell short of the greater potential savings which the broader perspective of a totally integrated study is sure to produce. True, departmental systems studies are of comparatively short duration and results come swiftly. Yet a properly planned total approach permits phasing to allow for intermediate changes to be put into effect well before the end of the complete survey.

PLANNING FOR INTEGRATION

Planning for total systems integration is fundamental to its concept and objectives.

The development of the plan first requires that the organizational boundaries and the departmental segments within them be clearly defined and designated. The over-all goals of the plan should be outlined in general terms and a timetable established for their accomplishment. Both the objectives and the schedule should be accepted as flexible, for either or both may change as the studies progress.

Next is the preparation of a detailed blueprint of the plan. Programs and projects which may be developed separately should be identified, since this will be the means through which intermediate results may be obtained. Adjustments to the programs and projects will later be made from time to time.

It is also necessary to gauge in a preliminary way the expected results in economies and improvements for each project as well as for the plan as a whole. More realistic estimates can be made as the work goes along. Actual results will later, of course, be compared with estimated results. Manpower requirements and other developmental costs of the studies should be determined.

It is well very early in the game to bring into the planning picture senior representatives of the major departments which will participate in the systems review and whose functional areas will benefit most from the ultimate integration of data and procedures. Finally, a form of progress reporting to control the carrying out of the projects is desirable so that the timetable may be kept up to date and management may know the status of the program at significant intervals.

ACCOMPLISHING THE GOALS

Implementing the blueprint in an orderly fashion will result in a comprehensive study in depth of the relationships existing among transactions and the summaries and reports derived from original data of all types. New models may be derived by constructing a series of graphic models which represent the data and the way in which they are processed, while identifying at every step the interrelationships which become evident. In the proposed models, all redundancy will have been eliminated in recording, processing and reporting, so that one recording, one listing, one series of summaries at all levels and one set of forecasts for each major function or combination of functions will suffice.

Thus, the two goals of total systems will have been accomplished. But of what use is this accomplishment to the company's operations and to its management? Aside from the obvious savings in time, money and people, what else is to be said on behalf of this all-inclusive exercise in scientific management?

It is axiomatic that top managements largely depend on timely, accurate and significant information in simple, condensed form for their decision making. A good information system presents data to them in conformity with these criteria. As competitive situations frequently require immediate and flexible decisions, only a good management information system can facilitate this kind of decision making. (By flexible decisions is meant a type of decision which can readily and quickly be altered as changing conditions warrant.)

BENEFITS TO COMPANY

The potential benefits to top management are as great as management's ability to use them. A proper system provides the steady flow of relevant information needed to set objectives, develop alternative strategies, make decisions and gauge results in terms of planned goals toward profitable operations.

A proper system will get to the grass roots of financial and non-financial information which is basic for planning, operating and controlling an enterprise for profit. Data are produced which are oriented to share of market, productivity, quality levels and the adequacy of customer service. Information on operating costs and profitability in the various operating functions are provided. A complete system, drawing from a data bank, gives information on marketing activity, levels of prices and other business trends.

Through the management information system, current knowledge is available concerning production planning, inventories, shipping, sales and controls of all types.

Above all else, a total systems program requires creative imagination on a management scale of the broadest type. Those engaged in its practice must draw upon many administrative skills and, temporarily at least, consider the entire range of executive perspectives, both one at a time and simultaneously.

Total systems development is the greatest challenge to the systems and procedures specialist since the advent of the electronic computer, for it runs the full gamut of this segment of management science. Success in this field is one of the most rewarding satisfactions which its technical practitioners can experience.

By Adrian McDonough
Wharton School, University of Pennsylvania

The Scope of Management Systems: Past, Present, and Future

PROGRESS IN ANY FIELD is determined by both the opportunity and the desire for advancement. The field of business systems is no exception. Growth in systems work has been generated by opportunities inherent in the increasing size and complexity of American business. As our society and economy sought increased rates of progress, there has been a challenge to increase the scope and intensity of management research and its expression in systems and procedures.

The systems man of the past developed as management specialties were organized into white collar office jobs and departments. Paperwork increased and overhead grew as line executives sought relief from the increasing array of problems that were becoming part of their jobs. As the executive became responsible for more problems, more decisions were necessary and more systems were needed to provide the information.

A conflict was set up in this early period of systems work that still exists. With the idea that only physical output was productive, there was great reluctance to increase "nonproductive" services, such as systems and procedures. Management wanted the help, but it was very difficult to rationalize spending money for activities that did not make a directly observable contribution to production.

Certain office functions left no choice — payroll, general accounting, purchasing and inventory control systems were finally accepted as necessary services that had to be performed. From that point, such services were to exist, but were to be under constant attack for cost reduction. This focus on cost reduction, plus the above mentioned relief to management, has formed the historical pattern of the specialized systems function in business.

Specifically, a good system could reduce pressures on (or be a substitute for) management talent, yet the increased costs of systems were hard to justify.

MANAGEMENT DRAWN TO SYSTEMS GROUP

Evidence that the systems group has been close to the decision makers' position is shown in the popular practice of assigning fire fighting chores to the members of systems departments. Another significant factor is the use of systems work as one of the training grounds for management development.

In general, there has been a movement from a negative view of systems work to a recognition that systems work is an integral part of the management process. The emphasis on cost reduction remains, but more and more, systems analysis is providing the background for management decision at the policy level.

The ultimate in systems work would be no systems work. All significant problems would be identified. All analysis would be completed. All systems would be installed and accepted and working according to perfect plan.

Fortunately, from the point of view of the systems field, the picture that has just been painted is more surrealistic than realistic.

We have not recognized all significant business problems. There is much room for improvement in the attitude and methodologies of analysis. The phases of installation and acceptance of new management methods are conditioned more by wishful thinking than by probability or predictability of success.

Deliberately, I have gone from one extreme to another — from the point where we know everything to the point where we know very little. But it appears to me that this is one of the fundamental problems for the business manager. It is so easy to believe there are a finite number of problems to be solved. At a moment in time, and in a specific job, this may be a useful point of view, but it is hardly the basis for a breadth of vision for management progress.

If we are to make progress and measure this progress, we must be realistic and recognize that there are an infinite number of business problems — an endless universe of unknowns.

Such thinking would at least force us to recognize there are no conceptual limits to how far we can go in management research. What limitations exist do so not because of limited problems and opportunities, but rather because of the technical, economic and political restraints existing in a particular situation, again at a given moment in time.

UNLIMITED RANGE FOR SYSTEMS APPROACH

One of the fundamental changes in the management field is this recognition that there is an endless universe of unknowns susceptible to the systems approach. Additions to the jargon of the field are evidence of this conclusion — operations research, integrated data processing, the total system and real time planning are but a few of the terms recognizing extended opportunities for systems work.

What has been said so far could be said about any field of knowledge, or about knowledge in general. Note that the systematic approach is a common denominator for advances in all fields of knowledge.

The medical researcher and the chemist, the lawyer, and even the musical composer, have their systems. Each has his approach to classification and analysis, each has his symbols and means of measurement. Each seeks to improve productivity within his particular field of effort.

If we are to appreciate the field of business management and to consider its future, a broader viewpoint would be beneficial.

For example, the business systems man today is feeling competition from, or at least feeling the pressure to add to his talents those of the mathematical programmer, the computer programmer and even the behavioral scientist. But here again, these competitive fields are not finite — nor self-contained. Rather, they look at the same, or similar, problems from different points of view.

There are no natural boundaries to separate the application of these approaches from those traditional to the systems field. There is, however, a very fundamental change taking place in the field of business systems because of the existence of the new approaches.

The characteristic in these new approaches is the willingness to look at business problems and business systems from a conceptual point of view. This is in contrast to the idea that systems work involves only concrete facts in concrete situations. The most difficult problems for a given management are not those involving concrete situations; rather, the most difficult problems are those involved at the conceptual level.

TIME FOR A CHANGE

To date, our systems knowledge has been achieved by trial and error.

The time is ripe for the development of a theoretical framework as the guide for larger systems analysis. At present, the systems field is lacking a philosophical or theoretical base. Any field that professes to be a profession has the responsibility to seek out and demonstrate the key relationships among the elements that make the field important to society.

It is only recently that business has even been willing to use the term systems theory. My prediction is that we can expect increased attempts to explain systems from a theoretical viewpoint.

We will look at more distant and broader problems and at the same time split problems into small characteristics and details.

If one accepts the goal or ideal of total integrated systems, he should expect that analysis must get to such a detailed level that common characteristics can be found which allow meshing of now separated systems. The dramatic analogy is the development of atomic energy. Success was achieved only after theories showed how to identify subdivisions of matter. At some critical subdivision, it became possible to connect the apparently quite separate elements into a really continuous system of energy.

The connection and conversion of energy in business information systems may require even more intensive analytical effort. It is my impression that success in this field will be more valuable to us as a society than that achieved in the development of atomic energy.

A corollary to the recognition of the need for systems theory is the growing acceptance that the work of the systems analyst is concerned with creating models of reality and not with concrete reality itself.

The very essence of analysis is the ability to abstract the significant factors from a complicated situation. Reality is too complicated. Analysis through critical abstraction is necessary to bring problems down to manageable size. To date, such abstracting has been intuitive. Now we expect to see the development of techniques that will help us to isolate the important elements in a systems problem.

Along with this development, there will be an incentive to consider the rhymes and reasons behind the classifications of business problems and to study the handles, or symbols, that are attached to these problems and their subcomponents.

A CONCEPT

In discussing the concept of a system, perhaps I should define a "concept." The dictionary calls anything that can be handled by the five senses, percepts. Anything that cannot be seen, heard, touched, smelled or tasted is a concept — that is, a mental image of some sort.

Concepts are the basic raw material of analysis in systems work. For instance, budgets, standard cost reports and invoices are concepts. Note that each has a physical representation which is only an application of the concept.

To these we can add some that are products of an even higher degree of imagination. For example, authority, office morale, good will, responsibility. Note that these are less tangible, and therefore the tougher problems that are logically assigned to higher levels in the organization and represent the more difficult systems assignments.

Without making any attempt to prove it, I would propose that as an individual is promoted, his ability to think in terms of concepts becomes more and more important. Thus, the systems analyst should ever be conscious of the level of the position of his studies and related conceptual requirements.

In many instances the main difficulty the analyst faces is a lack of understanding of this conceptual framework on the part of the line executive who must approve a study. I offer the following conceptual definition of a system for thinking about systems:

A ——— SYSTEM IS A LOGICAL CONFIGURATION OF THE SIGNIFICANT ELEMENTS IN A SELECTED PROBLEM AREA.

The unique factor in this definition is the blank before the word system. It reminds us that we must identify the particular field of knowledge in which we happen to be seeking improvement. By filling in the blank we determine how total a system we are considering.

Note that the definition is not limited to business systems. For example, we can say that a legal system is a logical configuration of the elements of criminal law, maritime law, patent law, and others. In business today we hear a lot about models. We can have three-dimensional models, graphical models, mathematical models, even models using electrical energy to simulate various conditions.

If we use the present definition of a system we can conceptually develop a "system of systems." In other words, what is the logical configuration of the significant elements in the problem of systems definition?

BREAKING DOWN THE MODEL

Here is a model that can be taken apart and analyzed piece by piece. Take, for example, the term logical. The dictionary says logical means results are obtained through a process of formal reasoning.

In business we know many decisions are made when the individual uses his intuition, so we have used the term logical to mean obtained through a process of formal reasoning, plus the support of intuition. We also note that there can be illogical systems as well, but for our purpose of conceptualization, we use logical in the sense of benefiting the organization.

By way of further inquiry, a question mark can be placed under the word benefiting. What do we mean by system benefits to the organization?

We will see this problem of values, or benefits, comes into other parts of the analysis. Logical means mentally created. Processes of logic, of the scientific method, where we hypothesize, analyze, bring back together in synthesis, test and apply, are derived from the ability of the systems man to reason, compare and, thus, decide.

A CONFIGURATION OF ELEMENTS

For the term configuration you may wish to substitute other words. For example, model, structure, chart, or image. This definition of system, in and of itself, is a form of configuration. Configuration implies pieces that have to be put together, or a set of relationships. These relationships are between and among significant elements. Normally these are narrowed or abstracted from reality, because reality is too complicated to handle with all possible elements in the configuration.

The concept heard in operations research circles of sub-optimism is relevant here. We cannot have the configuration unless we have the pieces or the significant elements. The elements are of no use unless they are put together into the configuration.

One of the difficult questions is, Do we build down from the configuration to the significant elements, or do we build from the significant elements into the configuration? Notice this is the process of classification. Much research is being done in this area. The information retrieval work now being given major attention is based upon classification.

To classify, symbols are required. Here we have an example of classification. If we are going to communicate, we are limited to words, pictures, or numbers. Thus, we find the significant elements in business systems appearing as words, in reports; pictures, such as charts; and various diagrams and numbers in the form of accounting statements or mathematical programs.

The terms significant and selected indicate alternative choices. Any time there are alternative choices, measurement is required, comparisons must be made, and selection must take place. Thus again we come to the question of required measurements in the appropriate values of the particular system. These values are not necessarily constant, so policing action is necessary when we find the values changing with changes in the problem area.

SELECTED PROBLEM AREA

There are at least two ways to look at the term, selected problem area. In the first instance, let us assume that all problems are classified. Our system problem then is, which one do we work on? If we assume a fixed inventory of problems and we have a large enough budget to have enough people, we can work on all of the problems. But, normally, we have limited resources and must be selective in picking our problem areas.

Secondly, and more complicated, is the situation wherein the problem universe has not yet been subdivided. The discussions on the total system concept center around this point. We are still trying to conceive and spell out a useful total system of a business. Some progress is being made. Note that automation — a term applied to the shop and later to the office — is now being applied to an integration of both shop and office.

The question of selected problem area has at least two parts: 1) What is the totality of the system, as just mentioned? and 2) How do we subdivide or set limits to the scope of the subdivision. Note that there are various restraints operating here. Let me cite just three restraints on how big a problem we can take on:

One, in practice, each of the separate systems, covering separate problems, has usually been developed to the limits of comprehension or conceptual ability of those involved in its design and utilization. At some point things go out of focus and out of control. A manager who does not admit the infinite possibilities of complication will pay the price as his ulcer quotient goes up. Though there are no natural boundaries to systems, there are administrative limitations.

Second, there are no instantaneous business systems. The business system is meaningless when pictured as a moment in time. If we think of a system as a logical configuration, it implies a logical sequence of steps and for these logical sequences of steps there are time intervals as inherent factors in the systems. These time intervals may be quite different for various problems in the same business.

Third, each element covered by a system is, in the final analysis, a product of human judgment applied to the classification of activities. These classifications may be appropriate in one period and less appropriate in another. For example, the first week in the month versus the last week in the month.

Thus, we must either have alternative classifications or, of necessity, work with averages or optimum classifications. As a conclusion, we can say that separate systems covering quite different problems can often justify quite different classifications. Any attempt to standardize is accomplished only at the price of further averaging and this barrier often sets a limit in systems scope.

STRIVING TOWARD INTEGRATED SYSTEMS

What I am implying here is that as we try to increase a system's scope or take on larger problems, there are geometrical, compounding complications pressing back on us from these restraints.

Total systems are not good in and of themselves. I might refer to the production environment where we had something similar to a total system years ago when one very large motor would drive many machines through a series of belts.

More recently we have found it advantageous to set up separate systems with individual motor drives on machines. It was only when we were able to conceptualize over-all relationships of the individual machines that we were able to move to integrated production systems. Even now, this covers but a very small percentage of our physical productive capacity.

To generalize, I think that life in management systems in the future is going to seem just as challenging as it is today. By this I mean we will solve certain of our business systems problems — but we will take on even more complicated ones. My reasoning is this:

1. There are many business problems that are not yet in focus — not yet understood well enough even to describe.

2. Integrated data processing is a glib term. It is not easy to integrate. The restraints and restrictions on integration of systems and reports builds up like the compounding of interest.

3. As with other advancing fields of knowledge, greater degrees of specialization can be expected.

4. These degrees of specialization will require that greater attention be paid to coordination of systems work.

5. As a result of coordination efforts, management research, operations research and systems research will be shown to have apparent, rather than real, differences. Less effort will be wasted in polarizing professional achievements.

6. As a result of the maturing of the systems function, the highest level of systems work will have the opportunity to achieve the professional authority and status of business legal and medical advisors.

CHANGES EXPECTED

These six predictions are admittedly general in nature. Let me cite some specific changes in management systems orientation that can be expected.

1. Information systems will be designed with the admission that they are to be used to formulate company policy. This will require a relaxing of the assumption that all policies are set at the top. It has been said knowledge is power. With complete information available, the decision or policy may already have been made. Another way to say this is the facts speak for themselves and require only a formal acceptance and stamp of approval by the line executive rather than a decision.

2. Information systems will be designed simultaneously with the design of organization patterns and job responsibilities. Here we will see a synthesis of organization planners and systems designers. Jobs will be described in terms of their problem content and related information needs rather than in the present jargon of authority and responsibility.

3. The rate of insertion of new problems into the organization will determine whether or not companies centralize or decentralize. If we assume that there is only a certain number of problems for management, then any improvement in systems or the use of computers will lead towards centralization. A more realistic approach is to recognize that centralization-decentralization movements are a function of relative rates of changes.

By E. R. Dickey and N. Louis Senensieb
Space Technology Laboratories, Inc.

A Total Approach to Systems and Data Processing

WITH THE GROWTH in size and complexity of modern business organizations, information processing has posed a complex of such proportions that, despite the mounting administrative costs which engender even more critical problems, business continues to need more efficient systems for producing accurate and timely information for the ultimate goal of managerial decision making.

Due to a background of rising costs and inadequate communication lines, business turned eagerly to the capabilities that electronic data processing promised in the early part of the last decade. It seemed that a tool had been fashioned that could process information rapidly and reverse the trend in high clerical costs. Many accepted electronic data processing as the panacea for most administrative problems. What has been learned from experience with this new tool in the last decade?

First, the information problem remains. Electronic computers have been able to produce a large volume of data in short time spans. But a large volume of data is not necessarily equivalent to useful, accurate and timely business information.

Secondly, in many cases clerical costs have not been reduced, and where costs reductions have been realized, they could not be attributed directly to the use of automatic data processing. Furthermore, a growing communications barrier is being recognized between the personnel who operate the electronic data processing equipment and the operating personnel and managements of the organization concerned. Is it then that electronic data processing equipment cannot do the job? No, it certainly is a most valuable tool. But like any tool, it can be misused.

Data processing departments, in the hands of specialists, have been service oriented. They have mechanized specific problems on request, nearly always on the false assumption that something done mechanically is done in the most economic manner.

In this respect, electronic data processing has fallen into the same fire fighting approach that has traditionally plagued all forms of systems work and industrial engineering. If anything, electronic data processing personnel have been even more removed from a management orientation that a business is an integral whole whose sub-parts or sub-systems can be joined together by an effective management information system. The net result has been the tragic misuse of these powerful new tools as high speed typewriters.

Business Week, in its special report on computers in the June 21, 1958 issue, raises the need for "acceptance of the computer as a systems tool and not simply a fast office machine." It points out that "Manufacturers concede that if companies made the same intensive analysis of their systems — and the necessary changes — without the spur of an incoming computer, they might sometimes eliminate the need for one."

The report mentions that one company's "computer men will privately concede that many applications are marginally justified at best. The hitch: The data processing center has been conceived simply as a 'service of existing departments.'"

EVOLUTION OF NEW SYSTEMS CONCEPTS

There is an obvious need to discard both beliefs in electronic panaceas and traditional systems fire fighting approaches to business problems. The recent management literature gives increasing attention toward putting fundamental management principles back into perspective. The emphasis is for their effecvice implementation through revised system concepts geared to the modern dynamic business environment and utilizing the full capabilities of new tools, such as the electronic computer.

John Diebold stated: "Sometimes what we believe to be our problems are in reality symptoms, the true problem lying far deeper. It is important that we do not try to automate in order to tackle symptoms. A thorough systems analysis and careful thinking through of objectives is the best means of defining the true problem. At the same time an adequate systems study can save management from the opposite, but equally serious mistake of trying to make too fundamental a change in one pass."[1]

He also pointed the way for electronic data processing utilization by indicating that "the big benefits from automatic data processing will come only when management learns to use automation for its unique ability to provide better, more accurate and more timely information about the operation of a business."[2]

Ralph Cordiner likewise expresses this conviction as follows: "This deep communication problem is not solved by providing more volume of data for all concerned, by faster accumulation and transmittal of conventional data, or by holding more conferences . . . What is required instead, is a far more penetrating and orderly study of the business in its entirety to discover what specific information is needed at each particular position in view of the decisions to be made there."[3]

RATIONALIZING BY MANAGEMENT

In order to make a thorough systems analysis, define the true problems, and provide the right information to the right people at the right time, management people rationalize that any business can be analyzed as an over-all information system composed of inter-related and integrated systems and sub-systems.

Elaborating upon this concept, Virgil Blank, of Haskins and Sells, observes that: "An engineered approach to system development is based on a frame of mind . . . which accepts the business enterprise as a high order system composed of interdependent parts. These parts are people and their methods and procedures of sales, production, purchasing, accounting, etc., working towards a common goal.

"These parts are usually separated into departments for organizational reasons but not for data processing reasons. In systems development, then, the organizational structure must give way to the data-flow structure . . . The business system, being interdependent, acts like any servo-mechanism . . . sensitive to various economic and commercial forces. There is a balance of relative effectiveness of each part within the enterprise acting in relationship with every other part to produce the performance of the whole system."[4]

Blank spells out the objective of such an engineered systems development approach as one "to optimize performance within the enterprise through achievement of proper relationships between parts of the business system."[5]

He sets "profit improvement — not cost cutting" as a proper goal in systems design work, stating that "this implies that the system analyst be management oriented in his thinking so that he can visualize the business as an over-all operation and not as a set of separate parts requiring cost reduction through mechanization."[6]

Stanford L. Optner, management consultant and UCLA instructor, postulates in a similar manner that "business operations consist of a set of intimately related sub-systems. The integration of sub-systems is the key to effective and economic operation."[7]

He describes integration in sub-system design as "the key concept of systems analysis in business. Integration of systems postulates the trade-off between the functional requirements of a sub-system with its immediately related sub-systems.

"Integration in this sense also means the inter-compatibility of sub-system design. Each sub-system becomes a black box when viewed by the systems engineer. Using the data at his command, the systems analyst observes the sub-system operation, looking at inputs, outputs and the processing device (the black box) to determine whether each sub-system is making the desired contribution to the over-all system requirements."

Optner describes the art of systems analysis as "the ability to find the correct sub-system or to identify the proper systems elements. As in any other field, the ability to perform efficiently is to some degree a result of the participant's training, experience and ability. Thus, the business oriented systems analyst can make a major contribution because of his knowledge of business operations, generally."

THE DYNAMICS OF THE BUSINESS SYSTEM

To take a total systems approach to the problem, we must define rather explicitly the total dynamics of the business system. A business system ranges from the most abstract concepts of objectives to the most concrete conditions of processing of materials. The organization structure also approximates the same abstraction ladder, in that it begins with the board of directors and top management who concern themselves with more abstract ideas, and ends with the workers doing routine tasks at the bottom of the pyramid.

Exhibit 1 depicts the dynamics of a total business system. Note how it is divided into four quadrants. In the top two quadrants we

Exhibit 1

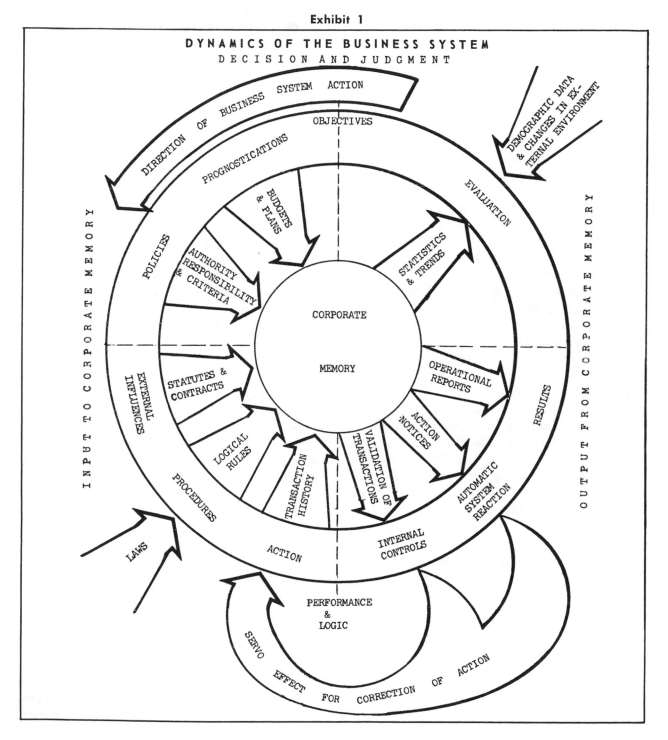

have pictured the abstract part of the business, while the bottom half represents the concrete. The quadrants on the left indicate actions contributing to input into the business intelligence system or corporate memory, while the right quadrants represent output from the intelligence system.

The input to the corporate memory must be logical and structured data to have any meaning. No input is expected from the statement of objectives which is far too abstract for inclusion in our system. When the objectives are stated in a logical manner by prognostication and statements of policy, the ideas then can be logically stored, manipulated, and retrieved. The ultimate in systems design would automate this intelligence system, but these basic concepts remain true of any manual system.

The dynamic process of the business system starts at the top of our circle and proceeds counter-clockwise. Since the process is dynamic it is continuous; action is the result of decision; and objectives are altered as a result of action. The cycle starts with the board or principal who arbitrarily establishes some objective for the enterprise.

Caution should be taken here since the classical motive of profit may play little or no part in the objectives. If this is not recognized, the systems designer will be designing a system for objectives not considered desirable by top management.

The next step in this dynamic process is prognostication. This is the first step to be reduced to logical terms, and constitutes a statement of plans and budgets that can be manipulated by man or machine processes. The prognostications are a matter of judgment and decision and cannot be derived directly by rules applied to data, as can a payroll.

POLICY — A KEY WORD

The only function left for decision and judgment on the input cycle is the establishment of policy upon which to build the procedural processes. Again these policies are arbitrary, but are fashioned to be the basis for accomplishing the objectives and prognostications.

Since the word policy has been badly abused in business parlance, we shall use the word to mean authority, responsibility, and criteria. Once a policy has been reduced to logical statements and stored in our corporate memory, the area of decision and judgment is just about accomplished.

At this point we enter the area of performance. Here procedures as to how the information system will operate are designed. These procedures not only must conform to the policy statements, but also to any statutory impingements that are applicable to our enterprise. Procedures must also take into account any contracts with suppliers or customers, since these affect our rules of procedure.

The last item to enter our intelligence system is the history of transactions. At this point we have a well designed system accepting into the corporate memory explicit and logical statements of all our plans, rules, legal situations and record of transactions.

With all these statements being not only logical but also highly structured, we are prepared to manipulate and retrieve information or data. We may, at this step, retrieve data organized in patterns that can be only vaguely helpful to operating personnel or we can extract the essence of information. Information is data that can be used, and aside from fulfilling legal or curiosity requirements, is the only data that is valuable.

OUTPUT ON CONCRETE LEVEL

The first output from our business system is on a highly concrete level. The consideration of internal control and validation of prior transactions is paramount. By manipulation of the rules established in the policy statements with the procedure, transaction history and time, we are able to extract from our system action notices, such as low stock notices and employee review periods.

These outputs will trigger a servo effect at the performance level. They also act as correction stimuli to operating personnel much as a thermostat starts corrective temperature action.

The next concrete level output is in the form of selected operating results. These are at a very detailed level, and to be useful at all, must be associated with the prognostications. This is true of formal, informal, manual or automatic systems. It is in this area of operating reports that the greatest amount of money is wasted because of the outpouring of great volumes of paper containing only data that has low information content.

We have now arrived at the last and probably the most important quadrant of our cycle, that of output and evaluation of the essence of information relative to the health of our enterprise, and the art of comparing the situation of the enterprise with external conditions.

It is extremely important that the information (not data) at this point be valid and complete. It is also essential that great competence be exercised by management to determine if the dynamics of the organization are correct, that the enterprise is healthy, that external conditions are such that success in fulfilling objectives will continue. If any of these factors are askew, correction or new decision and judgment must alter either the objectives, prognostications or policies.

TOTAL SYSTEMS CHARACTERISTICS

What, then, are the identifying characteristics of the total systems approach as compared to the action level, problem oriented, traditional systems approach? They are as follows:

1. Objectives are taken into consideration as a logical basis for formulating a basic policy framework. Individual policies must be evaluated in relation to each other to determine whether they are compatible with and reflect the organization's objectives.
2. The systems analyst can design logical procedures to govern all performance within the parameters of applicable policies, based on the knowledge of:
   a. The organization (organizational structure and the organization's objectives),
   b. The functional relationships of different parts of the organization and their specific goals as governed by responsibilities and authorities defined in policies.
3. Related procedures are integrated into logical systems governing performance.
4. Mechanization is conceived as the systems tool to:

   a. Perform procedures economically where possible — and mechanization may not be universally applicable to all situations,
   b. Process vital information more rapidly and provide the right information to the right people, and
   c. Protect the integrity of information by means of validation techniques.

This concept, governing systems work, should assure that:
1. Performance is geared to effective attainment of objectives, guided by applicable policies and governed by logical procedures.
2. Operating procedures are integrated into logical systems.
3. Mechanization is system oriented rather than isolated problem oriented.
4. The typical inconsistent patchwork of policies and procedures is eliminated.

The flow of information or data brings us to the final point in a total systems approach. This is a recognition that the management information flowing between component parts of an organization represents an over-all information system, just as an organization is an organic whole.

The design of an effective management information system that properly integrates administrative action is the aim of the systems analyst. The accomplishment of such an integration of information is possible today by the proper use of electronic data processing equipment as a systems tool.

REFERENCES

[1]Diebold, John, "Automation and the Manager," an address at the XI International Management Congress, Paris, France, June, 1957, p. 21.

[2]Ibid, p. 7.

[3]Cordiner, Ralph, *New Frontiers for Professional Managers*, McGraw-Hill Book Company, Inc., New York, 1956.

[4]Blank, Virgil F., "The Relationship of the Systems and Procedures Function to Electronic Data Processing and Management," a paper presented to the American Management Association's S&P Course, Los Angeles, October, 1959, p. 4.

[5]Ibid, p. 5.

[6]Ibid, p. 7.

[7]Optner, Stanford L., *Systems Analysis for Business Management*, Prentice-Hall, Inc., Englewood Cliffs, N. J., 1960, pp. 17-18.

By A. Richard DeLuca
CIBA Pharmaceutical Company

Understanding Total Systems

IT IS THE PURPOSE of this article to provide background concerning the evolution of the total systems concept and to present a working framework which may be useful in developing a clearer understanding of this concept.

THE PROBLEM

The total systems concept means many things to many people. For example, to the harassed operating executive, it may imply a coordination of his internal operations so as to give him assurance that his own particular organizational unit will perform satisfactorily. To the data processing manager, it may be the dream of a central intelligence file into which all vital data are fed and from which any executive might select information, at random, which he requires for decision making purposes.

To the systems professional, total systems can be viewed in several ways:

1. From the individual systems project viewpoint, it may refer to the conduct of that assignment in such a manner as to assure that all interrelationships involved in the problem have been properly considered and provided for.

2. Viewed from a top management perspective, total systems may refer to the integration of all information which is processed by the various functions of the enterprise. The integration is handled in such a way as to facilitate efficient performance of all corporate operations and simultaneously provide management with the information needed for planning and controlling.

3. It may denote " . . . a single system crossing existing departmental boundaries and theoretically bringing all major operating systems into one functional organization."[1]

Let us look at the manner in which some current literature defines total systems:

1. Thomas C. Fisher, manager of data processing at Bell Helicopter, Fort Worth, Texas, describes total systems as "complete integration of all major operating systems within a company into a single operating system through the medium of data processing. In a sense, it is an extension of integrated data processing as we think of it today."[2]

2. To the systems planners of the Carborundum Company, total systems is thought of as integrated electronic data processing which serves two purposes:

   a. The processing and/or production of operating documents, records and reports, and

   b. The preparation of management control information through data reduction and analysis."[3]

3. A number of writers have attempted to define total systems in terms of objectives. For example, a recent article contains the following description:

   "The objective of total systems is to bring to bear all possible scientific disciplines in a quantitative way to create information systems that will make it possible for management to operate an organization in the most efficient manner."[4]

4. Another writer describes the total systems concept as follows:

   " . . . the total systems concept truly encompasses the entire business . . . developing a system for the operation of the company itself provides myriad patterns of interlocking data and information flows. One cannot get his arms around anything so complex, taken as an entity, so the total system must, for analysis and handling at this time, be broken into major systems and sub-systems.

"It is the writer's observation that too many approaches to total systems design put too much stress on specific applications and not enough on inter-relationship of systems. Too much emphasis is placed on doing a specific job with a specific piece of hardware instead of analyzing basic information needs so as to be certain unnecessary data and reporting are not by default carried over from a manual to a mechanized system . . . "[8]

5. The only direct definition of total systems which I was able to locate in the current literature is one developed by Roger Christian, associate editor of *Factory* magazine:

"By the total systems concept, I mean 'Integrated corporate intelligence systems designed to permit management by exception, based on timely information, randomly available, and guided by rigorously determined relationships and decision rules.' "[5]

EVOLUTION OF THE TOTAL SYSTEMS CONCEPT

Looking back at some recent history, I view the evolution of the total systems concept as follows. During the mid-forties, emphasis was placed on the development of paper work improvements, through the commitment to writing of all repetitive clerical procedures being performed throughout the organization.

We might label this evolutionary phase the total procedures stage. It is noteworthy, in this regard, that few of our present day enterprises ever completely achieved this first goal.

As time and technology progressed, the fifties ushered in the integrated data processing era, which concentrated upon developing the multiple use of input data. This concept was concentrated on operational improvements, rather than on management information requirements. Most recently, this concept has been modified by a newer approach, which deals with management information systems.

PRESENT INTERPRETATIONS

This brings us to today: Total systems is now interpreted in two major ways:

1. The older interpretation still holds sway in many circles. It emphasizes the development of integrated operational systems, referring to the creation of smoothly flowing paperwork systems which enhance routine clerical or other paperwork operations, such as purchasing, receiving, sales, order processing, production and inventory control.

2. In contrast to this older, traditional, systems approach, is a more recent development, namely the management information systems concept.

Indeed much, if not most, of the current literature has switched the meaning of total systems over to this newer viewpoint. It is a drastic innovation, emphasizing not the effectiveness of the operations being performed, but the needs of the manager himself — namely, the specific elements of information required for planning and control.

A NEED FOR INTEGRATION

We can see, from our review of the evolution of this concept, how these two major interpretations came into the forefront. Our problem now becomes one of properly integrating these viewpoints so that a common objective of all systems work, namely, the improvement of both management and operations within an enterprise, can be best accomplished.

Exhibit 1 is presented as a conceptual model — a very crude one at that — which can be used in coordinating the major elements of the two separate viewpoints described. Note, that the purely managerial functions of planning and control are depicted as the basic elements of the information system aspect of this concept.

The second portion depicts the operating element. When merged conceptually, as shown, these viewpoints serve to constitute a total management systems concept. I might add that this concept could well be used to educate management as to the potential scope of systems work within the enterprise.

Let us not deceive ourselves in regard to

any supposed simplicity in this concept. We are dealing with a radical approach to the discipline of management.

For many years, the developers of scientific management concentrated on the mechanical aspects of the science. The net result was an extreme devotion to the concept of specialization of effort to the extent that the more fundamental concept of integration of all functions and activities within an enterprise toward a common objective became a mere platitude.

Members of the systems profession have for too long promoted a servile devotion to this concept of specialization. With the advent of computer technology, however, we have been forced to shift our sights to the more fundamental problem of how to integrate all of the complex interrelated elements of an enterprise.

NEED SOUND FRAMEWORK

Are we up to this task? It is my belief that we can only begin to understand the immensity of the challenge if we first become more serious students of the discipline referred to as management. The need for a sound con-ceptual framework, within which we can classify our thoughts, has never been more urgent. As a system authority states:

"To understand the objectives and characteristics to be built into a management information system requires understanding of the basic processes of management. The majority of specialists in systems and data processing must become more profound students of management than they have been in the past.

"But a knowledge of systems techniques and data processing hardware, however expert, is not enough. The ability to perceive management information needs, and a capacity to translate these needs into an information systems program, even in limited applications, is essential."[6]

Within this perspective the conceptual framework described here is presented in the hope that these concepts will be investigated, studied and improved.

IMPLEMENTING THE TOTAL MANAGEMENT SYSTEMS CONCEPT

How can this broad framework be imple-

Exhibit 1

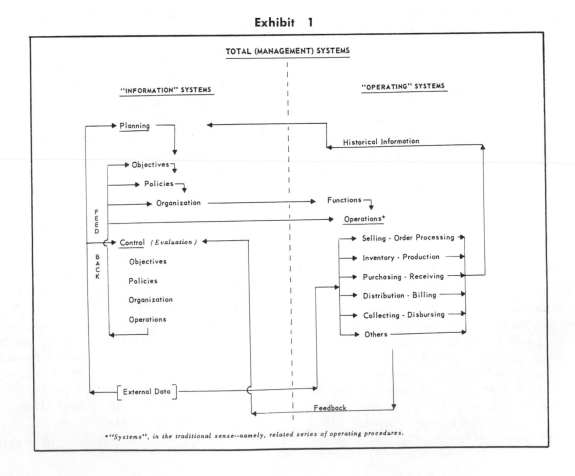

*"Systems", in the traditional sense--namely, related series of operating procedures.

mented? The reader is invited to consider each element depicted in **Exhibit 1** so as to further dissect each element (preferably in diagrammatic, or flow, form), and possibly establish the key components (sub-systems) of that particular element.

Once this conceptual framework has been completed, depicting all elements of the total management systems concept outlined in **Exhibit 1**, the systems planner will possess a new analytical tool, useful both to himself and to the managers with whom he will work, in determining all information required for both operating systems and the planning and control activities of management.

Perhaps most significantly, such a conceptual device will point out many of the complex interrelationships which exist between the managerial and operating elements of the enterprise.

FIRST THINGS FIRST

The development of such a conceptual framework should serve, at the least, to enhance any existing systems programs by inviting a more profound study of the particular application(s) being developed. Concentration on the development of operating systems, however, will not begin to accomplish the goal of creating a completely integrated management information and operating systems network for the enterprise as a whole.

It will be necessary for the systems professional to first tackle a far more difficult and challenging task. This consists of obtaining from management a detailed statement of objectives; then, working from the stated objectives, all functional responsibilities must be identified and clarified.

These actions will bring the systems analyst into the delicate and perhaps dangerous area of organization. Aren't most of management's problems, if probed deeply enough, found to be in essence problems of organization, such as overlapping or missing responsibilities and illogical relating of functions?

The importance of clarifying and, if necessary, modifying organization to provide a rational base from which to determine and build the planning and control information systems needed so urgently by management, cannot be overemphasized.

One director of systems and procedures expressed this opinion:

"Designing the information needs and report structure of a business is indeed a challenging responsibility. I know of no greater challenge than faces systems and procedures people today. . . . The job of isolating key elements of planning and control requires much brain power and little, if any, computer power at the outset."[7]

CONCLUDING REMARKS

In conclusion, I would like to stress these points:

1. By far the toughest assignment facing any systems man is the job of helping managers define, in detail, their personal information needs for planning and control.

2. The task of defining the problem requires brainpower — not computer power. How can you use a computer for implementing a total systems concept, if you haven't thought out, in specifics, a complete picture, or model, which represents the total system?

A computer is a tremendous tool; but it's only a tool. Too many systems men have been bitten by the computeritis bug — fascination with the means, to the sad neglect of the ends. Why not take off our technician's helmet and put on our own 10-gallon hat . . . the headpiece of the management architect?

REFERENCES

[1] Spray, Norman, "Total System Concept In Action at Bell Helicopter," *Paperwork Simplification*, Issue No. 58, 1960, p. 5.

[2] Ibid, p. 5.

[3] "Carborundum Co. Develops 'Total Systems Approach' in Data Processing," *Office Management*, January, 1959, p. 21.

[4] Sprague, Richard E., "Advances in Data-Processing Hardware and Software," *Advances in EDP and Information Systems*, American Management Association, New York, Management Report No. 62, 1961, p. 75.

[5] Christian, Roger, *The Total Systems Concept*, from a talk delivered before the 14th Annual International Systems Meeting, October 8-11, 1961, Cleveland, Ohio, p. 8.

[6] Gallagher, James D., *Management Information Systems and the Computer*, American Management Association, New York, Research Study No. 51, 1961, p. 25.

[7] Hendrick, James G., "Management Information Systems in Focus," in *Advances in EDP and Information Systems*, p. 21.

[8] Ewell, James M., "How to Organize for a Total System," *Systems and Procedures*, Nov.-Dec., 1961, p. 5.

By William B. Worthington
Fort Huachuca, Arizona

Total Command, Management and Administrative Systems

IF THE ESSENTIAL INFORMATION needed to manage a business were in an electronic memory and well indexed, you could hit a button and get what you need to know, or, if an automatic machine needed instructions, it could hit its own buttons and proceed without delay or error. Further, if the memories were interconnected by an interrogation network, any point of need could get what it needed without duplicating files. It is this aspect of electronics, call it a *network of automatic memory*, that is the principal component of the electronics-for-management dream.

The available languages are confused, so call it what you wish. The business journals speak learnedly of *information technology*, the scientists write of *information storage and retrieval*, your secretary probably says filing, and an old-time punched card salesman would have said, maybe, "Anything you want to know, just *run the cards*," just as glibly as I said, "*Hit the button.*"

I think the first thing to do is to take a look at the basic information problems of a business, or any other kind of organization of people, whether manufacturing, retail, railroad, bank, college, military, or federal government. The common characteristics are:

1. They are composed of *people*.
2. They have a *head man*.
3. They have *goals*.

By *goal* I mean an objective, some reason for existence; the boss wouldn't be *head man* if he didn't have some kind of goal, or star to hitch his wagon on. How does he lead the organization to the goal? Obviously, he has to *estimate his situation*, dream beyond present time into the *future*, and set up the *goals*, the *targets*, to be reached, since any of them take

time, and we have to allow time for the doing.

Somebody has to *do* something. Whether he has 10 or 10,000 helpers, the head man can't know all and be all to all people, so he appoints a VP for Operations and expects him to know and handle the *do* part, the *doing*. Now, this VP can't do anything without people, so the head man appoints another VP to provide *people*. Let's call him VP for Personnel. People need tools and materials to work with, so we get a VP for Things who is responsible for pretty much anything that can't talk back. Someone has to keep records and see that the dollars are allocated and get value according to plan, and to keep the head man informed of how well his plans are working out, so we get here a VP for Control. And back in the beginning, somebody helped the boss scout the future, check the markets, estimate the situation. Let's call him VP for Information.

What have we drawn?

1. *A network of human memory* — If the head man wants to know what the situation is in operations, he'll put the finger on Joe, VP for Operations, the *do* man, and say, "Joe, what gives?" And Joe is supposed to have in his mind what the score is and give it to him *instantly* . . . well, as instantly as he can.

2. *A staircase of actions* —
   a. Plan this way: *Information* to *goal* to *do* to *people* and *things* to *dollar requirement*.
   b. Act this way: Get dollars, then people and things, do job, evaluate and replan.

3. A set of feedback cycles — This is the rolling pattern of control that maintains continuing change and evolution: Plan,

write orders, do it, feedback what happened, and replan, on into the future.

SKULL, PAPER, AND AUTOMATICS

Joe at first tried to keep it all in his head, then made notes in some kind of a butcher book, and finally set himself up with a set of files: mental files, in the persons of his subordinates, and paper files in the familiar cabinets, with maybe a few automatics in the form of punched cards. The subordinates multiplied in accordance with Parkinson's Law and communicated and made work for each other as well as helping each other, Joe, and the other four VP's, who followed the same procedure and process. Is it clear enough that we're dealing with a large and tangible memory network composed of people, paper, and a few automatics?

Now, suppose that in the *do* area we've planned a job and know it will take 12 people three days and XYZ materials, and that this detailed specification is in the do procedures file, ready for use and proven because it worked OK the last time the job had to be done.

Let's use a little blue sky imagination and say, "Well, we could avoid delay and follow-up and get a prompt answer if we just had a machine that would read that spec, query the people and files for when we could have the 12 people and the XYZ materials and bring back an answer in a few milliseconds. Then we'd know right away what we could work on, and we wouldn't get into any cross-promises on what's available to do it with."

We get an immediate qualitative improvement — from a practical approach to the real problems of running a business — but is it blue sky? Or is it an everyday practical approach, like it sounds?

QUALITATIVE IMPROVEMENT

Ask for an airline seat from, let's say, New York to Washington. The lady uses a flight tag that resembles a gas station credit card, puts it in a small gadget on the counter, then punches a button that asks a question of the system: "Do we have an open seat on that flight?"

That inquiry goes by wire to an electronic memory in one central location, and if there's an open seat, sends back a green light that says, in effect, "Yes, we have a seat; does your customer want it?"

She asks the customer, and he says yes.

She punches the other button, which changes the color of the light and deducts one seat from the central memory and in effect has said, "OK, that seat is now reserved for your customer, and nobody else can have it unless you release it."

Is this unfamiliar to anybody? It is a basic sort of system: an automatic memory that can be automatically interrogated in milliseconds from a number of points located at considerable geographic distance, without delay, confusion, errors . . . its sheer simplicity makes it unimpressive!

QUANTITATIVE IMPROVEMENT

However, when you think about it, such simplicity is not the way Joe VP's system of operation works, nor was it always the way the airlines' reservation system worked. Until recently, about the only common systems that stayed up to date with the current situation were the stock quotations and the parimutuel machines at a race track, and if you know those at all, they worked but without simplicity.

Operationally, the potentials are fantastic. Applied to the major working files of an organization, such methods can enable a manufacturer to prepare a major bid in hours, a government administrator to rough out next year's budget in minutes, and a military commander to set up a counter-move while his enemy is still routing paper between totem poles.

The files may be 40 miles, four floors, or a slow elevator away, but it is possible to set them up electronically so that buttons, displays, or other files can get at operating information with the speed of light. Now, such a system can work only where precise questions and answers are possible, but we have reason to believe that about 90 percent of business planning and communication are in this category, and that one half of the cost of doing business is not an impossible target.

MEMORY MEDIA

The key word here is media, or we could call it method of memory. Except our own brains, there's a fairly consistent pattern of geometric shape and use of different materials and symbols. Let's back off and look:

1. *Human* — The best and most flexible of all memories is still the space between two ears. If we're married, we know how well this space retains ideas and can bring them out at high speed. However, it doesn't have the exact accuracy of other means of holding information.

2. *Paper* — More permanent and changeless than human memory is paper, and the principal shapes are scrolls, books, sheets, cards, and tables. These developed as ways to hold symbols so we could get at them most easily for particular usages, and these shapes repeat through the newer methods, for about the same reasons of limitations and convenience.

3. *Carbon* — Roughly 50 to 75 years ago carbon came into use for easy copies. It is used in the same shapes, scroll, book, sheet, card, and tables, plus special constructions such as continuous, fanfold, strips, snap-outs, and coatings.

4. *Masters* — Many ways developed to multiply one setup in the same pattern of scroll (tape), book, sheet, card, and tables; address plates, blueprint process, white-print, photo, hectograph, stencils, offset printing, and others. Also, Gutenberg invented movable type about 500 years back and the end result, printing, is still one of the very best ways to spread information.

5. *Holes* — This was a new kind of machine-readable symbol on all of the old shapes of tape, book, sheet, card, and table. Jacquard looms wove tapestry from punched cards 150 years ago; teletype and IBM cards date over 75 years back. A card file is equivalent to a scroll or tape and reel in the limitations that sequence of data imposes on searching for a specific item; both are clumsy.

6. *Spots* — Spots are mostly magnetic, though sometimes chemical. The big advantage of both is no inertia in reading as speeds approximate light itself. However, with the one exception of core matrices, the shapes are as clumsy as ever:

    a. Tapes have to search back and forth like a scroll or reel (start-stop).

    b. Drums are nonstop loops, in effect; no start-stop can run at speed.

    c. Discs are another way to get more surface on a nonstop loop or drum.

    d. Ramac is a juke-box arrangement of discs. The reading device moves.

    e. Sheet is being developed for machine selection from a file box.

    f. Cards are cut tape three inches by one inch in development.

    g. Cores are devices in 3-D matrix for direct access.

7. *Other* — Many means are not yet developed; i.e., chemical means, low temperature storage or currents (cryogenic), storage in structure of matter by use of an electron microscope. Who knows what actual break-throughs will come next? Dimly, we can see possibilities approaching those of the brain in capacity. So far, all the King's horses and all the King's men haven't even come close to the speed, economy, and capability of the original human model.

The words core and core memory can be used to characterize the three dimensional matrices that are at the heart of the speed and capability break-throughs in data equipment.

It's a method of suspending a spot of information in a set of three way coordinates so that an electronic impulse can reach it, and store or read that particular spot without moving parts. This part is ancient.

What's new is that ways and means are being found to pack these into reasonable space at low cost so that in some years twice as many go into half the space at half the cost, so that a reading speed of a million words a minute, which was meaningless when there wasn't anything that would hold a million words, becomes a live and real capability.

This million words a minute puts a terrific stretch and strain onto the imagination of a lot of us. For instance, for the last 85 years the commercial communications industry hasn't had to deal with anything on the ends of their lines that could take it in or put it out much faster than the 100 words per minute of a teletype tape or a normal speaking human being. Now, this raises their sights by 10,000 to one, and some near at hand developments are likely to multiply that by another 100 to make it a million to one.

Some current accomplishments go even further into the fantastic. Right now, capabilities that were hailed as tremendous accomplishments in a half acre or so of tubes and wires, are being duplicated in portable and mobile models of about the cubic volume of your own desk.

What this means to you and me is that in fewer years than we imagine, costs and capabilities will be not only within reach of any business but will be necessary to business survival, just like telephones and some of the other automatic gadgets we take for granted. But they're coming at rates of speed that are 10 and 1000 times faster and that means that you and I have to stretch our thinking in bigger, simpler, more fundamental jumps into the future, in order to be ready to handle these things.

It is true that nobody is yet forcing us to even consider them. We live in a free country and can ignore them all we want to. But the catch is that invention is mothering the necessity of application for the eminently simple reason that if you and I do not employ these capabilities, we'll probably find ourselves competing with someone who has put them to his own use.

Fortunately, we have a model that's still 1,000 to one ahead of all of these things, and we can use it as a guide in how to organize and employ these fantastic gadgets that we'd like to take in stride for commonplace usage during the next ten years; and the model is human.

HUMAN MODEL

Let's jump to pure theory for a moment. Management, or command, or administration, whichever you want to call it, is first of all an entity consisting of:

1. The top man himself.
2. His helpers, who extend his own capabilities.
3. The management system used to run the business.

The people, paper, methods, policies, practices, and procedures have to be considered as replaceable parts and subsystems of this management entity, which is first and foremost a thing composed of people and their activities. New organizations are shaped by the top man and the situation, and in old organizations, it's a toss-up whether the entity shapes the top man or vice versa. Either way, the top control is an entity-in-change at all times.

Human components have to be arranged in such a way that they conform to the capabilities and characteristics of people, and so do the non-human information media such as paper, holes, spots, and all systems of hardware. They're all parts of the same machine, and even though they are part of the change pattern, they can't escape the basically human pattern of the whole.

This human pattern is frequently spoken of as the shadow of one man, the one at the top, and even though that fellow as an individual sometimes becomes a hazy ghost of himself and all his predecessors, I think we're justified in concluding that at the very least we're working to a type of human model, and frequently the specific habits, language, and character of an individual.

I think we're fortunate in having this human model to use as a guide, because it is the one element of genuine stability in the whole future picture; it's reasonably certain to remain relatively constant, in spite of the fact that the technologies are changing like crazy.

For example, let's dream some more about that automatic memory. Assume that the top man wants to bid on a lucrative contract, that all information is available somewhere in the organization, but by paper methods it would take three weeks to gather it. Would it help the top man to be able to assign a helper to punch buttons and have the answers in a couple of hours? Would it help him in competition?

Now, looking at the other side of the coin, consider what happens to your top man, your company, and yourself if your competitor can consistently get out bids in two hours and it consistently takes you three weeks. Using your knowledge of the human model, does it take long to figure out what your competitor will do about it if he can, and what your own top man is likely to feel and do about the situation?

I think the answer is obvious that what's at

stake is the question of who survives in the competition through 1970 and beyond; and this goes for business, industry, military, and government organizations.

The way to get there first with the most, I think, is to start with the fundamental requirements of management, command, or administration and use imagination to determine their needs in speed and effectiveness. Then, assume that almost any machine requirement can be met by the explosive rates of technology, dream the ideal supplements to the human model that's still likely to be running these organizations, and work backwards from there to what we have to have installed and operating at any one time in order to hit the 1970 period with full employment of electronics. Set up a single plan in a moving series of two-, five-, and 10-year increments, and schedule each phase to be equipped with the best combination of skulls, paper, and automatics that's likely to be available in the period.

PRIMARY AREAS OF APPLICATION

The primary area of attention in application of electronics is the management entity itself, and the rest of the bits and pieces are governed by the nature of that entity and its activities and must fit into it. We start with the top man and develop needs outward from him as a human model of the total system to run the organization. But how do we look at these activities so that we can split out a piece and say, "Here is a place to start?" Let's make a stripped-down outline:

1. Top man, helpers, and system to run the business.
2. Information, do personnel, things, control plus specialties.
3. Relationships of files, people, and activities.

This is a general outline of the area and scope, but how do we get down to cases? How do we split out discrete data to automate? What comes first and why? What files are involved and how do we generate them? What about plans, requirements, lead times, schedules? What are the primary cycles of action and feedback to govern those cycles? Let's assume the existence of a top man and helpers, and ask the question, how do people get together to do a job?

There can't be much argument that the exact processes and communications between these people on any one matter of policy or project would make a chart that looked like a five-pound ball of wet fishline, yet there is a sequence of steps with much feeding back and forth of information and alteration of premises. We can show this general sequence, and the major responsibilities that have to coordinate:

1. What's the situation?   — Information
2. What's our objective?   — (All)
3. What has to be done,   — Operations
   how, when?
4. Who's to do it? Skills,   — Personnel
   when?
5. Do it with what? Tools,   — Things
   materials?
6. Money, values,   — Control
   estimates?
7. How about a plan and   — (All)
   a budget?

Although these sequential steps are general to any kind of organization, it will be easier to look at them individually if we assume one type of company and go through the relationships. A combined sales and manufacturing company will do as well as any to illustrate the files and subfiles that back up each of these areas, and what can be done with them.

Information — This area of information is an anomaly in that it is probably the most important of all to the top man and his helpers, the most directly critical to them, and one of the very best areas of application of electronics for display, research into markets and operations, estimating a situation, and general decision making. However, I'm going to bypass it and come back to it when we've gone a little further into what's available in usable information and how to use it to feed back into decision making . . . frankly, we'll get here quicker by traveling the long way 'round.

1. *Sales* —
   a. Customers—Who can we do business with? Name, location, characteristics?
   b. Products—What things and services can we sell? Name, identity, details?
   c. Sales Order Cycle—Sales order writing generates sales orders, delivery schedules, shipping schedules, order

status, order history, invoices, accounts receivable, statistics of orders, customer history, and, indirectly, production schedule files. Call this a sales order cycle, from customer through our company and back to customer; feedback on status and adequacy of performance keeps all operating files and both customer and product information files accurate.

d. Order Writing — You've probably seen sales orders written without finger motion by using some reproducible format from the customer and product files such as: masters (address plates, ditto, other), holes (cards and tapes), and spots (magnetic tapes and juke-boxes). The point to remember is that by setting this information up in usable files once, it can be accurately and rapidly put into the order-action-feedback cycles and thence multiplied 100 or 1,000 times automatically into the remainder of the cycle as needed. The files thus generated are available to report status of the situation and history of what happened.

e. Accuracy of Files — If an action order is printed directly from what's in the files, we have a very fast and reliable assurance of correction. He who has to act will make rapidly certain that the file-keeper gets told in terms that are not uncertain — he may even include remarks about it's human to err but long-eared to repeat — in any case the master data gets corrected promptly and very little inaccurate data gets into the much larger operating files. This process is a form of feedback control of accuracy.

2. *Manufacturing* — In our assumed business, the kick-off for manufacturing action is either the requirement generated by a sales order or a forecast of many future requirements. Let's look at some of the files we'd find:

a. Bill of Materials — First, even on Sunday we could find a bill of materials, call it a B/M, filed to show what we need and have to put to-

gether to assemble the XYZ gadget called for by a sales order. Now, we're not accustomed to thinking of B/M's as being generated by anything other than human effort, but it's not impossible for large parts of them to be generated by constants on file in engineering — such as standard B/M's with minor alterations to customer's specifications — and there have been plenty of computers put to work in determining what those alterations should be.

b. Operations Sheet — Second, even on Sunday we could find something on the procedure for making each individual part and assembly. This "how to make" part of the files, sometimes called routing sheet, consists mainly of steps covering how, when, who, tooling, machines, set-up time, running times per unit, materials, design responsibility, and so on. These were produced by people.

c. Manufacturing System — Kicked off by a sales order, the information on the bill of materials and operation sheet can be used to machine write a work order, which directly and indirectly generates work schedules, machine schedules, work loads, manpower requirements, material requirements, shop and department schedules, and all the rest of the production system of the company. All told, it results in maybe 100 to 1,000 times the quantitative volume of data that was in the base files.

d. Key to Automated Manufacturing Information — So, if you get this B/M and operation sheet information into automatic files in such a manner that it can be used to generate other files, you're well on your way through automatic information to automated manufacturing.

e. Cost System — Incidentally, your cost system starts with the estimates from the operations sheet; most of the detail can be generated accurately from the operations sheet codings, and the labor and materials feedbacks serve to keep the B/M and operations sheets accurate in both estimates and procedures.

f. Feedback Cycle — Action isn't complete until what happened matches what was planned. Sometimes this comparison is called plan vs. actual, sometimes variance.

g. Schedules — Once there's an accurate pool of information on what has to be accomplished and approximately when, which we generated by the work order writing process, the way is open to use computers in optimizing the best sequence and utilization of manpower and equipment, usually by a mathematical process called linear programming, plus adequate change procedure. However, here is a warning. Anything in scheduling is a change system rather than a computation, and to work, it must be approached on that basis.

Things — A by-product of the process of generating orders in the operations area is a requirement for things: materials, tools, facilities, and whatever. The key to this things area is to start all thinking and procedures from these things requirements. The files are:

1. *Status of Each Item* — This is the key file and consists of:
   a. Requirements — What and when to support operations?
   b. Orders — How many coming, when, to meet requirements?
   c. Receipts — Which ones came? How do the others stand?
   d. Use — Issues, usage; as planned or not?

2. *Item Files* — Specifications and constants about each thing to be used.

3. *Vendor or Source Files* — Who furnishes what we need?

4. *Purchase Order Cycle* — If the status of each item file shows not enough items on hand to meet requirements, the item and vendor files are used to write bid requests and purchase orders. This initiates the purchase order cycle, receipts, follow-up schedules, payables, etc.

Personnel — A by-product of the process of generating orders in the operations area is a requirement for people to do the job. The key to this personnel area is to start all thinking and procedures from these personnel requirements. The files are:

1. *Status of Personnel* — This is the key file here and consists of:
   a. Requirements — What and when to support operations?
   b. Orders and Availability — How many and when to meet requirements?
   c. Receipts — Who arrived, and how do the others stand?
   d. Use — Present location and assignment?

2. *Personnel Files* — Individual status, history, capabilities, and other.

3. *Personnel Pay and Deduction Files* — These two generate about 95 per cent of the detail in pay orders, payrolls, earnings and deduction records, union check-off lists, hospitalization, etc. This isn't all; there are roughly 100 scheduled outputs possible from this area, plus unscheduled and nonpredictable requests.

Control — The key here is plans, maintenance of how we stand in actual against the plans, and corrective action to replan and update as required. We have already described 90 to 95 per cent of the detail data that has to be tapped to run the business. That same stored information is available for control purposes. Finance is a specific area that needs real-time handling and in which the inquiry-interrogation pattern is of real interest to the top man and his helpers. How do we stand on our allocation of the number one resource, which is money?

The standardization of files, data, routine, and programs is one of the most difficult and also one of the most productive activities you can engage in. Let's look back a little and see what kind of questions and possibilities we have ahead:

1. *Questions* —
   a. Items bought, items sold; any inherent difference?
   b. Buyers and sellers; they are both people are they not?
   c. Orders to receive and to ship; two ends, are they the same deal?
   d. Orders to buy, orders to sell; same thing reversed?

e. Orders to people to do a job of work; all spell out what, where, who, when, how and why, with some estimates of how many. Can you think of any really basic difference other than prestige between work orders, maintenance orders, engineering orders, development orders, project orders, reseach task directives, standing job and production orders, and open work accounts?

2. *Possibilities* —

   a. Articles handled; be they items bought or products sold.

   b. Outside contract files; be they vendors or customers.

   c. Contracts; be they sales or purchase or subcontract orders.

   d. Operating orders; produce, research and development, maintenance, engineering, printing, sweeping and other.

   e. Operations planning; requirements, costs, controls.

3. *Examples* — A standardized system's chief characteristic is simplicity of pattern after standardization; that is, after solution the answers look stupidly simple.

Information — From here on to the end of this section on primary areas of application of electronics we're talking generally within the information area. I said we'd get back, and we're there. I'm going to bypass such things as market research and combat surveillance and other areas outside your own company. Partly, they're obvious and valuable uses, and partly, you've already thought about them. What I do intend to show in some detail is that in the internal part of your information system you need to make full use of information from outside the organization, and something of how one works with the other in decision making.

FEEDBACK

Feedback is the corrective report of outcome that is used to redirect a succeeding action cycle. All of the automated management systems that have ever worked, electronic or any other, have been based on well defined files, adequate feedback, and adequate change procedure to incorporate the experience fed back from the firing line. I have never seen or heard of one that got into successful operation until somebody worked these things out and nailed them down into a smoothly working part of the system. This may not be the story you hear either during or afterward. The steps tend to be taken in the dead of night and to be hopelessly unexplainable to the front office, so that your narrator probably never heard of them. But you can bet your last two bits that: (1) Nothing moved until the files were established, and (2) nothing was satisfactory until feedback kept them clean.

If you want a procedure to follow to assure proper attention to files, get Dick Canning's book, *Installation of EDP*, published by John Wiley, New York, and follow it.

What can you do about feedback? This isn't quite so pat as following a book; you have to follow your own nose and judgment a lot more. The ideas are beautifully defined, but in so many languages and contexts that you have to be able to recognize the patterns and cycles of automatic redirection wherever you find them, be it in humans, machines, paper systems, automatic machinery, missile guidance, navigation, management, gunnery — almost any human activity. In management systems, you have to find the cycles for yourself, though we can set forth a few rules of thumb in how to handle them:

1. Sales orders, purchase orders, work orders, research and development orders, task orders, operation orders, move orders, shipping orders, any orders.

2. Order cycles, from start to close, are action cycles.

3. Feedback of results can come from any point in the cycle.

4. The man doing the job or action owes reports on troubles.

5. Inspection specialists normally report qualitative trouble.

6. Quality control specialists feedback design troubles.

7. Accounting specialists report variances from estimates.

8. Unions frequently feedback estimate and plan troubles.

9. Customers feedback many kinds of failure information.

10. Many subcycles can exist within an order-action cycle.

11. Trouble should reflect in the file that wrote the order.

12. The shorter the feedback period, the quicker the files are clean, and the quicker the system operates successfully.

In navigation and guidance, the course is planned, and a monitoring system fixes actual track and deviation and feeds back an opposite correction to get the ship or missile back toward the planned course to the target. In automatic production, autogauging measures deviations and corrects machine settings back within quality tolerances. In heating your house, the thermostat remembers the temperature you set it for and keeps turning your furnace down and up to keep it there. In auditing and accounting, the thing is quite well described as internal check and control. In management, the process is sometimes called management control, and sometimes described as management by exception, where reports indicate the need for corrective action. Task management covers the same field.

OTHER APPLICATIONS

There are other and better publicized uses for electronics than these I've discussed as primary areas for application in your own companies, but if you shoot for the files and the feedback cycles, the others will come relatively readily as by-products or obvious developments. Reports, for instance, are sometimes a statement of situation, sometimes a guess into the future, and sometimes a form of feedback on the past. There are three kinds:

1. What's the status of the situation? Get these by output from current, updated files; keep them as real-time as a race track tote board, and arrange for output to answer any question the boss can ask, and answer it now, when it's needed . . . say, in under 10 minutes, or less . . . and preferably, do it by display rather than print-out on paper, of which we already have entirely too much.

2. What's the situation developing toward? Develop workable methods for advancing the current situation and showing the future probabilities for use in management decision making.

3. What's the history? This comes in at least three major bags. First, for any one period, what happened, what lessons can we learn from this feedback against our plan? Second, the historical, chronological record: for taxes, for law suits, for settling disputes, for seeing where we now stand, for audit and internal check, for contract renegotiations, for experience factors in planning. Third, you have here a valuable reservoir of company experience, from which you can derive totally unforeseen answers to even less foreseen questions, which naturally develop on a crash basis. Here you have the problem of information storage and retrieval in its classic form . . . large gobs of seemingly unrelated and unindexed facts. Be sure to keep it in machine usable formats. You'll find you're digging into this pile of data for the next 10 or 20 years and deriving useful trends, slants, statistics, and future guides. Tape reels and microfilm are both possible storage answers.

OPERATIONS RESEARCH

This is the pay-off area in application of electronics in your companies and organizations. Perhaps you noticed, perhaps you didn't, but I moved bag and baggage into the area of operations research in discussing reports, particularly items two and three, which boil down to advancing the situation to develop, optimize, and select the best and "least-worst" alternatives, and to searching and researching into the past operations of the business to find out what makes it tick so you can make better guesses on the future.

You are most certainly entitled to ask a question at this point: "If you consider operations research to be so important and profitable, why have you been so bashful about mentioning it?" To answer, let's review a bit:

1. First things first — The fundamentals that concern a manager: We began at the concept of automatic memory, the networks we use to run a business, and the idea of information being accessible from a distance as rapidly as wanted, via interrogation of automatic files. We went on to use of a human model as an element of genuine stability in a picture of technological change that is absolute-

ly fantastic, and we named the probable real objective of our present efforts: ability to survive in the competition to 1970 and beyond.

2. Second — The primary areas of application of electronics: We began with the procedural steps and timing of the management entity itself, breaking it into subsystems and specific files. We suggested automating the small files that generate order-action-feedback cycles, and then expanding within these cycles, with the larger files being generated as by-products of each cycle. We discussed standardization, the importance of files and feedback, and the development of reports on the past, present, and future . . . especially developing workable methods of advancing the current situation and showing future probabilities for use in management decision making.

3. Third — (and this is the crux of my reluctance): Successful operations research depends almost wholly on availability of data, of information, concerning the operations being studied. It needs not just data but reliable data, accessible data, and plenty of it; preferably, in electronically usable formats so we can crash-retrieve data from past and present files to develop answers usable in decision making now, not next year or even three months hence. Also needed is fast feedback based on current developments, to follow and amend a line of action stemming from operations research answers and their underlying assumptions if those assumptions suddenly turn out to have been glittering but not gold. It seemed best to me to outline the essential data system and some of its characteristics first, and after that, suggest that operations research should be an application goal, based on a solid information system, and used primarily in management decision making.

MODEL DEVELOPMENT

The basic procedure is to develop a model that behaves like the real thing, and then use the behavior of the model to predict the behavior of the real thing under various conditions. One of the questions that invariably develops is this: "What values are we basing our measurements on, and just which measures have any real merit in determining which of these proposed courses of action is the best one?" Now, this sounds like one of those totally impossible situations, but it isn't. The test is, does it work?

The model itself can be of many types: displays, games, charts, plots, three-dimensional scale miniatures, pilot operations, selected samples, overlays, pictures, symbolic logic, profiles, statistics . . . let's say, any way you care to name of representing something else. But what we're usually thinking of is mathematical models that can be set up as stored programs and held in a library.

There is another aspect here too. It is amazing how many situations have repeated themselves time and again in different organizations, and the solutions have been worked out, stored, and reported in the various journals of the model-makers so that:

1. Bits and pieces can be borrowed frequently.
2. Applicable simulations occasionally are found.
3. Total development from scratch is getting rarer and rarer.

What does it take to work with this field? Probably the most important attributes are understanding of the problem to be solved, an active and original imagination in developing postulates, and sheer doggedness in testing to prove the validity of relationships, assumptions, and postulated patterns.

What kind of models would be useful? How about of various classes of customers, to pretest a new sales plan or product? Or of a principal competitor, to see what he'll do in any given circumstance? Or of the operating system of your own company, to test how it will perform on a new bid, let's say, of large money and tight delivery date?

We just summarized this section in reviewing the buildup to operations research. But we can take it down to a few memory aids that are neither brilliant nor complete, but may help:

1. Scope is the system to run the organization.
2. Understand that system, its parts, and its goals.

3. Automate the files that generate other files.
4. Automate the order - action - feedback cycles.
5. Use operations research models in management decision making.

TECHNIQUES INVOLVED

What kind of techniques do we use in doing this job? They are:

1. Common sense and management planning.
2. Organization planning.
3. Work and work measurement.
4. Records management.
5. Forms and the fifty formats.
6. Archives, languages, symbols, codes, and coding.
7. Classification, identification, and handling of data.
8. Manuals, charts, writing, mathematics, and programming.
9. Standardization.
10. Survey.

It may be that you can get through these areas on the basis of intuition and what you already know, but a lot of the detail procedure in making your studies and system designs is indicated in this material, including the fundamentals of the coding systems you'll have to eventually get down and sweat out.

COMMON SENSE AND MANAGEMENT PLANNING

The first technique is common sense, and the second is the same kind of management planning that we've been discussing as the primary area of application for electronics.

ORGANIZATION PLANNING

We've just been deep in this one. As a standard technique, the problem is the continuous development of an organization to meet changing conditions. Right now, planners are having to aim five, ten, and twenty years ahead because that technological race we discussed is essentially a lead time race, and it's the early starters and the time compressors who come out on top. I don't know of any better way to hurry than by better planning, but there's so tremendously much that isn't very well understood here that I sometimes think we'd do better to deal with it as **organization research** and development and give it the full plush treatment.

WORK AND WORK MEASUREMENT

Just like electricity and gravity, work is something we don't know very much about, but we sure do try to measure it, and we learn mostly where the sore spots are in the operation, the good and bad methods, and where the effort and return are out of balance. This technique can help you in evaluating what you're studying, but in application of electronics, accept a word of caution. You will be dealing with three different kinds of work — mental, manual, and machine. Standard techniques slant toward the one you'll practically never be comparing with, and that's the finger type of manual work on repetitive jobs. By definition, that's the kind of stuff that will be inside the black boxes, so don't ignore the principles of this technique, but do realize that you're pretty much on your own in developing your own applications to your problems.

RECORDS MANAGEMENT

On the surface, it's a study of files in their old age, when what you're interested in is their generation, preferably without work. There's no better place to learn the quantity, content, and access requirements of the information system, as well as the pattern of the business, than in study and management of the almost dead archives. Why?

First, a survey of old records doesn't involve the emotional upsets tied to current operations, and the basic patterns and trends of change in the business do not get confused with current fads, opinions, and personalities.

Second, you can start in the past, come up to the present and first thing you know you're staring far into the future, which is the thing you're really interested in because your automatic system is going to take a few years to install and you'd like to have it stick for a while.

If your organization has a records management activity, you can probably get your overall statistics on files, sizes, content, and access frequencies for the asking. Your first use should be in making out the remainder of your survey plan.

FORMS

In order to store information in an electronic memory, be it core, drum, tape, disc, or juke-box, you have to set it down in definite format and pattern.

It's the same information in essentially the same pattern either way, whether you're laying it out for the coordinates of a typewriter or the coordinates of a drum location.

It's for the same purpose of coordinated action, to keep everybody working together, whether you do it with lots of copies to lots of departments or do it with an electronically connected automatic interrogation network.

It's the same set of order-action-feedback cycles that bound the copies and files of a well integrated order form system; orders for work, sales, or purchases take off from the same small files like B/M's and operation sheets to generate the same kind of huge historical files, only they use carbon and ditto and offset, rather than electronic transmission and magnetic spots.

Yes, your guess is right; you can parallel the originations and cycles of a well done order form system with punched cards, punched tapes, and all manner of electronic gear, and feel fairly safe that you've grabbed at the right areas, limits, bounds, purposes, file points, file sequences, access requirements, and information content, even inclusive of most of the codes, languages, expressions, titles, captions, and instructions.

You can frequently find highly effective and solid information systems already set up in forms, so when you accelerate the pattern with electronics, about all you're doing is changing the media and some of the methods, with nearly no alternation in the basic system pattern and procedures. Now, this is relatively reliable in order form systems, that follow the order-action-feedback cycles; but in any other area, you're likely to land in a hugely snarled tangle of incomplete cycles, especially in accounting.

There are a couple of extremely cheerful items from out of the forms area that you should know. First, we are told that about 50 standardized forms would handle 99.44 percent of the data needs of almost any organization . . . not over 50, either. Once the common denominators are found, the solutions for standard patterns are stupidly simple.

The big thing this means to you is that if less than 50 forms will do the job, the odds are strong you can lay out the total electronic system for your entire organization in terms of about 50 standard patterns also (which is far different from the 50,000 you were thinking about!), and most of your programming can be automatic in extremely high degree after you get those 50 formats found, tested, integrated to each other, and sweated together into a single simple set of beautifully standardized designs that are fully compatible in all directions. The other item of cheer is that if you were ever able to do this with forms, you can do it just as well or better with magnetic spots. The 50 formats are also a large part of the solution to your complexities in coding, terminology, standardization, and interrogation networks. If you're wondering why you've never heard this before, consider: How would a math or E.E. major ever find it out?

ARCHIVES, LANGUAGES, SYMBOLS, CODES, AND CODING

It's a clear case of the shoemaker's barefoot children; offhand, I do not know of any area of the arts and sciences that is foggier in its terms and languages than those areas that deal with terms and languages. Maybe a couple of guideposts will help in cross-indicating what you need to know:

1. *Archives* — Data, information, records, files, information storage, memory and an almost unlimited number of other synonyms, and such associated terms as archivist, librarian, library, central files, and records management.

2. *Languages* — This is a broad term. There are national languages such as English, French, German, Russian, and Chinese, and infinite subvarieties. There are trade, occupational, sectional, scientific, and joint military languages all of which are different. Machine languages cover a huge variety of types, all different. A language seems to be anything expressed in symbols and codes, and this includes mathematics, which is one of the better languages for expressing action.

3. *Symbols and Codes* — These are the languages in which a language is ex-

pressed. A symbol is anything recognizable that represents something else, and a code symbol is a symbol that is translated from, and represents, some other symbol. The word code is sometimes used alone to mean a system of symbols and/or code symbols, usually with fairly well defined meanings, which is almost never the case in the so-called natural languages, which, like Topsy, just growed. Most machines operate spots or holes for symbols, and the combinations are called codes.

4. *Encoding and Decoding* — This means going into and out of a second set of symbols.

5. *Coding* — This means sitting down and making up your own tightly defined language the way you want to use it, no matter how the same symbols are used outside of your own internal systems and procedures. The usual method of doing this is to list the entities you want to express, group them the way you want them grouped, then divide the entities into the number of available code symbols and use that interval in assigning codes to each entity. There isn't much in print that's definitive on this subject, but IBM's *Modern Methods of Coding* is at least fairly standard in its use for this purpose. Decimal codes expand to the right, serial codes expand serially, alpha numeric codes leave spaces to insert additional words and maintain both sequences, mnemonic codes have something in them that resembles the entity identified, and there are many other varieties.

If you don't know what entities you want to express, but can make a guess what the pattern will be, you can set up the code pattern and assign specifics as you find out what entities are involved.

If you can't even make a guess at what the pattern will be, then you are forced to grab for whatever national, trade, or other language you think will come closest to expressing the ideas you're dealing with, and try to redefine it as you go, so that it gradually becomes yours and yours alone . . . and some of the technical glossaries and thesauri

can become genuinely ferocious.

If there were such a thing as a general purpose, flexible, completely defined language that everybody could understand, it would simplify tremendously our various problems in information storage and retrieval, but there does not seem to be such a thing in existence. Probably the closest to it is the thoroughly standardized version of Latin that has been used for internal communication by the Catholic Church for something over 1,500 years . . . we may have to borrow it yet.

Do you see what you're up against? You either adapt a long-form natural language and cross-index yourself crazy, or make sure that you've included the total pattern and then invent your own short-form coding within it.

CLASSIFICATION, IDENTIFICATION, AND HANDLING OF DATA

A down to earth and practical approach to any type of automatic data equipment requires that we deal with discrete codes and use them as modules to build up clusters of constants permanently tied into standard packages around each of the dozen or so basic entities of the business, and then handle these packages of classification constants by means of the "handle," and entity code that is short-form, nonclassifying, and nonchanging.

1. *Find your entities* — In each specific case, just what are you dealing with? A customer? A vendor? An employee? An organizational unit? A job of work? A tool? A material? A product? A piece of paper? A location? A characteristic?

2. *Identify each entity* — Arrange coding so there's a specific identification for each discrete entity, such as a man number that means Joe Smith and nobody else, a catalog number for each material, a code for each customer, a serialized identity for each piece of paper, and so on. Fix this so that Joe remains #1492 regardless of where he works, and Department 47 remains 47 no matter how often the totem pole is shuffled. To do this, you must limit this code to identification; none of the business of mixing, of saying that #47 is by definition one

of the departments that comes within scope of #23. Limit the meaning to the unit and group only; for the other, indicate this by #23-47.

3. *Use codes of discrete entities to classify other entities* — Joe is in Department 47 which is a subdivision of 23? Say: 23-47-1492. Joe moves to another 23 subdivision, number 12? Say: 23-12-1492. Or if Joe and 47 both move over into Division 83 say: 83-47-1492. In other words, build your short form internal code on a module basis so that now or later you can shuffle the arrangement of the building blocks all you wish with no change in coding. This means nothing to change, especially in the actions of those skulls, papers, and automatic memories that have known Joe as 1492 and the unit as #47. Now or 20 years from now, they can still identify who did what to whom and maybe how come.

4. *Entity clusters and entity codes* — Entity Code 74711 can mean Smith Company, a customer, with maybe 1,000 characters of addresses, shipping data, and discrete nonchanging codes for type, city, branch, state, and so on. Set them up, carefully check them, and put the whole package of constants into the system. Do likewise for Product Entity Code 11423, and include all the technical descriptions and discrete codes for classes, such as from Department 47, product line, model and catalog, drawing, weight, shipping class, package, assembly it goes into, sales and engineering responsibility, estimated cost data, and so on. Maybe 1,000 characters could be 20 to 20,000. All these extras classify for files and analysis.

5. *Handle entity clusters by entity codes* — Just as there may be 1,000 gadgets in a suitcase but you can pick up the whole works by using five fingers on the handle of the suitcase, we can use entity codes of product and of customer to activate a couple of clusters of 1,000 characters each and originate a 2,000 character sales order. We just avoided:

   a. Look-up and writing and key input and key verify of 2,000 characters.

   b. Cranking 2,000 characters through the input of the hardware.

   c. Delay and mistakes, through automation of 99.5 per cent of input.

I call this automation of files that generate files. You can see how it can handle the detail of subsequent shippings and billings. Can you see how this can contribute to the formats by further using entity clusters as modules and combining them, as we did to make that sales order format? Hang on to this one. It's important.

MANUALS, CHARTS, WRITING, MATHEMATICS, AND PROGRAMMING

I'm lumping these into one progression because as far as you're concerned in application of electronics, they're all extremely close kin, considerably interchangeable, require the same kinds of qualities in the people who work with them, aim at the same general ends by the same general rules, and as in our earlier comments on skull, paper, and automatic media, we can say that the emphasis of study and installation shifts gradually from left to right of both sequences. Collectively and individually, there are aspects basic to your efforts:

1. *People* — To do successful work in any or all of these five techniques, the number one requirement is to understand the subject matter: the management system, its parts, how it works, who's involved, and the relevance of the particular topic to the whole. Fortunately, people who are skilled in any or all of these techniques usually understand this and are therefore relatively easy to teach. Given half a chance, they may even improve your own facts on what you think the situation is. But you might as well know now that unless you do organize and formally present an understandable frame of reference, these people will work from the mental picture of what the score was in their last employer's system of running his business. This can stop your team as effectively as a left-hand thread. The easy way is to start at the beginning with initial orientation and continuing briefings, plus continuing opportunity for each individual to fill in on the tech-

niques he does not possess, such as mathematics for writers, reading and writing for mathematicians, machine programming for both, vice versa as required, and general business, military, and government operation for the whole crowd. I mention all three because it helps tremendously to be able to pick ideas from all three. Each is ahead of the other in various fields and there's no sense reinventing what's already been worked out.

2. *Manuals* — You may be able to lift a good deal of your orientation program from the top policy, mission, organization, and functional responsibility manuals available. If your own company's manuals are terrible, which is not at all unusual, borrow somebody else's for a comparable operation, and don't overlook the military and the government. They've been forced by size to operate from manuals, and they do a pretty fair job in the fundamentals you'll need.

3. *Charts* — This is an art and not a science. A chart is a picture, and you can frequently augment it with photography. Forget the flow notion; it's like mapping the world. You need the land masses and the water in between, then you can draw in the trade routes between the concentrations of people, the two way paths of information and goods. For a management system draw the people and the files first, then it's easy to see the pattern and the unlimited paths in any direction between them. Most important: if the meaning isn't obvious in one glance at six feet, the chart is no good. Do it over.

4. *Writing* — You usually have to have something written out, accurately, before you can translate into either mathematics or machine programs. The normal language is English, and this is also true of the statements of problems that you usually need before you can solve them. It's a high skill, and the biggest part of the time and labor is usually the getting, developing, and organizing of the information you want to set out so somebody else can read it. And by the way, who must read it, and what lingo does he understand? And for what purpose is he going to use the information gained?

5. *Mathematics* — You can consider this as just another language, which sometimes you need and sometimes you don't. Mostly while you're getting started you don't. But you do have something else to consider: mathematics is the language of action, and as you get further along and start being able to provide information, you get deeper and deeper into what to do about that information. When you get this far, you're up to your ears in decision making and quantitative evaluation of action and interaction and probabilities and optimizing of choices. At this point you'd better be able to read, speak, write and think in this language of events.

6. *Programming* — This is translation from the human idiom to the machine idom. The human idom can be English, charts, mathematics, logic, or even forms; but you'll do far better if you see to it that it is a translation of some kind of human idiom that somebody else can read, understand, verify and properly fit into the over-all mosaic that is a management system. The alternative is to try to skip this explanatory and patterning step, and the result is bits and pieces that resemble my poker hands: nothing matches.

This isn't good if you want one part of the total system compatible with and accessible to all other parts, and that's what it must be, to do a job for your company. Here's where some of these other technical ideas come into use, especially over-all standardization based on the 50 formats, which in turn can be put together as entity clusters of relatively constant data, which in turn are moduled from entity codes. You will need some variety of compiler to facilitate assembly of these codes, clusters, and formats. At this point you're bypassing the "gobbledegook" and up to your ears in automatic programming.

STANDARDIZATION

Maybe you're not out of trouble at all, because about here and now the horrible realization ought to be dawning that if the machine **idiom** of the automatic files has to be standard in all parts of the system — or face a crazy quilt of conversion routines — then the original English and mathematics and system pattern should have standardized notations, patterns, nomenclature and definitions too. That brings you back into some of the natural language and internal language problems I outlined. You keep on going back and back, and pretty soon you say, "Why, this thing should have started toward uniformity of pattern and language from the start!"

I say you're absolutely right, and there isn't any reasonable alternative. For that reason you do have to start with the management entity, which is the only place in the company that they all meet and have a common denominator in the person of the head man. From there you have to study equally outward into all major areas — information, do, people, things, and control — break down and co-ordinate the top files that generate files, and then make your installation along the lines of the order-action-feedback cycles. During all of these activities, the entity clusters and the entity code lists are probably your best working tool for keeping the whole ball of wax tied into one package.

SURVEY

In making a survey of feasibility you'd best be putting about 60 per cent of your time on the problem, about 30 per cent on the techniques, and about 10 per cent on the hardware proper, the equipment. If you set the problem up correctly, you won't have much trouble picking which techniques to use in synthesizing solutions, and once these are done, selection of media, and in turn the hardware to handle the media, isn't too bad a job. The answer to each step becomes obvious as you get to it.

By Enoch J. Haga
Editor, SABE Data Processor

The Systems Approach to Effective Management

THE SYSTEMS APPROACH to effective management represents an attempt to coordinate and control the affairs and course of enterprise, whether public or private, by making it possible for timely and adequate data to be placed in the hands of those individuals charged with the authority and responsibility for making decisions. Such an approach to management is neither new nor wholly dependent upon automatic data processing.

At the Arsenal of Venice, in 1436, an eyewitness reported that in the span of six hours, 10 galleys were fully provisioned, armed, and manned — simply by being towed down a waterway, the Renaissance equivalent of a modern production line. By the time the King of France visited the Arsenal in 1574, a newly built galley was launched and readied for sea, fully armed, in less than a single hour. Implicit in such speedy production is planning, the heart of the systems approach. By making use of this approach, rather than trusting to luck and hoping for the best, managers plan in advance for the successful achievement of the aims of their particular enterprises.

TOTAL INTEGRATED SYSTEMS

Today, managers are becoming interested in what may be called total integrated systems. It may be taken for granted that each enterprise exists for some primary purpose. With business this purpose is usually, if not invariably, the maximizing of profits. Systems are, therefore, simply well organized and implemented plans for the achievement of this aim. The word "integrated" implies that the various plans will fit and function together as parts of a coherent whole. The word "total" indicates that no part of the management of enterprise will be left entirely to chance. An effort will be made to plan, control, and coordinate the use of all the human and material resources that are to be used in the production of economically useful goods and services.

Management itself is the most important factor of production, for the fortunes of empire and enterprise rise or fall with the right or wrong decisions of men. The Chinese emperors knew this when they planned for the provincial administration of China. They wisely provided for the periodic rotation of governors. Further, no governor could rule in his native province. Nepotism, graft and corruption were thus reduced. This was an attempt at systematic and orderly government. The Chinese emperors believed that if a man was a good administrator or manager, his talents would be equally useful in a variety of posts.

Until the opening of the twentieth century, managers usually relied upon their own judgment and upon the advice of trusted associates, in conducting the affairs of business. They trusted to their own knowledge, skills and shrewdness in the process of decision making. The last vestiges of such a philosophy of management are seen today in the professed ability of some managers to size up new employees during interviews, to make quick decisions on the basis of scanty information and to operate generally on hunch and intuition. That such practices sometimes seem to have a measure of validity is no more surprising than that sometimes the weatherman should turn out to be correct in his predictions.

But the concept of total integrated business systems aims to plan the affairs of business in such a way that its course can be plotted, checked, and reoriented at every step of the way, so that preordained results may be achieved in accordance with expectations.

It is generally supposed that the art and

science of management developed and arose out of the Industrial Revolution. It seems likely, however, that the reverse is true. For it is inconceivable that any enterprise could succeed — financial, industrial, military, or otherwise — without the planning, control and direction which must necessarily proceed from management. There is evidence, for example, of a total systems approach being used in the Birmingham factory of Boulton and Watt prior to 1805. This factory used time and motion study to establish job standards, incentives and costs. Applied managerial talent at this early factory was considered to equal, if not surpass, the development of actual manufacturing skills. The cost accounting system used was superior to that of many successful twentieth century firms, with forecasting being used to plan production.

MANAGERIAL CLASS EXPANDS

As the factory system developed, larger and larger amounts of money were needed to acquire and maintain the men, plant, equipment and materials needed for the productive process. As the factory system expanded, the managerial class tended to expand also. This expansion brought about a shift in the character of management. At first the owners of capital themselves controlled its use, but gradually financiers tended to employ managers to oversee the productive processes. Managers were hired to perform a function, much in the same manner that ordinary laborers were hired. Today, it is not uncommon for managers to have no direct financial interest in the businesses whose affairs they manage. In this respect they are in no better position than the workers they supervise.

At any rate, the managerial class has grown to the extent that the field of management encompasses a diversity of areas including administrative, financial, office, personnel and production. Each major function, administrative or productive, requires a manager. As organizations grew and expanded, each expanding function required a new division or department. Often the growth was haphazard and undirected. A manager might do an excellent job of running a useless department. In the absence of adequate information, management guessed on the basis of what it did know and hoped that things would turn out satisfactorily.

Gradually, some of the leaders in management began to realize that an attempt should be made to obtain information as a basis for decision making. Indeed, while it seemed that the whole function of management was to use information, guesswork was still the rule.

Charles Babbage wrote what is perhaps the first modern book on the science of management. His *On the Economy of Machinery and Manufactures*, published in 1832, was the result of a decade of study directed toward finding a way to manufacture his engines, or computing machines. What Babbage was trying to do was find some systematic approach to management that would help to bring about a breakthrough in manufacturing technology. Babbage failed to get his engines built, but his ideas were basically sound and today he is considered to be the originator of the systems approach to data processing. Babbage intended to control his machines with punched cards, an idea picked up from the weaving industry which had used punched paper tape to control looms as early as 1725.

The Swedes, George and Edward Scheutz, contemporaries of Babbage, did succeed in building a more modest difference engine. This machine was purchased by the Dudley Observatory of Albany, New York, and placed in operation in 1858. Thus, nearly a century before the first electronic computer, its mechanical prototype was placed in operation on American soil.

Scientific management, the precursor of the contemporary systems approach to business management, began in the U. S. in the late nineteenth century with the work of Frederick W. Taylor. Taylor, who in 1878 began his meteoric rise in management as a laborer for the Midvale Steel Company, today is considered to be the father of time and motion study. Twenty years after his stay at Midvale, Taylor went to Bethlehem Steel, where he was responsible for vast improvements in methods of handling pig iron, shovelling coal and ore, and especially important advances in metal cutting. The result of Taylor's work was invariably greater production and higher wages for the workers using the improved methods.

It would be possible to catalog the work of many other leaders in the advance toward scientific management, but it is sufficient to show that the systems approach to business management did not suddenly develop overnight. Instead it incorporates and extends most of the principles of scientific management, the chief principle being that events which are planned in advance have a higher potentiality for occurring than events which are not planned. An official of a company which used Taylor's principles of management reported in 1911 that his company was able to do three times the previous volume of work with the same number of men and at the same cost. The essential difference was that more men were used in planning and management, and less in production.

ORGANIZATION IS KEY WORD

What is really new about the total integrated systems approach to business management? Very little. The scientific approach is still there, as is the emphasis on time and motion study, job standards, incentives, increased productivity and lower costs. True, the scientific approach has been borrowed from the factory and applied to white collar work. True, the mathematical and statistical problem solving techniques of operations research give promise of making the scientific approach more sophisticated. But what may be really new is an increased awareness on the part of management that it must make use of and plan for the gathering of information to be used in the decision making process.

This very realization has called attention to the fact that business enterprises must be organized in such a way that they can be managed. Those enterprises that are not well organized must be reorganized and those that are well organized must be kept that way. New businesses must be planned so that the management hierarchy is able to initiate and maintain effective control and coordination of operations.

Recently, the managers of even large enterprises relied chiefly on historical accounting data as the main source of information on operations. Managerial decisions were made on the basis of whether or not the company had a profit during the preceding accounting period. The efficacy of the decisions made was almost a direct function of the adequacy of the firm's accounting system. Even small companies were forced to gather some information about themselves for tax purposes and reporting to various governmental agencies.

Today, the means for rapid gathering and processing of data are available, and the most advanced enterprises are using them to collect data in time for it to be of positive use to management. Financial reports several days to several weeks old are of little current value and the trend is toward getting information about today's happenings so corrective action, if needed, can literally be taken immediately for the improvement of tomorrow's operations.

The fact that the accountant provided almost the only useful information about the success or failure of business operations, in large measure, accounted for his great influence and importance in the realm of management. But there are other aspects of management and with the increasing use of data processing systems and automatic computers, the role of the accountant in management may diminish or the accountant will extend the range of his profession. In any event, managers of the various departments are going to be able to get information from business systems of such accuracy and quality that their value to their companies is going to be measurably enhanced. Already this is true. Managers who have valid information as a basis for making decisions, and who use it, are bound to be more useful than those who do not.

Data processing systems can be used to provide rapid analyses of large quantities of paper work relative to practically any aspect of administration or production. Does the sales manager want to know which territories provide the highest volume of sales? Does the personnel manager want to analyze the characteristics of his work force? Does the inventory control manager need to know when to reorder materials? Does the production manager have the responsibility for setting and maintaining complex production schedules? The computer can be used as a tool to provide the answers.

In some lines, such as insurance, the company that does not automate will soon find itself unable to compete and out of business. Data processing can help managers to become better managers, but the managers must know what kind of information they need in order to make decisions. Reports produced by the computer that are never used, or that are unnecessary, are no better than useless hand written reports.

Here, it is important to again note that a total integrated systems approach to business management does not necessarily imply that automatic data processing machinery or computers must be used to provide data for management. Many businesses can operate quite well without computers. Others can make use of the facilities of data processing service bureaus. But the systems approach does have some common principles, whether computers are used or not.

PRINCIPLES IN SYSTEMS APPROACH

First, the enterprise must be viewed as a whole. Such questions must be answered as: What is this company trying to do? How can this company be organized to achieve its aims? What kind of men do we need to run this company The whole enterprise must be planned from top to bottom. Nothing or nobody should exist without a function. No function should exist without a purpose.

Second, in the organization structure, form must follow function. The organizational chart of the company should reflect the various integrated tasks that are to be performed by each department. It will not be wise to form a department merely because another company has one similar, or because such a department has traditionally existed in a given line of endeavor.

Adequate exploitation of the benefits of the total integrated systems approach to enterprise dictates the emergence of new organizational patterns to facilitate the doing of old jobs in new ways and the performance of completely new tasks. The recent newspaper reports of pending shakeups in U. S. Army organization is a case in point. In California, the governor is attempting, and has partially succeeded in, a vast reorganization of state government. Old forms of organization must yield to new.

In the third place, men, materials and facilities must all be selected with the aim of fitting them to their tasks — not their tasks to them. In particular, machinery, especially automatic data processing equipment, should not be acquired before it has been determined exactly what it is to do. With new organizational structures and new tasks cutting across old departmental lines, personnel adaptable to new and changing job requirements must be secured.

Fourth, one of the characteristics of businesses using the total systems approach will be a heightened receptivity to change and to new ideas. Nearly all of the larger enterprises will make use of systems and procedures programs and groups, and even smaller organizations will have a systems and procedures program of some kind. New ideas and new machinery will be continually explored in an effort to find better ways of achieving the major goals of business operations. This is the systems approach.

REFERENCE:

Henry H. Albers, "The Management Problem: Past and Present," ORGANIZED EXECUTIVE ACTION: DECISION MAKING, COMMUNICATION, AND LEADERSHIP. John Wiley & Sons, Inc., New York, 1961. Pages 3-62.

By Richard W. Reynolds

Modern Management Concepts
of Computer Systems

AMERICAN MANAGEMENT has reacted vigorously and successfully to the challenges of booms and busts, innovations, wars and an environment characterized by continuing change over the past century.

Never before, however, has it been faced with a dynamic challenge of present scope and dimensions. The society in which it resides has become dramatically aware that it is locked in a genuine death struggle with a merciless and dangerously capable Communist enemy.

At the same time a revolution in technology has begun which many scientists predict will be remembered in centuries to come, not as the dawn of the space age, but as the birth of the computer age. The computer concept will have as significant an effect on man's understanding of himself and his powers as the Copernican and Darwinian revolutions.

Against the confusing transitional background of the past decade, American management found the newborn electronic computer delivered into its hands, and much like a bewildered father of the oldtime cartoons, wondered what to do with it. Decision on this moot point was delayed by most, but some managements decided to put the computer to work as a pioneering experiment. Results can be accurately described as minor mixtures of comedy and pathos, with a solid, extended base of productive experience. It is fortunate that we have developed such sound experience, for the computer system has become the key tool of the new technological age.

Concern with the concentration and focus of Soviet scientists on developing computers that reason with superhuman ability is voiced by many of our own scientists returning from visits to Russia. It is a fairly safe prediction to say the winner of the trade and military race will be the society that learned to use the computer system most extensively and wisely.

Discussion of management computer systems is a fruitless pastime without pre-recognition of basic reality in three areas: 1) the environment in which management operates; 2) the human resources which are utilized by management to obtain results; and 3) the management process.

THE MANAGEMENT ENVIRONMENT

The member of management belongs to a dynamic team which is engaged in an intense competitive struggle to provide some kind of value to society in return for a profit. Price fixing scandals notwithstanding, there are a great number of opposing management teams in this struggle, each team desperately trying to outwit the others in securing the identical proportion of profit from the identical society. Changing characteristics of the demands of society, new innovation of technical means and changing competitive strategies form the external environment which makes the concept of security an illusion for any management team.

The term management is imbued with the concept of getting goals accomplished through other people. The idea is easy to comprehend when we think of the owner of a small business with perhaps a handful of men in his employ. But when we try to picture the involvements when the organization is large enough to have a dozen or more vertical levels and perhaps hundreds of horizontal segments at the lower levels, it is often difficult to come into realistic focus on the situation. Each of the groups of people involved will have its own territory staked out in the current way of things. Each individual group will have its vision and viewpoint limited severely by the natural obstacles of both their organizational immobility and the narrow selectivity of communications parceled out to them by other areas of management. Group codes of behavior reflecting their job satisfactions and fears will be well established. Ordinarily, these codes will be designed to offer fierce, if subtle, resistance to any imposed changes that threaten the group securities of income, fair supervisory treatment, and other social or work satisfactions. This means that the key to successful changes of significant dimension is within the group itself. Any key of such intimate nature is best manipulated by the genuine leadership of management and, in fact, may not turn for any kind of authoritarian decree.

The desire of groups for the security of status quo is one of the strongest contributors to inflexibility in an organization. On the other hand, genuine leadership, if available and applied, can create a sense of greater satisfactions and securities to unleash a capacity for successful change.

The management process may be regarded as one great feedback control device. The concept of feedback control as used by management is simple. A target, or objective, is set, such as some future condition of the organization that might be desired. At the same time the means by which the future target condition will be attained is determined. Finally, a device is prescribed for gathering and reporting the necessary information to determine at any time how far away from the target condition the organization is. Ideally, the device also provides information as to the causes for being off course and off schedule, so that determination of efficient corrective actions becomes a relatively simple process.

The management process, then, is concerned primarily with the coordination of three main functions: 1) *Planning,* which includes the setting of objectives, development of plans for attaining objectives, organizing and staffing; 2) *Doing,* which includes the implementation of plans, and the directing of such implementation; and 3) *Inspecting,* which includes the gathering, interpretation, and reporting of the feedback information.

CHAIN OF COMMAND

Until this time, we have considered the management process at the very top of the organization. But how does this process work down through the various levels of the organization? When top management sets an objective, it also determines a means by which this objective (end) is to be obtained.

Supposedly, each means is then considered as a sub-objective and again means are determined to achieve each such sub-objective. The process is continued over and over again in a continuing delegation down through the ranks until objectives and means are established for the lowest clerks. Theoretically, there is constructed a neat means-end chain by which everyone in the organization knows precisely what his limits of means are to achieve those objectives. In theory, the functions of management become rather easy to handle, for every executive knows what his responsibilities and authorities are, and are not, in the areas of planning, organizing, staffing, directing, controlling and coordinating.

In practice, it is a difficult, if not an impossible chore, to find a large, complex organization that has such a neat means-end chain defined according to textbook prescriptions. One is more likely to find the same objectives and responsibilities split and hazily distributed among several segments in the organization in complete contrast to established principles of organization.

This situation becomes compounded with the periodic resetting of objectives to meet changing external conditions. Evaluation of a manager's performance becomes an embarrassment, since split objectives and split authorities and means simply do not permit straightforward measurement. The inability to measure performance accurately, lowers executive morale.

What managers and their groups are being held responsible for, and measured for, then, is something less than an integrated, productive contribution to a dynamic organizational leadership in the worldwide competition. Wherever managers and their groups are held responsible for less than this, the management process has deteriorated in some degree towards a deadening routine, and resistance to change is in danger of becoming an established way of life.

Wherever resistance to change has become an entrenched way of life, even the strongest kind of leadership will find devastating delay in effecting corporate reaction to the demands of a rapidly changing environment.

ABILITIES OF MODERN COMPUTER

The modern computer system makes provision for the trapping of pertinent data in mechanical or electronic devices. The device may be any of the following: punched card, punched paper tape, punched tag, magnetic tape, magnetic ink characters (MICR) and regular inked standard characters for optical scanners (OCR). The data may be transported physically, or transmitted electronically, to other devices which prepare the data for entry into the computer, or in some cases the data may be entered directly into the computer.

The computer itself has arrangements for storing data file informations, and its programmed instructions for processing data, either internally or externally. It has a capability of manipulating data and making decisions in this regard at fantastic speeds. New data are compared and processed against the internal or external storage that is made available for the length of the program. The proper calculations are made, history files are updated and data are read out.

The data that are read out are either printed in prescribed format as a service document, or an historical or control file, or are recorded on some mechanical or electronic device for transportation or transmission, and later conversion.

There are four classes of computer systems. First, there is the special purpose system which may be custom built for a particular company, or for companies having identical systems. In these systems, programs are generally built into the equipment and there is little demand or capacity for additional programs or reprogramming.

Second, there is the off line type of system. With this system, transactions are accumulated in batches and periodically run into the computer to update the master files that are processed at the same time. Interrogation of a single record is difficult, however, for the entire file must be hooked into the computer and run serially until the required record is reached.

Third, there is the in line system which incorporates a random access memory storage file. With this system any record may be updated or read out at any time regardless of its sequence in the file.

Finally, there is the real time type of system. Although to date, it has been limited to military applications, reservation problems, and production recording systems, this is possibly the management computer system of the future. Under this concept, data is entered into the system as soon as the transaction takes place. The data is immediately transmitted to the computer. The computer, in turn, immediately makes all decisions regarding records that would be affected by the new data and updates these records without delay.

REALIZING REAL TIME SYSTEM POTENTIAL

The technology of this real time system is available only to the extent that a small segment of a complex organization can take advantage of it. But the definitely obtainable goal set by the equipment manufacturers is a total real time system for management which will take care of every routine transaction automatically. With such a system, management will have to work out: 1) forecasting policies for each product; 2) optimum manufacturing and procurement plans; and 3) financial policies involving inventory and investment costs.

The computer itself, combined with operations research, will be of great help to management in devising these policies and plans. The informational flow of data will then be determined by the specialist team. This flow will include origination and inputs of data, transmission, memory storages and programmed instructions for data processing and decision making. It will also include proper transmission and output devices for informational reports of trends and historical nature, automatic decision and action documents, and exception (flash) reports.

In the past, we heard the old bromide about the computer being only an extremely fast moron. But today, it has become fairly well recognized that the computer acted as a moron because we insisted on communicating with it in moronic language. We also utilized it in a manner that did not make our own insight look too good. The computer can, in fact, manipulate all kinds of symbols besides numbers. Our present ability to communicate words is at a pidgin English level, but it is improving very rapidly.

Computers can be programmed to learn on the basis of experience and to reprogram themselves to do a better job — with a kind of inductive reasoning used by human beings. In a yet limited way, they can solve relatively ill-structured problems by trial and error search, by solving an abstract from the given problem, by using analogy, by means and ends, goals, sub-goals reasoning, and by adjusting aspirations to the attainable. The potential for increasing and utilizing this ability as computer technology advances over the next decade is awe inspiring.

What the computer system can do has been as much limited by our own unwillingness to understand and utilize its abilities as by any limitations of its earlier or present technical specifications. It is a fact that a primary benefit of installing a computer is the forced examination of current objectives and systems-means in the area of installation. The savings that result from such a forced examination seldom fail to surprise the management involved. As modern managements begin to apply computer systems to their problem as a whole, the forced examination of objectives and systems-means will have to be complete.

It will be found in a multitude of cases that, when considering the capabilities of the computer system, data need not be originated as it is presently. Neither do controls, files, and duplications have to be effected as presently, and the same applies to human judgments based on experience patterns and "rules of thumb." In fact, organizational units need not be continued in the same complex inflexible design as they are presently.

The computer will permit the design and operation of a much different, more complex system. However, the complexity will be generally contained within the equipment itself; it will not involve bulky organization. Further, the more complex system will supply management with information that is far more simple, selective, and pertinent to the problems involved.

THE ROLE OF OPERATIONS RESEARCH

Operations research is an activity which involves the application of mathematics and scientific thinking to the solution of business problems. It is generally teamed up with the computer system not only for the fast computing advantages, but also because the computer system is in the process of gathering business facts and making decisions in the most efficient manner available. Computer systems cannot give optimum benefits to management without the inclusion of applied operations research techniques.

Several operations research techniques have been devised which successfully relieve managers of a whole series of decisions including control of inventory, production, purchasing, warehousing, and shipping. Linear programming calculations to determine product mix, and simulation of airline operations for optimum decision making are but two other highly successful areas of operations research techniques. The increasing use of the PERT statistical method has already effected tremendous savings in management planning, coordination and control. This method involves defining, integrating and establishing definite control over all intellectual and physical activities essential for the timely achievement of program deadlines.

In most of these cases, an automatic data processing computer system has been involved. The established trend clearly shows elimination of much routine decision making from management. The eventual optimum use of combined operations research — automatic data processing systems techniques will permit management by exception to become a principle of continual use by the higher levels of management. It may also greatly relieve the need for a great proportion of middle management personnel to continue doing their jobs the same old way.

CLOSING REMARKS

To avoid being accused of taking an over simplified view, let us admit that the problems involved are formidable indeed. The earlier discussion of the environment of the management world and the management process was meant to emphasize the difficulties in the most important area of our discussion. Before a total computer systems approach may be taken by top management, a second philosophy must be thought out and put into practice in this regard. This will take some doing in itself. Then, before any available equipment can be utilized, top management must get sufficiently into each area affected by the study for the proposed changeover to actively advise on the setting of policy.

Such detailed activity by top management executives, although necessary, is very difficult for many of us to picture. Not withstanding the problems of getting top management involved to such an extent, the complexity of technical problems and considerations are tremendous, as are the resistance problems inherent in the vast bulk of organizational personnel.

Even with improved technical capabilities, it is likely that the application of automatic data processing computer systems will continue on a piecemeal basis for some time. Technically, this may be an inefficient method of utilizing the equipment. However, it is probably the most realistically efficient method of implementation under present circumstances. Piecemeal implementation gives the computer system a fighting chance against entrenched personalities, quill pen requirements and management unfamiliarity with the new informational tools available to them. A number of piecemeal implementations may eliminate enough unwarranted requirements and unfamiliarities to permit eventual management agreement toward a total system.

By Arthur H. Pike
Norwich University

Total Systems Approach to Business Management

MAKING DECISIONS IN BUSINESS is often like trying to catch fog in a fish net. Even with the best of systems, aided by electronic devices, decision making by executives involves complex procedures. Often, needed facts elude the decision maker, or data takes so long to assemble that its usefulness for current decision making is lost.

The success in the last decade of electromechanical and electronic data handling equipment in processing information for executive use is a familiar story. Executives initially expected such hardware would both speed up data processing and also result in cost savings in clerical routines.

But, in fact, the speed of data processing equipment alone, and its ability to provide comprehensive information for managerial use, resulted in widespread acceptance of electronic equipment, even where expected cost savings were not fully realized.

PROBLEMS ARISING FROM
SOME PRESENT SYSTEMS

The information an executive really needs does not necessarily result from the output of present procedures, even where electronic equipment is in use. Some present day systems are the result of a sort of patchwork pattern in which data handling equipment has been fitted here and there as business emergencies required. The equipment itself cannot provide an integration of system functions. Electronic equipment merely provides various means by which management may secure information. In an ideal system, the objectives of the processing routines would first be established, and appropriate hardware would then be selected for the attainment of these objectives.

PROBLEMS CONFRONTING
DECISION MAKERS

The executive who makes business decisions needs adequate data processed into usable report form. Then, according to his appraisal of the situation and his understanding of company policies or objectives, the executive selects his course of action. This strategy is largely based on conditions as he understands them from his study of the data.

Thus, the more accurate the data, the more likely are correct and profitable executive decisions. Executives are therefore understandably anxious to have complete and accurate information about all factors affecting their firms, within limits set by the cost of obtaining such data.

DATA PROCESSING EQUIPMENT
RELATED TO DECISION MAKING

Quite commonly, data processing equipment has fitted well into existing systems. Following initial success within an existing system, some executives have logically begun to consider the utilization of such equipment in a broader, more integrated scheme. Their ideas involve the concept of a total integrated system, using appropriate parts of some of the newly developed mathematical and electronic tools, designed to provide the more accurate and complete information needed by decision makers.

The two alternate approaches to system design are suggested by the following two rhetorical questions:

Should our firm continue to use data processing equipment and other new management techniques within the framework of existing systems, introducing them as easily, painlessly and profitably as possible? . . . or

Should we attempt to totally revise existing systems so as to establish a new relationship between men, machines and company objectives?

The success of electronic data processing equipment makes it possible to plan a total system that will perform at high speed and with great accuracy. Computers, for example, with new types of input and output devices, coupled with new techniques of scientific management, permit the more rapid and accurate processing of data expected in a total systems approach to data processing.

Heretofore, hardware has often successfully handled individual operations involved in processing data. Tomorrow's executive will use data processing equipment for much more than handling simple routines, so that the complex interactions among the many individual operations of a business firm will merge into a total system.

THE INTEGRATED FIRM CONCEPT

Perhaps an utimate (and today visionary) goal is the complete integration of all systems within a firm, to result in an automatic firm. Within this hypothetical firm, all phases of production, sales and data handling would be instantly responsive to each other, to the external world and to pre-established decision patterns. In addition, the whole network would report information to management as required and would be instantly responsive to revised management decisions.

To date, some electronic equipment installations have partially attained completely automatic operation. Whether the ultimate automatic system will result from a part-by-part building block technique, or whether a firm must start anew with a master plan, is often debated. It is probably fair to say that practical considerations, for some time to come, will dictate block approach.

AN INTEGRATED BUSINESS SYSTEM

An automatic firm may or may not be presently possible. However, the concept of the integration of business functions is being considered by many firms today. Basically, in an integrated business system, transactions occur, are recorded, communicated and stored largely through the use of electronic devices. Managers consider facts reported to them as outputs of the system, consult company policy, make decisions, transmit these decisions to others, who, in turn, use this information as a basis for further decision making.

Such a concept of an integrated system also sounds somewhat visionary today to some executives. The concept is not that of an automatic office, without human operators, but of the integration of data handling routines in such a way that humans are assisted in making decisions, not replaced as decision makers.

Unsolved problems of supplying data at input stages, and equipment limitations, exist as difficulties in the paths of designers of integrated business systems. One of the major problems in the total organization of a system is that the hardware required is not yet available in the form of any single device. In fact, the trend in hardware seems to be toward the manufacture of more and more pieces of equipment. Even a drawing board design of a total system requires the designer to choose from a greater variety of basic units to accomplish his task. The amount of new equipment introduced each year clearly indicates that there can be no universally optimum choice.

INTEGRATED DATA HANDLING SYSTEMS

As part of a total integration of systems, many firms are installing integrated data handling systems. Such systems are usually planned with a capacity for growth and change as needs of the firm dictate. Many of these systems succeed in cutting away useless and outmoded procedures not contributing value to the firm.

Designers of such systems have a difficult task cut out for them. In addition to an evaluation of the data output needs of a firm, they must plan a program for such a system, establish codes, design new forms and reports, select and supervise installation of equipment. They will also plan for the collection of input data in a form suitable for automatic processing.

Integrated system designers treat hardware as a part of the total system, using it appropriately to achieve their objectives. Both the objectives of the system, and the limitations and requirements of the equipment, are considered. Compromises are made to obtain optimum equipment utilization and system balance.

An integrated system is a constantly developing one, often of tremendous complexity, with equipment used in the total system where it best appears to function.

CONVERSION PROBLEMS

The conversion from an existing system to an integrated data handling system cannot be expected to proceed without problems. Among difficulties often reported are those resulting from forms changes. Human problems also often occur at several levels within the firm. The heavy financial investment in terms of new equipment and system design cost may also be an adverse factor, and may influence management to continue using existing systems, even where integration appears feasible.

There are also problems in maintaining the accuracy of the system. The speed and complexity of a total system requires that special attention be given to insuring accuracy of the input data, of the equipment during processing, and in output results.

For example, where a manual system is in use, gross errors in input data may be detected by the clerks processing the data and corrected. But with the use of automatic input data, either erroneous input data or machine malfunction might introduce errors.

Techniques for checking the accuracy of the machine work are provided in the design of some equipment. Internal audit techniques, perhaps of a sampling nature, may also need to be considered at sensitive points in the processing routine, even though such checks may slow down procedures.

CONSIDERATIONS INTRODUCED BY HUMAN FACTORS

Wholehearted acceptance of new concepts of system design by executives and by workers cannot always be expected. Vested interest in present methods almost always exist. Inertia and resistance to change will be encountered, especially where major changes are introduced. Questions dealing with the job fates of clerical workers have to be faced. Very real human problems have to be considered.

Finding solutions to problems of this sort may be difficult for management during early and transitional stages of installing a total system. But it is probable that such problems begin to solve themselves, at least in part, during the rather lengthy period of time re-

quired for the completion of the transition to a total system.

Careful attention to other personnel problems should smooth the transitional stages as much as possible.

Many new management concepts are being developed today. Among these, two seem especially worth consideration as bearing upon the concept of a total integrated system scheme. These two are, operations research and systems analysis.

OPERATIONS RESEARCH

Operations research is part of newly emerging decision theory studies. As such, it has a direct bearing upon the concept of the totally integrated management information system, particularly at the output and beyond levels.

Operations research involves the use of mathematical and statistical techniques. Models are created and the best (or least painful) solution among many alternatives in a decision making situation is sought.

At present, the operations research theory is especially well developed in production areas, where more certain control of all factors may be attained. It is somewhat less developed in marketing and administrative areas, partly because of the interrelations implicit in these areas which are beyond the control of experimenters.

New techniques suggested by operations research are primarily mathematical in nature. The merging of some of the operations research concepts into a total integrated management information system suggests greater success in planning and controlling business firms, especially where patchwork or hunch methods formerly were used. Many of these new operations research concepts are in their early developmental stages, and practical applications are not yet too plentiful. Nonetheless, the potential implications of operations research techniques in the handling and analysis of management information are tremendous.

THE SYSTEMS ANALYST

System analysis is required to some extent whenever equipment is used. But systems groups become especially important and even central when a total integrated management information system is under consideration.

The role of the analyst involves the development of effective ways and means for people and machines to carry through a business operation.

Involved are problems concerning adequate design of documents and forms, the flow of information, how information originates, how it is to be processed and the means by which it is to be used to control the operation. Selection of equipment, as has been mentioned, is usually a task for the analyst.

The whole system concept is often first advanced by the system group. Basic to the concept of a total system is the thought that the system will lead to an improvement in management.

The goal of a systems group is that it utilizes hardware most effectively in an integrated method leading to the greatest realization of company objectives.

THE TOTAL SYSTEM CONCEPT IN SMALLER FIRMS

The concept of a total system of information handling need not be limited to large firms able to afford costly electronic equipment. Small or medium sized firms may also use the concepts of such an integrated system, without necessarily spending the money required to buy or rent electronic equipment.

Time on such equipment, where it seems necessary to employ equipment in the system, may often be leased through commercial sources. A total integrated management information system may thus be contemplated by the management of almost any sized business firm, and is within the reach of all managements.

By H. E. Schmit
IBM Data Processing Division

Data Processing Techniques for Management by Exception

To APPRAISE the real value of good management, the objective of manufacturing in depth must be considered. Consider the cost of certain events which occur in many plants. For instance, what is the complete cost of stockouts? Schedule delays? Production bottlenecks? In terms of dollar value, what do they mean to the plant? What is the cost of a report which comes too late to correct an undesirable situation?

These are some of the questions that make up the nightmares of management men. The answers are critical in almost any type of manufacturing operation and they can mean the difference between profit and loss.

Management, of course, has been facing these questions for a long time. In the past, however, there was a certain amount of guesswork in the answers. The need for rapid decisions often forced managers to seek shortcuts. The human error factor in compiling detailed statistics might throw the results way out of line. The size of the problem frequently left blank areas in management's plans.

Today, management has a technique for tackling these critical questions. Control of manufacturing cycle functions, from raw material to finished product, can now be combined into a single data processing operation developed by International Business Machines Corporation, called the management operating system (MOS). MOS is designed so that sales orders, entered into a data processing system, will aid in sales forecasting, materials planning, inventory management, plant scheduling, work dispatching and operations evaluation.

MOS is not a new machine, but rather an organized plan of control that can be adapted to any existing computer with random access memory. The basic principle of MOS is management by exception — bringing to management's attention only those items which demand special action. Management thus has more time to concentrate on its primary task of managing problem situations.

AN INTEGRATED PLAN

The idea of computer control over manufacturing functions is not new. Inventory control, sales forecasting and manpower planning through data processing machines have been used in plants all over the country for a number of years.

As a first step in introducing manufacturers to MOS, an analysis of the current manufacturing cycle is conducted. The main objective is to determine the basis for the interaction of what heretofore had been considered separate elements of manufacturing. The next step is to reduce this knowledge to data processing programs and allied record-keeping functions that constitute an integrated management operating system.

To get an idea of how MOS works, review these components of business: Every manufacturing company uses materials, machines, manpower and money in order to provide goods for its customers. Now, if these four elements were available on an unlimited basis, management would be an easy task.

But there's one element missing — profits. A manager must keep all functions within carefully delineated limits so that manufacturing costs do not wipe out profits.

Special conditions arise often. There are always pressures being exerted on the manager from competition, sudden market changes, tool changes, breakdowns and a number of other factors. And if the manager cannot shift his production plans quickly, he and his company may lose business.

The problems that can develop in a manufacturing situation are many. Inventory can rise excessively, tying up an excessive amount of capital investment; or fall too low, jeopardizing the fulfillment of customer orders. Machines may not be utilized effectively. Manpower requirements can deviate drastically from previously determined plans. Manufacturing cost can climb to levels which completely absorb profit potential.

Many manufacturing companies have avoided some of these troubles with the aid of data processing systems on specific applications. This type of improvement might be called "sub-optimization" because only partial improvement of the total system is achieved. Thus, although the system may ensure minimum inventory levels, effective use of machine facilities may be impossible due to fluctuating plant loads and unrealistic plant schedules.

With MOS, management can be informed about a capacity problem in time to take corrective action. Management by exception focuses attention on the areas where management help is needed most. As a result, the company gains a more efficient use of management talent while maintaining a tight control on manufacturing.

FOR EXAMPLE

Assuming a plant uses a Ramac data processing system with MOS, the procedure would be as follows:

Certain factors and data relating to manufacturing operations and plans are stored in the memory of the machine. As work progresses, factors which might affect manufacturing, including orders, shipments, inventory transactions and labor tickets, are fed into the computer. The Ramac, in turn, makes the necessary adjustments to all six basic areas of manufacturing. The MOS program is also designed to effect changes in engineering specifications at the most economic point in the cycle. Considering inventory position, machine utilization and manpower distribution, the computer informs management when and where it would be best to begin the changes.

In all cases, management plays the key role. Although the data processing equipment carries the heavy burden of decision making, it is up to management to interpret the computer's results and carry out the decisions.

RAMAC - MOS ACTION

These steps are taken:

1. MOS starts with forecasting. Sales management provides a forecast of the end items needed during a specific period. If the items are a combination of devices of special features, the Ramac will adjust the end item forecast to determine the proper mix of devices needed. To do this, the computer calls on the previous sales history stored in its memory — and comes up with a finished product plan.

2. The finished product plan is automatically fed back into the system for materials planning. The plan is passed against the bills of materials stored in the computer's system, and a complete analysis is made from the top level of finished products down to the individual components. At this phase of MOS, total material requirements are determined by the computer.

3. Inventory management goes on concurrently with the previous two phases of manufacturing. The computer's memory is loaded with such factors as minimum and maximum inventory levels, economic order formulas, item usage, and cost and lead times. As the machine checks the material requirements against these factors, the Ramac initiates orders when necessary.

4. As far as scheduling is concerned, MOS plans each manufacturing order according to the master operations and loading formulas. The manufacturing plan is broken down progressively so that each person involved in the production cycle has a detailed set of instructions needed to carry out his function. Thus, shop orders, labor tickets, move tickets and raw material requisitions are produced as a regular product of .the Ramac system.

5. Dispatching is the next area covered by MOS. The computer implements the manufacturing plan by creating a daily work priority. Each work center will normally have more than one shop order

ready, with the priority constantly affected by customer needs, shop order costs, inventory levels and production performance, as orders move through the plant. This is designed to provide peak customer service, while considering economy of manpower, machines and money in the handling of an order.

6. Finally, MOS monitors the five preceding manufacturing functions by operations evaluation. Any pertinent variations from established standards are promptly reported to management as an exception. Also, operating data is passed against stored budget, cost, capacity and similar controls to provide management with a current picture of manufacturing operations.

In short, control of manufacturing is integrated as a series of interrelated production functions. The computer is programmed to look at the plant operation as a good manager would look at it — from a profit standpoint.

SCIENTIFIC MANAGEMENT

But, from the standpoint of management, possibly the most valuable aspect of MOS is its ability to answer important questions on forecasting.

A management science program recently made available is the Inventory Management Simulator which allows the user to test and evaluate inventory systems and select the system best suited to the firm's objective. With the program the computer can assist management in formulating effective inventory policy.

Also available, using similar concepts, is the Capital Investment Program, which enables management to determine the profitability of a proposed capital investment, and forecasts the return to be expected on investments. The program is flexible enough to analyze such diverse proposed investments as equipment replacement, facilities expansion, acquisitions and mergers and research expenditures.

These applications, plus many others, can be solved with certain management science techniques. One of these, called linear programming, is used in the solution of allocation problems. The technique states that, given certain factors in a problem, an optimum solution can be found mathematically.

For example, if it is known how many products can be manufactured, and the cost and selling price of each product, it can be determined how many of each product should be manufactured in order to realize the optimum profit. This technique can be applied to many, many business problems. The conclusion, of course, can only be realized if all variables, in addition to cost and selling price, are known.

By James L. Becker
RCA Service Company

Planning the Total Information System

PLANNING is the selection of means to accomplish a goal. A plan has two dimensions. One of them, plotted in space, is called organization. The other is plotted in time and is called the schedule. We shall discuss both dimensions of a plan for a total information system. It would be begging the question, however, were we to start this description without first discussing our goal: an operating total business system.

Your business is an integrated organization. Its daily control depends on the orderly flow of certain critical data. The flow and processing of this data, whether it is done by machine of by a series of forms, is an information system. A total information system is a medium for recording all significant actions of a company and logically assembling and screening them so they can be quickly interpreted and easily controlled.

To place this definition in context requires an understanding of the structure of business. Let us analyze an elementary example:

When John Jenkins inherited money, he decided to go into business. John was a shoe salesman, so he bought a shoe store in Murdock. When I met John two years later, I asked him how this venture fared. "That caper died six months ago," he commented, and went on to rationalize the circumstances.

John's business was not successful. It nevertheless had every resemblance of a true business. First, John had resources: money, his talent for selling shoes and a thrifty wife. Secondly, John decided to direct these resources toward a productive goal. Finally, the execution of John's decision took time.

MEANING OF CONTROLS TO BUSINESS

Even this elementary example illustrates the three parameters of a business: resources, control and time. When controls are imposed on resources the result is generally called cost (even though it may be difficult to put a price on talent or a thrifty wife). When controls are imposed on time, the result is called a schedule.

Management is the agent of control. A successful manager, however, must do more than merely determine costs and schedules. John's business failed because it did not even regenerate the resources it consumed. The successful manager so controls time and resources that he regenerates his capital and produces a profit. Thus, control is the fulcrum upon which is balanced success or failure and profit or loss. We should give close attention to this function while planning our information system.

Controls can be categorized in many ways. One method which is useful in planning an information system is priority. With this technique we divide situations that demand immediate action from those that tolerate deferred attention: a hot story breaks while the next edition is already on the press; a key worker on an assembly line suddenly takes ill; a client is upset over a delayed shipment. Decisions on these situations cannot be delayed.

Deferrable controls are the most common. Hiring a salesman, replacing wearing machinery and painting the office are tasks which we know must be done; but we can schedule them in harmony with the business routine. Both immediate and deferrable controls are made on every level of management, but immediate controls, because of their need for quick action, generally occur near the base of the managerial pyramid.

Many controls are determinable. They either follow predictable cycles or can be predicated on other decisions. Controls which are not determinable are called free controls. Free controls are management decisions which require data that the information system was not designed to report, because the need for such information could not be determined by analysis of the operational nature of the business. Thus, free controls are generally preceded by a special study.

The common method of plotting the relation of control functions in a company is the organization chart. Such charts suggest that management is organized like the root system of an oak tree. This is not true, because the interface between departments is more critical to the business operation than are vertical channels of control. Sometimes this horizontal interface is depicted by the use of three dimensions or color, but how we describe it is not important if we recognize that horizontal and sometimes oblique channels of communication are vital to a company's efficient operation.

SPECIFICATIONS FOR THE TOTAL SYSTEM

Let us summarize this analysis by stating our conclusions as specifications for the total system. The total business information system must:

1. *Deliver information when it is needed —* Situations requiring immediate control should be reported swiftly. Frequent summary reports should be issued to provide timely attention to deferrable control.

2. *Provide for total horizontal distribution of information —* Every office should obtain all the information required to properly execute its function.

3. *Filter vertical distribution of information —* Circumstances that require control should be referred to the lowest level at which action can be taken. Higher echelons should be informed only when subordinate management does not cope with the problem or is tardy in remedying it.

4. *Readily assemble information for special reports —* All the information in the files should be randomly accessible to support management decisions in unpredictable circumstances.

5. *Execute through its internal logic as many controls as are feasible —* Management then governs by controlling exceptions rather than every incident.

THE SYSTEMS PLANNING ORGANIZATION

Now that we know the specifications for the total system we can organize a department to develop such a system in your company. Varied talents are required, which must be welded into a team. The team is a department because it must freely function with other departments, and its activity will be a permanent component of the total organization. Relations between functions of such a systems planning department are shown in **Exhibit 1.**

There are five functions of the systems planning department:

1. To analyze the business organization and design a model for the total system.

2. To specify and procure hardware and programs for implementing the model.

3. To inform management and educate the labor force about their role in the system and obtain their cooperation.

4. To manage the interface of the new and old systems thereby insuring the uninterrupted flow of all critical data.

5. To coordinate and administrate intradepartmental functions.

Analysis should consider the work of each department in the total perspective. Sometimes management thinks each department can separately automate its own functions and these can later be joined together into an integrated system.

Even a management which initially agrees with an integrated approach, often compromises it for a short term gain. But if the total system is to be what its name implies, management must be understanding and patient with the problems and slow pace of an integrated analysis.

Selection and procurement of programs and equipment is an important function. To avoid a critical failure of the system, provision must be made for duplicate or emergency equipment. Keep programming flexible so the system can function even in the absence of some of its inputs, and keep it simple to accommodate the changes that may frequently be made. Changing a complicated program even with the help of common languages and compilers is bound to be expensive.

LACK OF EDUCATION

The most neglected function of the total systems department is education. A large steel company installed a system with data capture equipment spread throughout their mill. They were prevented from operating the equipment due to opposition from the union. Here failure in human relations and training caused failure of the entire system. Management is also frequently uninformed. Often vice presidents are ignorant of details of the system; they nevertheless make the decisions that influence its success.

Education is more than training and informing. It creates a giant spirit wherein everyone cooperates. Each person associated with generating, processing or using information must participate in planning the total system. Each person's ideas must be educed

and communicated to the whole. Each individual should realize that he is a part of the system, not as a mere cog in a wheel, but as a contributor to the success or failure of his company.

Since you are now in business, the present system of collecting and processing information apparently must work. Very likely it arrived at its sophistication through a series of trials and errors. The new system based on analysis and logic may lack some of the heuristic wisdom and possibly falter. For insurance we keep the present system operating until the new has demonstrated its reliability. Since the approach to the total system is asymptotic, the interface between the new and the old will always be present.

Coordination, administration and control of these functions is a task of management. Naturally its chief concern is with cost and schedules. PERTAC (PERT- Time And Cost) is a new tool designed to seek out a schedule that provides the optimum relation between cost and time. There are also other approaches

Exhibit 1

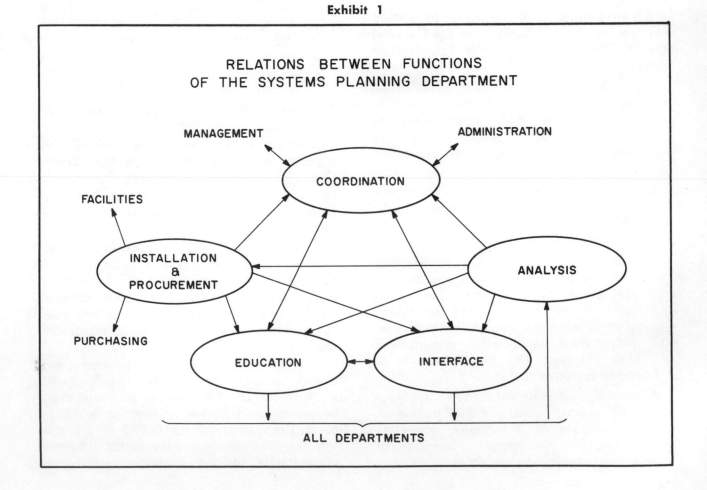

to the problem. For instance, scheduling early completion of those portions of the program that offer quickest amortization.

Exhibit 1 illustrates the relations between the different functions of the systems planning department. The department's operating efficiency depends not so much on any one function as it does on the interplay of the functions on one another. Several functions are tied directly into other departments of the company and for this reason the systems department is usually organized at a high level. However, since the department acts as service to management, it is staff rather than line in function.

SCHEDULE FOR IMPLEMENTING THE TOTAL SYSTEM

The other dimension of our plan is time, described in a schedule. A typical implementation schedule for a total information system is shown in **Exhibit 2**. The schedule for implementing the total information system varies depending on the needs, size and structure of

a business. A large organization may require five to 10 years to install a total information system. Since it is customary to plot a schedule along a time weighted critical path, we will discuss some of the events that are likely to occur along the critical path of the total information system.

The principal event and other events that occur at the same time as the principal event can be grouped together into time units called phases. We will describe eight phases in the implementation of the total system: proposal, analysis, installation, run, data capture, integration, display and operation. Each of these is named for the principal event that occurs during that phase.

The proposal phase begins when management decides to investigate the feasibility of the total system and ends with approval of plans for implementing the system. Between these events the information upon which management bases its decision is gathered.

Management will want to know the status of the present system, the advantages of a

Exhibit 2

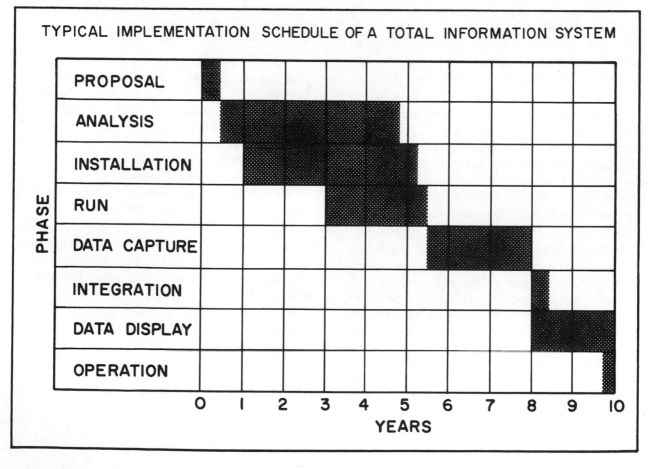

TYPICAL IMPLEMENTATION SCHEDULE OF A TOTAL INFORMATION SYSTEM

total system, who will implement it, what will it cost and the length of time necessary for installation. The credance management gives to the answers and arguments in the proposal will determine the future of the total information system.

The first task of the organization established to carry out this decision of management is anaysis. Analysis will be climaxed in the completion of a design for the total system. Generally this work will be broken into discrete sections and associated sections of installation and run phases will be mingled with the analysis. For example, while inventory is being run, contract negotiation programs can be debugged, and the engineering function analyzed. The schedule in **Exhibit 2** illustrates the partial simultaneity of these phases.

Generally, there is a one year lag between the selection of a computer and its installation. However, during this time, the installation activity is not idle. A site for the computer must be prepared, service routines, compilers, and other programs must be selected, and programming can commence. The use of electronic data processing service centers will expedite the installation. RCA, IBM, NCR, and CDC provide centers where computers can be rented for short intervals until the company's own system is ready.

The run phase begins when the first actual business information is successfully translated on the system. It ends when all business information has been successfully processed. Although most of the information will be electronically processed, the system can still be considered total if some of the operations are performed manually, provided these are integrated into the total system.

Once the data processing system is operating, attention can be given to automating data capture. The computer has been relying on punched cards, by-product paper tapes and data transcribed from business forms. Manual communications often have been slow, errors frequent, and data sometimes incomplete or biased by the personal interests of those who recorded it. Data capture equipment will speed communication cycles, provide more complete data and protect the reliability of the data

submitted. The work force will also be relieved of the irksome chores of paperwork.

Several varieties of data capture equipment are available today. Data collection equipment must be able to accommodate a variety of data producing situations with a minimum of human control. The data collection phase is completed when collection stations are transmitting their information to the data processing site.

Since there are problems peculiar to installing a data collection network, it is at first operated off line. After the reliability of the system is proven, it is integrated with the computer. Expect further analysis, additional programming and some modification of equipment during this phase.

What data capture will accomplish for the work force in the preparation of reports, data display will accomplish for management in the interpretation of reports. Here we design special equipment which will quickly and clearly communicate to management what is occurring in the business in context with projected costs and schedules.

The event that terminates the implementation of the total system is the successful operation of all portions of the system as a single unit.

The system will meet opposition. Some jobs will vanish. Employees will resent the disappearance of familiar faces. Lower management might claim that they worked more efficiently under the old system. Documents might even support this because business forms are often completed with a certain bias. Upper management has always been aware of this, but they too are frequently shocked when the bias has been removed.

Planning for the total information system is not an easy task. Your organization may differ from the organization proposed here and your schedule will vary from the one we described.

Our purpose was to alert you to some of the dangers and difficulties bound to be encountered if you become engaged in the long, steep climb to a total system. Being aware of them may make your journey easier, and of course the goal is adequate recompence for your efforts.

By Harry L. Spaulding
Woodward & Lothrop

Effective Electronics Planning and Programming

TODAY, a person can go from New York to Los Angeles via numerous routes and many modes of transportation. Those companies already in automatic data processing certainly have chosen their modes of transportation. It becomes the function of the Planning and Programming Section to optimize the use of the equipment with effective planning and programming to accomplish the goals of management and to recommend future equipment.

Seven years ago, a master automation plan was drawn up for Woodward & Lothrop. Data processing was designated to be the hub of a wheel, with the operating departments located around the circumference. Each operating department would channel work into and out of the data processing center in an integrated manner. The planning and programming staff was assigned the function of implementing the master plan.

With a small staff and limited equipment, it was an impossible task to accomplish the master plan in total at one fell swoop. An evolutionary process developed. Throughout the years, as more and more applications were programmed, larger equipment was acquired. Today, this company is achieving payoff results in automatic data processing.

To operate efficiently, electronics planning uses a basic operating method, which plan applies to either a large or small operation. For all assigned studies, rigid standards are necessary for:
1. System directive
2. Planning approach
3. Programming
4. Operating procedures

THE SYSTEM DIRECTIVE

The manager, electronics planning, is the contractor for work in his department. At this stage, basically he should be involved in discussion with management of new systems or system changes.

His background should provide him with a thorough knowledge of the basic operations of his company and he must know the basic new concepts in his field, plus having a full knowledge of planning and programming. As the expert in his line and management's representative for the automatic data processing system, it is his responsibility to equip management with feasibility studies and cost figures.

To carry out the new changes, he must write the directive for this system so that his department can carry it out. This directive should contain the following:

1. *The system's function* — Discuss the purpose of the system briefly, referring to the type of input and output and what this program does. This directive should carry the signatures of those people in management who were involved in original meetings concerning this system and who have agreed to it.

2. *The input* — Detail the source input as to fields or positions on tape layout forms. Indicate significant codes and fields that the planner or programmer need know and also sequences and quantity of input.

3. *The system's purpose* — State the action to be accomplished by the system. The more detail, the easier it is to plan and program. Account for the exceptions and what must be done to get around them.

4. *Type of output* — State what the output is, whether tape, cards, or hard copy, or any combination and quantity. Give the disposition of this output.

5. *The controls* — After the process is completed, output totals must be tied back to input. Audit trails must be established.

The manager, electronic planning now gives the directive and an assigned target date for completion to the planner who will handle this new system and schedule it in the department.

THE PLANNING APPROACH

At the scheduled date or earlier, the manager, electronic planning meets with the planner, reviews the directive and discusses with the planner anything he needs to know to acquaint him with his new project.

Normally, the planner's first task is to draw a flow chart of the operation and question every step. This flow chart serves twofold because it forces the planner to draw up the complete project so that he also picks up minute points not covered by the directive.

The manager must be available for brief meetings throughout the planner's flow charting. Reviews of the flow charts give the manager a quick picture of the planner's ability for grasping the subject. Also, if there are errors in the logic of the directive, the manager can change or modify his original directive. Most often corrections are in the processing part of the new system, and not in the input/output areas. A change in input/output areas requires an additional clearance with those affected.

When the flow chart has been approved by the manager, the planner must design appropriate report forms, if forms are necessary. Forms must be sent to those concerned for clearance and approval. Where forms become a major element of the overall system, and quantities involved are large, the manager may have these worked on first because of the necessity of buying them economically.

Forms normally take from 30 to 60 days to design and print. However, if the need is critical enough, and a relatively small number is required, a premium rate will get them completed in only 10 to 15 days.

The planner next makes a detailed logical flow chart which pictures the systems in detail, telling the programmer what happens at each step. It shows exactly the decisions to be made at each stage of the program. The logical flow chart is turned over to the programmer.

The planner concentrates on the chart and the handling of the input/output.

PROGRAMMING

Programming, to be efficient, must be logical and simple. It is too expensive to spend 10 days or even 10 hours on a particular computer program routine to gain 10 milliseconds in processing on a weekly program.

First of all, a company normally does not get back a sufficient return in time or money to warrant such finesse. Also, complicated programs can become difficult, time consuming and costly to change, especially if done by someone other than the original programmer.

A good example of this is the recent change in F.I.C.A. (Social Security) on a complicated fully packed program. Any company programming payroll during the last three years should have allowed three places to the right of the decimal point. Actually, how many payroll programs created during this period contained the expanded memory area for this kind of contingency?

Basically, only when the program exceeds the capacity of the machine should the program become complicated by tricks. This does not mean that the programmer should not do the best he can. It means that straightforward, logical and simple programming is the cheapest and best way for a company to program a computer.

Keys to consistent programming include:

1. A basic programming system.
2. Fields names and names carried throughout the program.
3. Remarks frequently used.
4. Program sheets filled out in a consistent manner. For example, a zero to the programmer may be an alpha 'O' to the keypuncher. Uniform and understandable symbols are vital.
5. Common numbered machine stops. Typical stops we use are:

   Ø Ø 99   End of job.
   Ø Ø Ø 1   No lead card.
   Ø Ø Ø 2   Card out of sequence.
6. A program to eliminate manual tasks whenever possible.
7. Editing of all input data prepared manually to insure proper data sequence, and coding.

8. An error routine program to check input media for errors and to transfer these errors to an error tape or deck of cards.

9. A program routine for dumping totals from memory when the machine stops unexpectedly.

After a program has been encoded, keypunched and listed, the programmer must review his work to assure that all possible errors have been found before compiling. The object is to assemble a program as economically as possible. Programmer's time at this stage is cheaper than computer time. Based on experience, we employ these procedures to achieve economic programming and computer usage:

1. The programmer must desk check his coding. To facilitate this, another programmer is assigned to actually take dummy cards through the program step by step. From this check, errors in logic can be found and corrected.

2. Routines and sub-routines must be checked for exits and entries.

3. Branches must be followed through to their ultimate conclusion. Desk checking can save valuable machine time later.

The programmer must prepare a complete set of test cards as well as error cards. The program, after desk checking, must be assembled and checked out. Machines are exact and the test deck will identify and select out most errors. However, until real media is used, all bugs will never be worked out.

In this operation, the programmer is responsible for running his program until it completely checks out. After checking out and operating procedures are written, the entire package is turned over to the manager, electronics planning. He and the manager, data processing review the program. If common agreement is reached, the data processing center assumes responsibility for processing the program.

OPERATING PROCEDURES

Planning and programming can do the best job in the world, if the data processing center cannot produce this in a normal manner, then the whole thing is a failure. The planner must write the overall procedure from the creation of the input, to its assembly, processing and final output. The procedure must be clear enough to let the data processing center manager turn the operation over to his operating people to produce, but still be able to answer most technical questions which may arise. Again, the operating procedures must be logical and simple.

The implementation provided by a planning and programming section when operating according to a plan, provides the tools to be efficient and effective. The manager, electronics planning, must keep on top of his procedures so that his automatic data processing programs will produce invaluable and timely data, processed economically and efficiently, and thus provide management with one of its most important decision making tools.

By Carl B. Barnes and Charles C. Weaver
U. S. Department of Agriculture

Total Systems Approach to Automatic Data Processing Planning

EVERY COMPANY has a system of data. Parts of a company may use the same data differently. Without a total concept, data handling can be costly. The potential of the data may even be lost.

Today, every company using automatic data processing equipment needs a total systems approach. The goal can be reached with the assistance of three groups. Management must plan, the automatic data processing organization must plan, every organization in the company must plan — and they must plan together.

MANAGEMENT PLANS

The total automatic data processing system is a design. What is now being done is not material. What should be done is vital.

The first planning by management requires the selection of the minds to design the system. The talent has been found within companies or acquired from the outside. If from outside, individuals can be hired or their work may be contracted. If contracted, company employees should participate to reduce dependency on the contractor.

This is the most important single management action. Many poor systems; many futile uses of automatic data processing equipment; many wasteful, endless automatic data processing studies have had their start here. At this time, successful, experienced system designers can be hired or contracted.

However, if management wants to train one of its own men, tests are available to determine creative ability and aptitude. These provide greater selectivity than the manufacturers' programming aptitude tests. Creativity is a top consideration for qualified automatic data processing designers.

If internal auditors or an accounting firm are used, it is imperative that they participate. Do not accept the attitude, "if you can check it, we can audit it."

Use their expertise to reduce costs of audits. The auditor should be able to use automatic data processing equipment in the audit; thus, his understanding of the equipment reduces his time and the company's costs. Recognize that management is relieving the auditor of responsibility for errors in the system.

INCLUDE SCIENTIFIC APPROACH

The company should integrate scientific management tools into the total systems concept. Mathematicians should be added early to provide this potential.

The use of operations research is increasing at a phenomenal rate. It identifies and analyzes management problems; breaks each problem into all pertinent factors; places a measure of value on each factor; and uses appropriate mathematics to combine and solve factors in an optimum manner. Management thus gets a firm basis for evaluating alternate decisions.

All top level persons in the company must be conditioned to accept the system design functions as assigned by management. The automatic data processing organization should not just service the other parts of the company. Data should be processed according to the system designed, with unnecessary reports and controls eliminated.

The man heading the automatic data processing organization must be considered management. Consequently, he should look at the system design and operation from that viewpoint. Management should provide for his access to the man in charge of company operations. He must concern himself with management's needs for data for decision making and staff advice purposes.

He must emphasize the development of a system designed primarily to produce data when needed by management at the lowest possible cost.

AUTOMATIC DATA PROCESSING ORGANIZATION PLANS

Participation in a contractor's design of the concepts of the total automatic data processing system for the company should be the first project.

Regardless of the specific automatic data processing structure, the problem is to conceive a system from a management viewpoint. A system must process data that will produce transactions, supply information and provide scientific management tools.

This requires a new look at the company and its data. The company must be visualized as one entity. The design of a total data system, the vertical integration of application areas, and the synchronization of business and mathematical programs are the target.

MANPOWER AND EQUIPMENT

If the concepts are approved, manpower and equipment are the primary concerns. Efforts on each should proceed simultaneously.

Time on equipment within the company may be available locally, from a feeder station or a satellite computer operation. If so, manpower may be available, too. Training expense and time can also be saved.

Remember that time may be available from users in the geographic area who have equipment. Automatic data processing equipment can run 22 hours per day for seven days a week. Only a very few operators are required to use the night shifts.

From these considerations, it can be determined whether the company will do its own programming and whether the firm will install its own equipment.

When time and money are available, design and develop the details of the system concepts for the total system at the beginning. For some large companies, this is too great a task. In other cases, details must be developed for a section or application area within the total systems concept. These details, in addition to the total systems concept, are included in a feasibility study.

The feasibility study should be prepared as a document. It should state the problem, the proposed system or part of the system covered by the application area, the total costs, the results of installation, the impact on the company's organization, the difficulties and benefits, and the recommended actions.

GATHERING PERSONNEL

Preliminary recruitment can begin while the studies are being conducted. A staff composed of employees from the company, from universities, and from other installations is ideal.

Present employees bring an understanding of present operations and terminology; recent college graduates bring mathematical backgrounds, fresh viewpoints, and initiative; employees from other installations bring automatic data processing experience.

All should have high aptitudes. From present employees, it can be expected to find about one of 12 to have the necessary aptitude; from selected graduates, about one of two; and from employees in present installations, it will vary from over 90 per cent to less than 10 per cent, depending upon the method of selection. All candidates should be tested. Valid tests require from eight to 16 hours.

CAREFUL SELECTION OF EQUIPMENT

If automatic data processing equipment is acquired, it will have to be selected before the costing can be completed. If the company's policy considers all suppliers, a statement of system specifications should be prepared. The specifications describe the system, input and output volumes, frequency of processing and file updating, and special equipment requirements.

Since support from the manufacturer is very significant, especially to a new user, information should be requested as to generalized programs to all users, the identification of customers using the proposed equipment and the staffing of the manufacturer's local offices.

Visit some of the present users of the equipment before placing an order. Plan alternatives when the system is designed to use unproved input or output equipment. Professional advice in equipment evaluation, even if expensive, usually is a good investment for an inexperienced company.

After selecting the equipment, the proposed system should be timed out and computer costs, operating plus amortization of developmental costs, should be included in the cost study. The present system should be costed as it now operates, not as it could operate.

The proposed system should not take dollar credit for intangibles, for employees whose time will not be saved or diverted to other chargeable work, or for equipment which will not be charged to other projects. Make every effort to accurately state the cost result. Reductions in present cost of more than 25 percent should be investigated.

Assuming the feasibility study is approved, the next step is to record the cost of the present system. This will provide a firm base for the cost comparison.

When the computer programs have been written, debugged and compatibility tested, the cost computations should be adjusted as necessary to reflect a closer estimated cost of the proposed system. The adjustment, plus the approval of outputs, is sufficient for the experienced staff. Parallel operations are not recommended.

The manpower required to run two systems, if concentrated on validating one, gets better results at a cheaper cost. After the new system has been in operation for a few months, the actual cost of the system should be recorded. A final comparative cost statement should be prepared.

THE COMPANY PLANS

The total automatic data processing system is a company system. Previously, many organizations kept their own records, inventories, accounts and sales. Now, there is a company ledger of these operations and the records belong to everyone in the company.

The automatic data processing organization develops the system for creating and processing input to the system, manipulating and controlling data within the system, and assisting others in using the output from the system.

To gain the most from the system, all organizations need to understand it, believe in the objectives of management in having the system designed and installed, and support the further advancement of freeing themselves from laborious tasks.

This requires orientations for affected personnel, both those whose positions are affected and those whose work habits are changed by automatic data processing processes and outputs.

Top management in other organizations can be kept in tune with company management's objectives through membership assignments on an automatic data processing committee. This committee, if used as a work or approving group, wastes executive time. But as a policy and progress evaluation committee, it can be most useful.

The secondary levels of management — company and organization — are neglected the most. These can afford passive resistance. By affording personnel at this level an opportunity to contribute, their support is gained. Not only that, but the company's system benefits from their knowledge, both in design and operation.

Periodically, survey the use of output. Determine: What actions are taken on the basis of output data? What decisions are made? When was data needed, but not available? What recommendations or staff advice are made from output data? What output is not used by management? Is the reason inadequacy or untimeliness of data, or lack of understanding or initiative on the part of management?

The nature and use of output data is a never ending problem. The nature of the company's business and its economic growth, or lack of it, are factors which vitally affect company data and their use.

Data should reflect the heart beat of the company. This flow is the message to the brains of the company to take a particular action or absorb specific items of information significant to the company's health.

The total systems approach to managing data is management's means of keeping its fingers on the pulse of the company's heart beat. Management must doctor its company's ills. The prognosis must be scientific and timely, arrived at confidently.

As symptoms of illness appear, diagnosis must be precise and swift. Remedies must be prescribed. This can be assured best by good plans for a total data system. The better the plans, the better the system. There are few places where an investment of time and brains will provide more return.

By Robert V. Lewis
General Foods Corporation

Managerial Responsibility in Planning for Computers

NOW that we have picked ourselves up off the floor of disappointing and disillusioning experiences with electronic computers, let us ask why we've been let down with such a sudden, hard jolt.

Upon close scrutiny, most of this disenchantment may be traced to top management's lack of responsibility and involvement in the corporate electronic data processing program.

Top management must closely associate itself with the corporate electronics program for many valid reasons. Large scale computing systems are not acquired at the cost of a simple ten-key adding machine. The rental or purchase price of such a system involves sizable expenditures. The costs of pre-planning and installation are also very substantial. The total cost of the overall project is usually large enough to require presidential or directors' approval. Previously installed office equipment was often approved by middle management personnel alone.

COMPUTERS INFLUENCE MANAGEMENT

Electronic computers have drastically affected the methods of management control. The form, content and timing of management reports, which may upset traditional means of control, must be considered by top management. Computers now make feasible new analytical methods. This ability to produce a rapid and varied array of analytical reports may sometimes backfire and management must guard against an over-indulgence in report generation. Executives must not become so absorbed in reports of what happened yesterday that they neglect their primary mission which is to plan and direct for tomorrow.

Changes in corporate policies and practices may be necessary to optimize the objectives of an electronic data processing program. For example, a policy of almost complete decentralization of management and staff functions may have to be modified to best benefit from the computer's ability and efficiency in handling repetitive, high volume operations. Decentralized plant or division functions including accounting, billing, inventory, payroll and similar applications may have to be taken away from autonomous units and centralized. Many accustomed practices, such as billing, may have to be dramatically altered to meet the requirements of the computer system. It is changes of this nature that should receive top management's attention.

TOP MANAGEMENT'S ROLE

In an attempt to integrate the data processing function, the work of some units and departments may be completely eliminated, or dramatically reduced, while at the same time work flow relationships are seriously altered. Changes of this order are usually resisted, at times vehemently, and the support of the company's executives may be required to effect them. Conflicts of interest will undoubtedly arise and can only be resolved by senior officer arbitration.

Top management must participate in getting the computer program off the ground. Primarily, top management should issue a statement of basic objectives and how they are to be achieved. This will provide a framework of study and recommendation for those individuals who will be personally responsible for the success of the project.

If the committee approach is used to initiate the program, the various departments affected are usually asked to be represented. These representatives should be men of proven ability who possess a deep knowledge of company-wide systems, operations and objectives. Often these men are a valuable asset to their department manager and there is a strong hesitancy to lend such men to an electronic committee. Once again, top management must step in to keep the program rolling.

Convincing top management to accept an active role in developing an electronic computer program accomplishes nothing if management only does lip service to what was mentioned earlier. Management must help to clearly define the goals and objectives of such a program and, at the same time, be firmly convinced there is a basic need for an electronic computer. This action should precede any approach toward a detailed feasibility study. Motivations for embarking on such a study are extremely varied.

PROGRAM OBJECTIVES

A few of the more common objectives of an electronic data processing program are:[1]

1. A worthwhile saving in clerical costs is expected to result from automation and systems changes.

2. Inventory investment can be lowered through better methods of control and closer estimates of requirements.

3. Better control over the enterprise is expected to result from faster, more detailed analyses and reports.

4. Electronic data processing will increase both speed and accuracy of accounting and paperwork.

5. A competitive advantage may be achieved through lower costs or through the ability to give better customer service.

6. The application of mathematical aids to management (operations research) will be facilitated.

7. Automation seems to be the only way to solve, or at least reduce, the growing problem of finding and training clerical personnel.

8. Reduction in clerical personnel will save a company the expense of acquiring larger office facilities.

9. Current methods of data processing will, in the foreseeable future, become incapable of handling the increased volume and complexity of paperwork.

10. The intangible benefits are attractive if a computer installation can break even on costs.

11. The dramatic impact of electronic data processing can pave the way for a much needed systems reform.

Quite often management has been motivated by one or a combination of the aforementioned benefits. In the early blue sky days, some managements went ahead with studies even without any definite idea of what benefits could be expected. Many such companies have clearly regretted their lack of advanced planning and detailed preparation.

WIDE APPLICATION SCOPE

For maximum effectiveness, the scope of the application should be broadly defined so that most, if not all, of the facets and data processing requirements of the business are encompassed. Little or no benefit is derived by limiting the program to a conversion from punched card procedures to an electronic computing system. Similarly, except in rare situations, application of a medium or large scale computer to the data processing requirements of one department seldom proves economically sound.

An example of an objective statement by one management is the following:[2]

"To enable the company to earn a larger net profit than it could otherwise do under its present system of operation or under any practical improvements in its present system. The larger net profit is the sum total of improvements in many specific areas, such as reduction in clerical work, lower inventory investment, more rapid collections, better customer relations and service and better and more timely reports for use in management decision making."

This particular management went on further in each objective area and set down specific sub-sets of objectives. For example, the following inventory objectives were specified.

1. To increase inventory turnover.

2. To keep an inventory in each warehouse

---

[1] National Industrial Conference Board's *Studies in Business Policy*, No. 92, p. 7.

[2] *Journal of Machine Accounting*, September, 1959.

which will be the minimum necessary to meet sales demand.

3. To reduce reshipment of inventory between field warehouses.

4. To provide current, accurate information on inventory and inventory requirements.

The above specifications clearly indicate the company's desires for more than mere mechanization of existing procedures. The list indicates the need for a complete systems evaluation and for the application of sophisticated operations research techniques to the inventory problem.

Management must keep a finger on the pulse of the project's progress by establishing financial and time budgets for such functions as the survey of the existing system, development of an electronic computer system plan, staffing and training and, finally, selection of the equipment.

STAFF IS A VITAL LINK

Typical of any man-machine system, the human element involved in electronic data processing is often the limiting factor of a successful installation. This point must never be let out of sight. The selection, training and development of an electronic data processing staff should be of vital concern to management. Despite articles and speeches on traps and pitfalls, management at large has assumed that it has the experience, presumably from previous systems work, to go into an electronic computer program. Accordingly, in many cases, the work has been delegated almost completely to personnel not properly equipped by training or background to do the job without proper guidance. Once the job is delegated to weak or incompetent hands, management is in for many headaches.

The place of the electronic data processing department in the corporate structure must be clearly and definitely defined in the early stages of the program. If the duties, responsibilities and authority of the computer department are not clearly understood and respected, organizational chaos can result. The electronics committee approach to computer department administration often results in a weak, loosely defined and ineffective organization. The electronic data processing department should be managed by a mature individual who has a broad understanding of company operations, policy, organization and customs. Experience has proven that a workable knowledge of computers can be more easily acquired than attempting to train a computer technician in the ways of a company's business.

To date, many large scale computer ventures have been or are unsatisfactory to some degree. This appears to be due to an uncontrollable tendency to mismanage this type of project, probably resulting from underestimating the planning and skills required or from overestimating the value or expectation of other types of experience.

Mismanagement has resulted in disappointing experiences when initial goals and objectives have not been achieved. Two areas in which results have not measured up to expectations are worthy of mention. These are, failure to achieve a net savings in costs and lack of any substantial increases in speed and accuracy.

DELAYS IN PROGRESS

Among the more prevalent reasons cited for not achieving these anticipated objectives are the following:

1. Quick and dirty systems analyses.

2. Over-sophisticated and exceptional type programming.

3. Acquisition of a computer really too powerful for the company's needs.

4. Failure to avoid unsuitable applications.

5. Failure to rent excess computer time to potential users.

6. Unrealistic estimate of the time required to attain the level of activity contemplated.

7. Systems and programming work more time consuming and costly than anticipated.

8. Failure to realize that systems and programming work is a continuous activity and part of the regular operating costs.

9. Underestimating the number of interruptions during processing and the effect they have on running time and unit costs.

10. Failure to eliminate as much of the old equipment as was planned. More work still remained to be done on the old

equipment than was anticipated.

11. Reluctance or neglect in releasing employees that have been displaced by the computer system.

12. Communication costs much higher than expected and still rising.

13. Decline in business which lowered data processing volume with no corresponding reduction in the cost of operating the computer.

14. Experimental and test work requiring extra shift operations not planned for.

15. Failure to provide for reduction in expense (what to do with excess personnel required to get program on the air, coupled with the advent of advanced machine-aided programming techniques [for example, ALGOL and COBOL]).

Although the tone of this paper may sound pessimistic, I sincerely and definitely feel that the future for electronic computers is healthy and bright. We have revaluated our expectations from electronic data processing in a frame of reference far more sensible and realistic than existed in the mid 1950s. Computer users, until very recently, set standards of performance which were much too high. The infancy of the field and lack of practical experience five years ago gave no justification for such Utopian hopes.

Earlier attempts in electronic data processing expected perfection and looked to the computer as some sort of panacea or opiate. Well, the drug has finally worn off and the pain, which is a healthy sign, is helping us to diagnose the ailment. Management's role must be that of the respected consulting physician whose prescription will be followed. This is to be distinguished from nursemaiding the project, which management is not advised or expected to do. However, the organization must provide for that type of care, to be given by those directly charged with the responsibility for the computer installation. The honeymoon is over and now comes the period of adjustment and learning to live together. Married life experiences are growing daily and coupled with lowering appliance costs the future life for computer families definitely appears favorable and promising.

The foundations of today's successful computer installation rest on the pillars of technical and managerial proficiency. Respect for the technical problems and considerations by top management was readily given almost at the dawning of the commercial computer age. However, what top management did not fully appreciate was the fact that electronic data processing would also create many new and difficult managerial problems. The many successful installations operating today reflect early recognition of the many and complex managerial problems created by automatic data processing.

Selection, training and development of personnel fall directly within the responsibility of management, and only through careful and thorough analysis of the data processing problem can management realistically estimate the investment of time and money that must precede a successful computer program. Review of past experiences in electronic data processing has revealed an almost consistent underestimation of expenditures of time and money.

Computer management must continually review the basic needs which originally dictated a program of electronic data processing. Business automation is a dynamic challenge and can never be considered static. Data processing's management must recognize that its function is to perform worthwhile services and must be organized accordingly. Flexibility must be maintained if the installation is to survive. Processing rigidity cannot exist in a successful, business-oriented computer program.

Very often, the capacity to serve the various departments or divisions of a corporation is the strongest selling point of management when initially gaining corporate acceptance of an electronic data processing program. To further instill confidence, an extensive corporate educational program should be developed. The mystery of computers must be dispelled and the limitations, as well as the capabilities, of the equipment must be understood by all involved in the data processing and information handling function.

Success depends upon understanding which, in turn, can only be disseminated through a well functioning and respected organization. Intelligent organization, skilled personnel and, above all, the assurance that a recognizable and justifiable need exists for the application of electronic computing equipment are all inherent to the administration of a successful automatic data processing program.

By E. F. Cooley
Prudential Insurance Company of America

Planning Considerations

WHAT DO WE MEAN BY "a total integrated business information system"? How total is total? What does integrated mean? Just what is business information? We'd better start by defining a few terms in common, everyday language.

By total we mean that the paperwork needs of the whole organization are considered, without omitting any part of it. The word integrated implies the same idea. Nothing is segregated. The existing organizational lines won't stop us from making combinations which improve efficiency. But if our understanding of total is as broad as it should be, this word adds little to our concept of a total system.

Let's drop it therefore as redundant, affected and subject to the suspicion that we are trying to claim some superior, mystical and miracle-working power.

Business information covers almost everything in the paperwork line that an organization needs to exist, including accounting data, reports to aid management, reports to government and documents to customers. Literally every report the organization produces, whether for internal or external use, falls under business information.

If we are going to plan a total business information system, we must study the whole company and analyze each product of data processing, whether it be a computer or a ballpoint pen. We must try to combine functions across existing lines of authority so that we make the most efficient use of every transaction.

We had better be realistic and admit there are going to be failures. Every report won't be included in our first attempt, but our target should be to present as close to a total system as possible.

SIMULATED BUSINESS OPERATION

As an example, we will say our business is selling sea shells. We receive an order for nine gross of our assorted size packages from a shoe manufacturer. He is an old customer which means he has our catalog with the special order blanks in card form, each one punched with the customer identification number.

When the order is received, a card, which contains descriptive information on the particular sea shells desired and the price per gross, is picked from the file. The quantity ordered is marked on the card.

Two cards are then sent on their automated way, one describing the product, the other indicating the customer. The computer consults its memory for complete address and credit data on the customer, computes the amount to be billed and adjusts the inventory record. Because there will be less than 1,000 gross left in stock after the order is shipped, a letter is written to the factory requesting more shells.

An account receivable item is set up in disk storage so that when a notice of payment is received, the account receivable can be added to merchandise sold, year to date.

A special memo to the vice president for sales might also be initiated, advising that the salesman handling this particular customer is doing an outstanding job.

With this type of operation, input data is reduced. The computer uses what is in storage, combined with the input data, to produce at one time all the outputs created by this particular transaction.

While this input is in the spotlight we do all that we can so that there is no need to have it be returned. Billing, inventory, shipping instructions, accounting, sales analysis and bolstering the ego of the vice president are functions completed at the same time.

CLEARING THE WAY

It is important to understand your objectives in anticipating a total systems operation. The company wants to make money, pay bigger dividends and raise pay scales. Try to get a clear agreement about what has to be done to attain them. There may be some difficulty in determining which procedures are essential and in what priority they should be initiated.

Next, analyze outputs to understand what they contain. It is vital to know what items are needed to make up the essential documents, reports and accounts.

The items come from two sources, some from files in the company offices. More items are furnished as input, which originally is obtained from customers, sales people or other companies. We back track to realize what the sources are and where we can first acquire them with the least effort.

Another factor to be considered is the manner in which we will receive this information. It may be punched into cards, retrieved from storage or computed.

There are other problems. Determining what outputs are essential and in what form they will be most beneficial is an area that must receive plenty of attention. Accounting records probably are specified by the accountant or the auditor. We may try to have him prove all the records are essential, but we can't expect to accomplish much reduction in this area.

More important is the question: What kind of documents are going to our public? Perhaps we are sending them only bills and material designed to separate them from their funds for our benefit, and, of course, to make our services available to them.

Is this effort effective? Are the forms designed to get the best result? Is the timing right? Are we providing all the information they could expect or want? Are there safeguards to ensure that the information is accurate and timely?

What kind of service are we able to offer? When a customer places an order, when do we deliver? He perhaps wants the merchandise the same day the order is placed. Can we act that fast? If he asks for information, can we give it to him quickly? If he phones for information, are we able to deliver a prompt reply? What would be the effect on sales if we were able to give improved service?

All these are questions we should answer in making a total system study. The paperwork of a business is its life blood. If we can construct a paperwork system that will cause that life blood to flow more freely in our organization's veins, the company will be healthier — provided our system isn't so expensive that it causes bankruptcy.

COST ANALYSIS

Another phase of total system planning is to develop a cost analysis system that will tell us the important facts about our expenses. But remember it is possible to overemphasize costs to the extent that no one dares make a decision to spend.

Perhaps the most controversial area of output for internal use is that of sales management reports. If our company has a widespread sales force, we will undoubtedly receive a tremendous quantity of production reports for each level of supervision. Very likely, there are variations by regional managers, with different needs perhaps, but certainly different ideas on what types of reports are worthwhile.

What shall we do? Shall we invent a new set of reports and try to sell them to management to replace what they are now receiving? There is a danger with this plan — we may sell the new and still have to retain the old. This is a difficult area in which we have to deal with problems of motivation. There is less agreement on the solution for such problems than in almost any other field.

We may, however, get the attention of the vice president for sales. If he is inclined to be skeptical about the value of a multitude of reports, perhaps we can eliminate some of his fears. If we work with the sales people in developing a new series, we may be able to achieve something more useful and economical.

A third possibility is that we may reach the conclusion there is little we can or should change, so we had better produce the present sales analysis complex as economically as possible.

There are several other categories of management information that must be investigated in detail. But the big three — accounting, costs and sales — seem to be universal. Service indices may be just as important, depending on the type of business. Inventory control activity obviously can be vital.

CONSIDERING THE EQUIPMENT

We want to design a system which will help to attain the objectives of the company as effectively as possible. We want to buy a minimum amount of equipment, but won't hesitate to purchase when we are reasonably sure the investment will be justified. If experimentation on a small scale is necessary before we can take a giant stride, we will follow that method.

We will consider hardware on the market and, perhaps, hardware in design. Reluctantly, we will consider having special hardware designed because special equipment is very expensive.

An electronic computer tops the purchase list. Without it, we will have no total system. The problem is in determining the size of the computer.

We will also need electronic storage of data. Acquiring random access depends on a number of things, particularly whether we plan a real time or a batch processing system. The preliminary decision will be determined by the type of service we wish to give and how current our accounting will be.

Data transmission equipment is included in the total system. Questions to be answered concerning this hardware include: Do we need to gather data from distant points, in less elapsed time than the U. S. mail makes possible? Do we need to disseminate data to other locations? These points are closely allied with the matter of real time operations.

If we intend to get our customers' questions answered within seconds of the time they are asked, we should plan on a real time system throughout. We will need a transmission network connected to the computer and the random access storage file by a message exchange. Equipment now in production will make this possible.

The big question is: Can we justify the expense? We must have a huge amount of facts, plenty of courage and a large supply of good judgment to produce an answer, because the benefits reaped will not be forthcoming from doing today's tasks with today's values, but rather in better products and better service for tomorrow's needs, evaluated from tomorrow's viewpoints.

EXECUTIVE FAVOR A NECESSITY

Best results from a total system can be expected only when the top executives of the company participate in planning it so that they will better understand and believe in the move. Then, old organizational barriers will not be allowed to restrict the system's operation.

The total system will truly be a master plan for much of the company's activity. It will be a large scale tool serving all management. The system will furnish management the information needed to control and plan, produce paperwork products for all departments and establish new standards of service which will enhance the prestige of the entire company and offer new opportunities to sales.

If the functions of management are to plan, organize, execute and control, then a total system, properly designed, will accomplish a large proportion of the execute and control functions and aid the plan and organize functions considerably.

A total system with full executive blessing and participation will be a tremendous advantage. Without executive approval, however, it will be useless.

By Stanford L. Optner
Stanford L. Optner & Associates

Systems Analysis—A City Planning Tool

THE METHODS to be employed by the systems analyst are new to city planning. These methods are science-oriented and have proven their value in allied fields, but have only once been applied to urban planning problems.

Systems analysis and electronic data processing are being used with a number of related conceptual and mathematical tools in the investigation of many aspects of contemporary life which can be conceived as systems. The application of scientific tools requires special training and experience in order to relate them to the restrictions imposed by the subject matter. The use of these tools makes it possible to analyze complex problems and propose a means of altering the way in which they should be operated. In city planning, the ultimate goal of systems analysis would be to improve the economic, social and physical well being of people dependent on the urban unit.

SYSTEMS ANALYSIS

Specialists trained in this field resolve problems into modules called systems. Each system has the component elements of input, process, output, feedback and control. The first requirement in applying the systems concept is to identify the system under study. In this case, the city will be the processor. The city system has as basic ingredients (inputs), its inhabitants, its man-made structures, natural resources and physical features. It has as its goals or reasons for existing (outputs), the optimization of economic, social and physical well being of the inhabitants. Controls over the city system are the laws, regulations and policies applied by municipal, state and federal agencies of government, together with other restrictions imposed by economic necessity. In the act of satisfying the day to day needs of individuals and their institutions, a large and widely variable number of acts are generated (feedbacks), in an attempt to modify the status quo.

The simultaneous operation of these elements is a continuous process. The city system breaks down into small systems (subsystems), which can be described in the same modular fashion, as a convenient method of analysis. Thus, the city can ultimately be described as a complex of systems and subsystems all interconnected and continuously interacting with one another.

The city as a processor provides the means by which the complex functional relationships between man, his culture and his physical environment are expressed. Subsystems express the functional relationships of less qualitative, general systems providing greater opportunities for understanding. The use of the systems concept in planning is aimed at describing the functional relationships of man and his city with more precision. As less qualitative systems are analyzed, it will ultimately be possible to relate the whole to its parts in meaningful ways.

The second requirement in this method of analysis is to state the outputs of systems and subsystems as goals or objectives. The purposes for which cities exist will reflect the wishes, or in some cases the conflicts, between powerful blocs within the city, and the ways in which inhabitants seek to exploit the man-made and natural resources. Goals will be stated generally at the outset. As subsystem definition becomes more precise, goals will be stated with more exactness. It is essential to state goals so the systems analyst can build a replica or model of the process being examined. This will be done symbolically through the use of techniques which provide the opportunity to test the validity of goals, bypassing the need to operate the physical system itself.

The third requirement will be to find valid criteria which are quantitative and therefore measurable. Criteria become indicators of the adequacy of the system, and measure the extent to which the outputs satisfy the system requirements. Identification of goals and criteria will reveal assumptions implicit in the system and provide opportunities to test the validity of concepts being used. Selection of criteria and tests of their usefulness in system design are dependent upon the use of a closely related tool, electronic data processing.

ELECTRONIC DATA PROCESSING

Computers have certain features unique in the machine computing world, the most spectacular of which is speed. Speed measured in the millionths of a second makes it possible to undertake large scale problems, impractical for humans to attack by manual methods because of the years of effort required.

City planning is a massive data processing problem scaled to the capabilities of a computer. There are other attributes, however, which make this tool ideally suited to handling problems of city planning.

Analysis of the city system is a problem of wide dimensions. Not only must vast quantities of data be analyzed, but it is already clear that one set of data may have to be analyzed many times, with slight variations in format. Computers are designed in such a way as to be capable of going from one part of a problem to the next without interruption. This automatic control feature eliminates the need to stop a long series of complex computations, minimizing the time required to complete the problem solving routine.

COMPUTER INVALUABLE IN CITY PLANNING

The computer is the ideal data handling device for complex problems of the city system. The complexity of cities indicates that the statement of city planning problems will be lengthy and very detailed. Because of the computer's internal traffic system, all problems must be reduced to simple instructions. The reduction of problems to mathematical form will require further translation to instructions in machine language. Once in machine language, problems are flexible and easily converted to other formats in which it is possible to expand the analytic process.

The computer is in many ways an ideal research tool; it will do anything it is instructed with 100 percent reliability. For all practical purposes it is error free, and can absorb tremendous computational work loads, up to the equivalent of thousands of people. Some computers even have the ability to solve more than one problem at a time.

The computer performs all basic arithmetic operations. In addition, it can perform certain logical operations. This attribute, sometimes called the decision making property of computers, is quite limited. It can select the larger of two numbers or choose alternatives, depending upon the previous detailed instructions it has been given. These kinds of choices are not what we normally think of as decisions. However, they are extremely useful to the man writing the computer's machine language, because they enable him to deal with all foreseeable contingencies.

The computer has a memory. Properly questioned, it can recall small pieces of data from very large files. Data can be put into temporary storage while the problem is in work and later be returned to the more permanent file without damage to the record being handled. Like the home tape recorder, it can read information or write over existing information. This process, file updating, is very important to city planning.

Because it can accept instructions as well as information, the computer can direct itself in a predetermined manner. In addition, it can check the results of its own operations and notify the men operating the computer when something is not functioning satisfactorily.

All problems in the city system must eventually be handled as quantitative expressions if they are to make use of the computer. The technique of systems analysis, so useful in analyzing the city system, would not be usable without the computer as the data processing tool. Together these tools of the technical world provide a powerful analytical package ideally combined for the solution of city planning problems.

A PLANNING DATA PROCESSING SYSTEM

A description of the tools applied in a study for the city of Los Angeles will serve as an example of city planning. This assignment was a feasibility study designed to determine if it was appropriate to use the systems tools in the planning area. This effort was also a design study, intended to outline the broad areas in which the new tools could be used.

To demonstrate this usefulness, the problem was divided into two areas: to deal with day to day information retrieval; and to deal with problems of wider scope where the need for further research was emphasized.

Thus, the first requirement in the Los Angeles study was to look at the existing operations as systems and attempt to define the various properties which were present or missing. After identifying the systems to be studied, the next requirement was to look at the purposes or goals for which these systems existed. Once the objectives were clear, it was possible to determine whether the existing systems filled the complete requirement. This led to a reappraisal of the objectives or purposes for which individual systems existed and provided a scope of study within which systems design would take place. A few words about the various systems will describe their reasons for existence.

THREE AREAS SELECTED

To cope with day to day problems, the report recommended that data processing systems be installed in three major areas: master plan, effectuation and planning economics.

In the master plan area, subsystems were recommended in the areas of population estimating, land use, schools, parks, public works and circulation. Many of these subsystems contain the elements of the existing systems currently employed by the Los Angeles department. However, through the added flexibility of the computer and the associated techniques mentioned, the systems are generally expanded to provide more information to planners as they accumulate data to analyze potential effectuations.

Using the five elements of a system, each detailed process in master plan, effectuation and planning economics was built into elementary subsystems. Each subsystem was designed to be compatible with all of the other subsystems to which it was related.

The combined systems of master plan were thus planned to be compatible with those in effectuation and planning economics and vice versa insofar as data processing was con-

cerned. This intersystem compatibility is called systems integration. Here is how the integration principle is applied in the Los Angeles system.

When there is a change in population, the planner knows that it may affect the circulation system because it will change transportation demands. In addition, a change in population may affect land use because the requirements with respect to living and working areas will have to accommodate increases or decreases in numbers of people. A change in population will likewise affect the public services which are available. Increases in population in certain areas will provide the need for more schools or more parks. It is also likely that, because of changes in some areas where people are leaving, the need for schools or parks may diminish.

Thus, a planning system would only truly be integrated if the computer could duplicate in its internal processes all of the operations the planner would undertake if he had the time and manpower to research an important action completely. This is precisely what has been done.

The Los Angeles planning system has been designed so that the planner will be able to gain access to all of the data pertinent to any action. Standard interrogation routines will enable the planner to do a complete research job in a fraction of the time now consumed. Research on this level of thoroughness has the potential of providing planners with an insight to their problems never before possible.

SUBSYSTEMS

The planning economics subsystem affords the planning department an opportunity to evaluate the economic consequences of anticipated effectuations. By adding the dollar dimension to planning actions, planners will have the ability to evaluate the long term consequences of these actions. Planners will be able to relate the ability of their city to undertake certain projects, versus the inability of their city to undertake certain large costs. In this subsystem, sources of revenue are balanced against expense and the planner can examine a very few numbers which will indicate to him the results of perhaps a million individual computations.

The effectuation system has been designed

to make available all of the data which is in the planning department's files. This means that a complete inventory of current, past and pending actions must be set up and an automated index used to gain access to the data which is required. This subsystem will make it a simple matter to obtain all of the data relevant to a pending action. It will increase the reliability of research into day to day problems, since the index will provide access in a number of different ways. The time requirement for research should be measurably affected, although the effectuation subsystem won't tell the answers — only where to go to find the information from which the planners can get the answers.

The population estimating subsystem will produce detailed breakdowns of population according to the concept of the statistical unit. Los Angeles would be divided into approximately 2,500 such units which will be combined by the electronic data processor in any way that the program instructions dictate. For instance, five of these statistical units may equal one census tract. These same five units plus 12 other units may equal a police reporting district. The original five units and 14 others may equal a school service boundary. This subsystem proposes an easy means of retrieving population information according to any desired service boundary with which the planner is concerned. Population has been chosen as the basic and underlying factor on which all master plan systems will be based for the simple reason that even in the atomic age people are still most important.

The land use subsystem operates on a complete inventory of existing and future land uses. The idea in the land use subsystem is to determine how well the existing land uses conform to the master plan. Through the planner's device of design standards or conventions, it is possible to look at the real life situation within an area from the standpoint of conformance to standards. These standards combine the totality of the planner's knowledge of what is best for the community with the various codes and restrictions placed upon the planner through his knowledge of good planning practice.

Standards become the guides for the design of an adequate city. The degree to which the city conforms to the state of these standards will be reflected in an index called a conformance factor, the purpose of which will be to direct the planner at areas which demand his assistance first.

The common thread in this description of planning systems is the ability to see a dynamic process, such as urban planning, as a system.

Planning systems are composed of many closely related, interdependent subsystems. The role of the systems analyst is to provide the method of operation necessary to design the system. The desired goal is to create a fully integrated system, where the subsystems interact within the framework of data processing, much as they react in real life. The execution of this data processing task is so monumentally large one can only think of it in terms of the computer which is the necessary processing device to activate these concepts.

ROLE OF PLANNERS ENLARGED

To those who designed the Los Angeles systems, it has become obvious that planning is the only department of municipal government dealing with the city's living problems in a horizontal fashion. Police, fire, public works and school departments, for example, are vertical in that they consider only their own problem areas in satisfying community requirements. Up until now, planners have been unable by the sheer size of the problem to create a complete picture of the city in order to deal with planning as adequately as they themselves have wished.

The use of systems analysis and electronic data processing opens the door to implement the planner's enlarged role in government. Only planners have a reason to assemble current data on the existing and anticipated population, land use, effectuation and economic status of the city. Only planners have periodic opportunities to evaluate objectively and reliably the current and alternate long range plans of individual service departments.

City planning can be a basic input to many of the municipal departments. It can be an effective control mechanism over the "city system" by generally raising the level of reliability in decision making. Only the planning department has the potential to develop all the tools and resources necessary to solve the complex urban problems which exist today.

By Charles F. Winter
General Precision, Inc.

Second Generation Computers

TEN YEARS AGO the computer was first applied to the processing of business data. Since that time there have been many changes in the design and use of electronic data processing equipment.

Initially, scientific computers were applied to solving business problems. But as business needs became more recognized, modifications took place within the computer to make it more adaptable to business needs.

Today, many companies and corporations are manufacturing computers designed specifically for business applications and for many areas of business data processing.

Some 6,000 to 7,000 computers, in various sizes, have been installed for business applications, with the greatest majority of these computer installations used for the processing of reports, records and statistics associated with the accounting department.

To this day most computers are being used to replace some or all of the punched card equipment previously employed in the processing of accounting department data.

But management needs and is looking for much greater accomplishments from its computer centers. To process data is one thing, to process automated, integrated data is another.

TIMELY INFORMATION IS VITAL

Information is both the basis and the result of executive management decisions. In these days of ever increasing competition, rising costs of operation and the development of new and better products, management sometimes finds it very difficult to know where it is going because it cannot find out, with sufficient speed, where it has been.

The lack of timely, accurate, available data relating to all areas of a business can result in some wild, impetuous and costly decisions.

It is not meant to imply that accounting information is not accurate, factual information. But the information, being recorded after the fact, is not always timely and not always available at the time it is most needed.

Modern corporations operate their plants and offices on pre-planned budgets and forecasts, with manufacturing schedules determined in advance. As long as everything operates within schedule, there are no headaches relative to orders in the house and work orders in process.

Under existing methods of operating a business, management does not know that the business is operating within budget or that the plant is on schedule until long after the fact.

If and when the proper tools are developed for processing information within a business organization, management will not have to spend more than half its time trying to find out what was done and what was not the general occurrence today.

With the possible exception of some payroll applications, the manner in which raw data is created, gathered and processed in our data processing centers makes it impossible for the accounting department to give information to management in much less than five days after the fact. Frequently this runs to 10 working days.

As information becomes available, under the present methods of processing data accounting can tell management what was done. But even with the delay in the processing of the data, accounting can seldom if ever tell management what was *not* done.

Under existing methods of processing data, where information is gathered on a department by department basis, the reports and statistics submitted by one department are not coordinated, or necessarily agree, with the similar reports and statistics submitted by other departments.

Management does not have the time — and should not be forced to take the time — to read reports and statistics covering what was accomplished, comparing them to plans and schedules in order to find out, by process of elimination, what was not done, what was not on schedule and what was an overrun or shortage in production. Management should be able to work on the basis that everything, except those specific matters which have been brought to its attention, was done in strict accordance with plan and schedule.

But even this type of reporting, now commonly called "reporting by exception," does not satisfy the needs of management nor can it ever fulfill the requirements of business until we have the ways and means of automatically gathering data at its source and processing it into the various avenues of reports, records and statistics, without any form of human intervention.

FACTORS TO CONSIDER

Time is the first important factor for consideration. Reports are meaningless if, by the time they have been created, they reflect only ancient history.

Although as important as time, accuracy of information becomes our next important consideration. Accuracy can not be assured with manual processing. At best, the human factor is only 99 percent accurate. When paperwork has been handled as many as 30 times the accuracy figure can drop to 74 percent. (Accuracy of 98 percent to the thirtieth power equals 54½ percent while accuracy of 95 percent to the thirtieth power is only 21 2/5 percent.) The only way to assure accuracy is to gather data automatically and integrate it mechanically or electrically, untouched by human hand.

The amount of paperwork that is manually created and processed within the plant, compared to that processed within the office area by punched card or electronic data processing, points out how backward the development of real integrated data processing systems has been.

Special computers have been and are being installed by many businesses to handle spe-cific, individual problems. But the actual use of integrated data processing systems is still very much in an infant stage, not because the methods cannot be devised, but rather because the computer system has not yet been built which can adequately handle and process data.

The word "computer" as such has been accepted by business management. Such acceptance, however, does not mean management is ready to install the equipment. This is far from being the case. Management realizes the full potential of the computer in its relation to business has not yet been reached. Furthermore, it cannot and will not be reached until manufacturers realize that in integrated data processing the ability must be present to:

1. Gather raw data automatically or semi-automatically at the point of its creation and carry it, electrically or electronically directly into the computer.

2. Provide on an on line basis, the ability to sort, collate and merge information in the process of integrating reports and records within the computer itself.

3. Without change of existing programming, increase the capacity of the computer through modular, building block construction.

4. Provide for the interconnection of computers so they may communicate with each other.

Unfortunately, computer manufacturers still associate the business computer with accounting and recordkeeping. They fail for some reason to see the potential of the computer in relation to the need of management for faster and more complete information necessary for improved decision making.

While a well planned integrated electronic data processing system will save many dollars in the cost of clerical labor, effective management now realizes that better decision making means greater profits. And greater profits mean far more than clerical savings, Such additional profits do not come overnight. Management must first learn how to use the new electronic tool to its greatest advantage.

DATA PROCESSING ORGANIZATION

Following in the footsteps of punched card equipment, computers were logically placed under the control of the finance (or accounting) departments when they were first introduced to business. In the early days of computer usage, this was reasonable inasmuch as individuals could see no immediate application for the electronic device other than ultra-high speed punched card type applications similar to, but far faster than, existing electric accounting (punched card) machines.

The original placement of the electronic data processing center within the accounting area has not proved to be too advantageous over the years — the computer applications have far exceeded the limits of the accounting department.

Management has begun to realize the emphasis should not be placed on the electronic device, but rather on the integrated systems throughout the entire corporation. The computer can make that possible.

The ability of a computer system to gather raw data in an automatic manner at its point of creation, integrate that with related data from all areas of the plant, as well as the office, has caused management to realize information can be provided for them as it happens rather than days or weeks later.

In the automated, integrated, peripheral computer system concept, the capability exists to provide management with information in a format usable for decision making, as it happens. This now becomes a management information service.

Companies which have had considerable experience with business computers have made several shifts in data processing organization. Initially, as it was realized the data center was working for areas well outside of accounting, the electronic data processing center was moved from under the authority of the controller to that of the chief financial officer (usually vice president of finance). When he found the job too big to handle, he created a new division within the financial area where data processing reported to a person of equal stature to that of the controller.

More recently, as top management realized the computer was the basis for better management information from and to all areas of the plant as well as the office, the direction of the data processing operation shifted from the financial area to a central management area.

Many companies of medium and large size created an entirely new area which deals only with systems and methods analysis leading to better management reporting and management decision making. "Management information services" or "management intelligence services" are replacing the more commonly known terms of "systems, methods and procedures" and "data processing department."

Corporate management should look into the new skills and decision making possibilities of management information services. Until management realizes that there is a growing need for better information and has decided upon what it needs in the way of a system, there is no need to consider or look at computer hardware. The potential of the computer to a business is directly related to the ability of the executive to change his pattern of thinking, planning and decision making.

It is interesting to note that in today's computer concepts, data entry is considered the key to an integrated electronic data processing system. At the AMA data processing conference held in March 1961, at least 75 percent of the 750 people attending favored, by a show of hands, that they require suitable data entry in their second generation computer systems.

It was also indicated at the conference that electronic data systems today are decidely lacking in sorting, collating and merging techniques and are equally lacking in multiple program techniques.

It was further indicated that sophisticated equipment will be required, by comparison to existing computers, before Pert, Pep, Line of Balance and similar records and controls can be properly processed by computers with associated XY plotters, or comparable devices for the drawing of charts and graphs.

Initially, the cost of an electronic data system was thought of in terms of the computer only. Now it is realized that the cost of data collection is equal to at least three times the computer cost.

In the past five years there has been a great increase in the number and sizes of computers and computer manufacturers. But in all computers to date, the data collection requirements have always been an afterthought and, as such, the computers fail to fully meet the systems requirements.

The present trend among potential computer users is to develop the complete system requirement at one time; it is realized that such a system must be completely free of flaws and errors which prompts the potential user to look for an on line, real time system that is truly automated, integrated and peripheral in concept and design. The fact that such a system design has not as yet been achieved has prompted the large majority of potential users to hold back on actual installation. They realize a conglomeration of auxiliary, peripheral and computer equipment, supplied by many different manufacturers, will never work perfectly together in producing an on line, real time, error free system which can provide accurate exception-type and overnight reporting.

Too many computer users bought their equipment first and then attempted to design their system around it. This will never work satisfactorily and is the reason so many data systems have been abandoned after installation.

A good electronic data processing system should provide information to the extent of need. It should be geared to supply information to the various levels of management in accordance with personal action responsibilities.

The significance of data is dependent upon the attitudes, situations and responsibilities of the interpreter. All information is interpretive and significant in terms of prior information and interpretation.

A data processing system should be designed to cope with the changing patterns of business. It should be a risk reducing, decision making aid to business. To be of the greatest benefit to business and management, the system should be so designed that the format can be changed as the business changes. Operations which have remained static as the overall system grows or shrinks should require no reprogramming. The resulting change should come from the size of the main data processing equipment.

A computer, regardless of size, has little or no value to business as a data processing medium unless it is designed to handle business problems on an integrated basis instead of on a special or single type basis.

The objective of an integrated system is to enter raw data once and have it perpetuated within the system where it can be acted upon and operated on by the system without further manual intervention.

Because an integrated system calls for data to be introduced only once it becomes a prerequisite and requirement of the system that all departmental lines of organization are crossed and that information is properly supplied to all such departments and areas.

There can be no restrictions placed upon those connected or associated with the data processing system in relation to the crossing of divisional or departmental lines. Any such restrictions would greatly impair the success of the system. A well organized integrated data processing system serves all departments and areas of the company. It serves all levels of personnel within management.

The personnel associated directly or indirectly with the data processing operations — the analysts, systems and methods men, the programmers and the data processing men — perform a service to all levels and departments of management. For this reason, management services, or management information services are designations used in order that the group which formally worked as separate entities can be more properly combined as a well defined team. The emphasis becomes one of providing management with the tools it needs for daily operations rather than to supply the archives with less effective reports and records.

An integrated data processing system when properly planned and executed, can provide management with far better tools with which to work than can an unintegrated system. However, an integrated system merely means information introduced to the system can be processed and reprocessed automatically. It does not imply the basic information fed into the system has reached that point on anything approaching a real time basis.

REAL TIME OPERATIONS

To approach real time operations requires equipment to be placed throughout the office and plant areas at the spots where information is created. It is necessary to have direct communications with the central data processing equipment in machine readable language, so that the main unit can act on new information at the time the event happens.

These units, spread across the office and

plant, are classified as peripheral equipment. Peripheral units must serve two purposes. They must send information to the data processing center and must receive information from the data center. With two-way communication, the plant or office area not only sends information to the center at the exact time of the event, but also is able to receive instantaneous information regarding any errors, variations in work performed, corrections in schedules, or new work orders.

When the integrated, peripheral system has been properly installed, both input and output at the peripheral location become fully automated and require a minimum of manual effort in creating or receiving data.

Theoretically, it is possible to reach 100 percent automation on input to the data processing center from the peripheral units. If this were done, the manpower currently utilized in creating input documents — writing, typing and key punching — could be eliminated. This, of course, is almost impossible to do in a manufacturing company of any size. Yet larger corporations that have installed fully integrated, peripheral systems claim that savings of 50 percent in such non-productive, indirect labor are easy to obtain in the original or basic systems concept. Some corporations claim to have reached a savings of 83 percent in these pencil pushing areas after the system has been fully installed and all the bugs have been eliminated.

There are good, sound reasons why only a few of the larger companies have extended the electronic data processing services to areas other than accounting. Some of these reasons are:

1. The length of time that it took to get data from the plant areas to the data processing center made information outdated by the time it could be processed.

2. The inability of a computer to sort, merge and collate at electronic speeds compatible to other computer functions prevented operations from being performed on an integrated basis.

3. To perform the necessary sorts, merges and collations, data centers must resort to off line sorting, merging, and collating on high speed punched card equipment. Because of the long series of integrated reports and records which must be processed, it becomes cheaper and faster to continue to use punched card equipment or to augment this existing equipment with electronic units manufactured by the same company.

4. The use of off line punched card equipment for sorting, merging and collating introduces to an otherwise perfect system the human error factor. This factor leads away from the true intent of integration, under computer concepts, in which it is expected that information once introduced to the computer is never again reintroduced by manual methods.

5. The volume of stored, repetitive or historical data used by the big company in its data processing made it necessary, even though costly, to sort, merge and collate its information on a combined on/off line basis. The small or medium size firm could not afford a similar operation and therefore could not justify computer usage except in the accounting areas.

6. Peripheral equipment, which has only come into being in the last five years, has not as yet been designed to work directly with the computer. Manufacturers of such peripheral equipment were interested in the sale of their equipment — not in the sale of a specific computer — and as such made their units so that they could work, one way or another, with any data processing system. The units, therefore, became a "jack of all trades — master of none" device which required the purchase or rental of additional auxiliary equipment for conversion of output to a code acceptable by the computer or punched card system. Furthermore, with minor exceptions, the various peripheral units were fixed in their capacity and rigid in their sequence of input/output which prevented their being used to the best advantage by potential users.

7. The association of punched card machinery with accounting department operations — the reporting of the systems, methods and procedures department to the controller — has made other departments shy away from data proc-

essing. This reluctance, on the part of other departments, to give up apparent (though not actual) control of their paperwork to accounting and to the controller, will continue until the words "methods" and "data processing" are dropped. A new name for the combined functions, such as "management information services" should be substituted, giving the feeling to other departments that the electronic data system and all persons associated with it are working for and with the management team and not merely for accounting.

The title or name, *automated, integrated, peripheral, electronic data processing system*, sounds very impressive, perhaps too impressive. Maybe it scares management executives who might feel it sounds too complicated to understand.

Actually, the title is very meaningful. Such a system makes the clerical functions of the office and the plant, by comparison, almost non-existent. It simplifies the paperwork functions of the overall business operations to the absolute minimum.

PAPERWORK PROCESSING

To repeat briefly and to aid in the explanation of a statement made previously, the following definitions apply to the processing of paperwork within a business.

Automated — a system or method in which the processes are automatically performed and controlled by self-operating machinery or electronic devices.

Integrate — to design a system in such a way that results of one report become the basis for another. To introduce raw data into the system in such a way that 1) it never has to be reintroduced by manual means; 2) that it perpetuates itself, mechanically or electronically within the system.

Peripheral — (distal) — farthest from the center or point of origin. This word is applied to the electromechanical or electronic devices scattered throughout the office and plant areas. From these locations, raw data can be automatically picked up at the point of origin and electrically or electronically sent directly to the data center without further human or manual intervention. "Peripheral" may also be applied to similar devices used in the same office or plant areas for receipt of information from the data center.

Electronic data processing — (EDP) — a computer of any size designed specifically for use in the processing of business information into reports, records and statistics

With automated, integrated, peripheral, electronic data processing equipment, the entire plant and office (paperwork) operation can function automatically.

From the physical receipt of an order or from the creation of a new product design, the paperwork is created automatically and flows, step by step, from one department area to another. In its automated integration, it

1. *Determines the presence or absence of needed items in inventory.*
   a. Creates its own production orders for replacement to inventory of "make" items.
   b. Creates its own purchase requisitions for items to be purchased on the outside.
   c. Makes necessary reservations of inventory items.
2. *Determines the logical manufacturing sequence of production operation.*
   a. Automatically checks and prepares machine loading requirements.
   b. Automatically checks and includes new production order into previously prepared manufacturing schedule.
   c. Creates the complete production order.
   d. Prepares individual job cards and parts requisition for each item on production order.
3. *Writes purchase orders when supplied with vendor's name, price and delivery information by purchasing department.*
   a. Supplies necessary follow-up to purchasing or open orders.
   b. Supplies receiving department and quality control with schedule of planned receipts together with card for each line item on every purchase order.
4. *Automatically maintains inventory records of all items in stock (both in pieces and in dollars).*
   a. Records all items on order.

b. Records all items reserved in inventory.

c. Records all withdrawals from inventory.

d. Records all receipts into inventory against purchase orders.

e. Records all receipts into inventory against returns.

f. Provides any and all inventory information upon request.

5. *From production floor.*

a. Automatically records the completion of each line item appearing on a production order together with quantity produced, operator (employee) number, and start/stop time.

b. Automatically records the withdrawal of items from inventory stores together with clock number of employee making withdrawal and job number on which item is to be used.

6. *From engineering*

a. Records any change in product design.

b. Alters and updates the required loading.

c. Alters and updates the over all manufacturing schedule.

d. Alters and updates the production order.

e. Alters and updates the job tickets and/or parts requisitions.

7. *From purchasing.*

a. Alters and updates changes in purchase orders and/or delivery dates.

8. *Automatically provides payroll information.*

a. Electronically records arrival and departure of employees, eliminating need for time cards and timekeepers.

9. *Provides management with daily reports.*

a. Each morning, upon arrival at the office or plant, executives, managers and supervisors are provided with exception reports listing those things which were not done as of the close of business on the previous day in accordance with plan and schedule.

b. Provides detailed records and re-

ports of all work performed — as and when required by prearranged schedule — including all existing documents prepared manually or by machine in all department areas.

10. *Sales and sales statistics.*

a. Will automatically provide sales with status reports of orders in progress.

b. Creates all shipping documents and invoices.

c. Provides all necessary sales statistics.

This listing is by no means fully detailed or complete. It is intended only to present an idea of how a single manual input to such an automated integrated peripheral system can do all of the paperwork operations of the entire plant with far greater speed and accuracy than can be done by other means.

Theoretically, all of the above mentioned automated, integrated, peripheral operations can be performed by a combination of auxiliary, peripheral and computer machines. To have such a system would be Utopian.

There are several reasons why this must still be classified as theoretical and why it is Utopian in concept instead of in fact. The most important reason is that no single computer has yet been designed and applied to such a business system that is truly automated and integrated in its operation.

Another reason is that many peripheral machines currently on the market were not designed to work with a specific computer or computer system.

Combining these two statements it can be said that except in special cases, the proper hardware to make such a system economical and practical does not exist.

When speaking of the very large corporations working in the broad field of electronics and space vehicles, there is an entirely different situation from the operation in the small, medium, and reasonably large companies.

Very large companies can afford communications networks of 100,000 or more miles. Their operations are such that they can substantiate a centrally located system for all their data processing operations. They can afford, under such concepts, a small computer operating off line to perform the sorts, merges and collations that cannot be done, or done profitably on the main computer.

Likewise, at a central location, they can afford the auxiliary equipment of many types and makes which are required to convert the output of the varied types of peripheral equipment into the common language of the computer.

PLAN FOR MANUFACTURERS

What must be done by the manufacturers of computers, auxiliary and peripheral equipment in order to interest thousands of potential customers in the Utopian economies and advantages of an automated, integrated, peripheral, electronic data processing system?

The computer manufacturer must make one of two choices. He must buy out a company manufacturing auxiliary and peripheral equipment or he must decide to manufacture his own equipment. His only other alternative is to work directly with manufacturers of auxiliary equipment and peripheral equipment so each of the three companies will manufacture a product which is fully compatible with that of the other two manufacturers.

The computer manufacturer must also solve the problem of integration by providing, as a part of the computer, the ability to sort, merge and collate at speeds which are equal to that of the other computer operations. Until such time as the computer can sort, merge and collate on line at electronic speeds, there will never be a truly integrated electronic data processing machine.

Until the computer can be tied directly to the peripheral input/output devices, through buffer storage and associated sequential scanners, the so called auxiliary equipment will not be eliminated and the costs of computers will not be cut to the point where they are practical and economical.

The possibility of complete reprogramming will linger until such time as the computer manufacturer, through modular, building block construction, makes it possible to buy or rent a small computer which can be built up in its capacities to suit the user's needs.

Until such time as the computer manufacturer provides for multiple programming of the computer, more than one tenth of a computer's capabilities will never be successfully utilized.

Until such time as a computer manufacturer evaluates all existing computers, auxiliary and peripheral equipment, and takes the best features of each and arranges the pieces so that they logically work together as if they were a single unit, that point of Utopia will not be reached where the statement can be made:

Here, for the first time is a truly automated, integrated, peripheral, electronic, data processing system that can eliminate 100 percent of the pencil pushing personnel.

By Maurice F. Ronayne
Federal Power Commission

Data Processing Follow-Up:
Feedback Plus Systems Analysis

THE RIBBON falls to the floor of the new electronic computer palace. The President of the company cut the ribbon, the computer manufacturer provided a computer, management followed the total systems approach in working out the new system from A to Z, systems analysts planned to the *nth* degree, and programmers programmed! Will our computer friend take over from here and resolve our management problems with his electronic impulses?

The answer is undoubtedly no.

Much has been written about automated data processing up to the point when the equipment has been actually installed. But little has been in print about what happens after installation day.

Anywhere from six months to three years may be spent in turning a mere electronic twinkle in top management's eye into an electronic computer system reality. Once installed, most management folk hope that the computer system will be operative for the next five to ten years, technological developments notwithstanding.

Today it seems fashionable to banter around the term "total systems approach." Many people use it without thinking what it actually means. Basically, total systems approach means implementing an automatic data processing system (anything from electronic computers to electric accounting machines to optical character recognition devices should fit in here) by covering all possibilities. It means that setting up automatic data processing is not a question of a single application approach, treating problems as separate entities, but a total systems approach, embracing a series of applications and their relationships to one another. Computers like to carry out every conceivable operation on a given piece of input data before going on to the next. Jobs have to be completely reorganized to be split up not by type of application, but by type of input document. Single procedures must be traced through all their branches, forgetting about existing organizational boundaries.

But what we want to talk over here is the implementation of a total systems effort; that is, the complete planning for this effort. Most regrettably, the most knowledgeable and experienced people often view the implementation of a computer system as ending the day on which someone plugs in the computer.

A year later they're hauling the computer out because it's costing more now than ever before to do the same old job! The reports are all mixed up! The system has to be expanded pronto! Prime shift time is only being used 50 percent! The clerks aren't coding the input data right! It's taking twice as long! And so on until top management screams, "Why didn't somebody tell us?"

Somebody didn't tell them because there was no system for telling (reporting to) anyone. The implementation of a total systems approach ended with the installation of the computer.

This could happen to you, and yours, and your organization if proper steps are not taken at the very on-set of planning for automated data processing. A total system approach means absolutely nothing unless you realize that the implementation of this approach, to its logical and ultimate completion, is the key to success.

Let's turn literary for the moment, and look

up this key word implementation. The dictionary says that:

Implementation is:

A putting into effect, fulfillment or carrying through, as of ideas, a program, etc.[1]

To be noted here is that implementation means carrying through a program to completion. This is also the heart of a successful automatic data processing program. Carrying the program through to its completion will help to tilt the odds in favor of its success.

Now is the time for all good automatic data processing people to look into the methods or techniques of the continuing implementation of an automatic data processing program through its actual installation to the time when at long last the hardware has to be replaced because of old age.

RECOGNITION OF THE PROBLEM

Once set up and running, an automatic data processing system can *not* be simply permitted to fend for itself. William H. O'Keeffe describes follow-up as being a most vital part of the total systems approach. He writes:

"A system cannot be left to maintain itself. Careful planning and skilled operation does not preclude the need for security of data processing systems. The speed with which the equipment executes the decisions of management requires that an equally accelerated means be provided to effectively analyze the system as it functions. If properly designed, the installation includes types of control and analysis programs that will indicate to what extent the system is realizing its objectives."[2]

RECOMMENDED TREATMENT

Regardless of the size of the computer system, there must be a plan for its continuous evaluation. Even in the vast electronic empire of the Department of Defense, located in the Comptroller's Office, a Data Systems Review Division has the military world of automatic data processing as its baby. It operates across the board to check on electronic computer installations throughout the military system. Its staff, formerly headed by Charles A. Phillips (of COBOL fame), has been " . . . responsible for review and evaluation of automatic data processing systems actually in operation as well as those proposed for test to insure that they will provide actual economies

and meet management needs effectively."[3] Alert civilian agencies as well as companies in private industry protect themselves with similar systems to make sure they know what they are getting out of their expensive black boxes.

LEADING QUESTIONS

To insure a proper review of new operations, top management must set up a reporting system to provide feedback information which will be both timely and accurate. Concurrently, and especially during the early stages of a computer installation, management must undertake recurring systems analysis studies to determine what is going on. Both feedback reports and systems studies will provide the answers to these vital questions:

1. Are predetermined schedule dates for application, conversions, schedules, and personnel considerations being met?

2. Have the major criteria goals of the new system been realized, *i.e.*, percentage of filled orders completed, days now required to process an order, inventory costs reduced, less clerical effort, skills released to do more important work, manpower savings, improved quality control, inspection elimination, production trends, reduced computations?

3. Has costing been applied to each application? Are anticipated cost savings being accomplished?

4. Are schedules for all phases of computer operation being used?

5. Does the quality of the information resulting from the system approximate planned standards?

6. Have intangibles been evaluated and assigned a monetary value? What other benefits have resulted? Have factors like timeliness, accuracy, and improved service been properly documented?

[1]Charles Earle Funk, editor, *New College Standard Dictionary*, New York: Funk & Wagnalls Company. 1953. p. 594.

[2]William H. O'Keeffe, "Step by Step," *Data Processing*. April, 1961. p. 24.

[3]"The Comptroller," *Armed Forces Management*. November, 1959. p. 50.

7. Have modifications or refinements in the system and in the written procedures been made, as justified by actual operating experience?

8. Have all replaced procedures and routines actually been discontinued?

9. Has the decision making capability of the computer been expanded over and above initial concepts?

10. Have additional areas offering a greater degree of integration of data, files, and processing been identified?

11. Can any data or information requirements now be added, eliminated or combined?

12. What new applications can be incorporated into the computer system?

13. Does the installation have the general appearance of a well run installation? Do the employees appear to be enthusiastic about the operation of the installation? Do the top administrator and his supervisors appear to have the work situation well in hand?

14. Is data output actually being used to measure organizational performance as a basis for decision, to reformulate policy, and/or to execute regular affairs of business?

MAJOR TOOLS TO BE USED

Two major tools, feedback reporting and recurring systems analysis studies, should provide most of the answers to management's fundamental question of "How well is the work being done?"

Feedback reporting provides measurement for all principle operations; controls to insure the accuracy of data reported; assurance that the uses of machine products are consistent with the cost, frequency, and promptness with which they are cranked out; and facts such as that one time reports are only done on the computer when proven advantageous, and that management gets the basic data it wants for statistical analysis and control.

Systems analysis includes recurring operations audits to make sure that policies, methods, procedures, and practices are being effectively administered by those responsible for the system. Systems analysis in this form will take the appearance of the periodic medical check-up where a study is made without

necessary prior knowledge of any existing problem. An established schedule for follow-up will leave nothing to chance. Techniques employed include measuring results of improvements through work measurement, statistical standards, work sampling, machine utilization reports, and cost analysis. An analysis of records may show a lack of adherence to prescribed procedure plus possibilities for further improvements. Random observations, interviews, and other appropriate survey devices can be used to note how things are going in the new installation.

IMPORTANT AREAS OF CONCERN

A model data processing center should be operated and administered so that the information for feedback reporting and systems analysis will be readily found in the installation itself. Here follows discussion of what management should equip itself with, to establish feedback reporting and recurring systems analysis for effectively, and economically, evaluating the performance of its data processing center, from the initial follow-up review to periodic ones thereafter.

BASIC INGREDIENTS

The most important ingredient for the follow-up of an initial installation as well as a continuous evaluation of its performance is a uniform procedure to collect and present carefully selected information on programming, workload requirements, and progress and operation of the hardware and of the overall system. Reports should identify the initial and cumulative benefits which have been gotten, on the basis of on site experience, from the application of automatic data processing to the data processing requirements of the installation. A definite demarcation should be made between direct and indirect benefits obtained in each major functional application (not forgetting even those discontinued during or before the reporting cycle). Definable management improvements should be identified, described, and credited to the application of automatic data processing techniques.

To establish an effective follow-up system which can be the concrete foundation for a continuous reporting system, it is well worth the effort to set up systems which use job codes, index numbers, file data numbers, work order numbers, and control and assignment codes, as well as a master job code directory.

A good standardized job coding system catalogues an entire workload into recognizable bits and pieces, ties the workload together through a total systems concept, and couples the whole ball of wax to an effective recording system, so as to provide nearly all the basic data to evaluate an organization's operation. It also ties manpower, machines, and other resources potential to the productive output, informs management on how the productive effort was divided, offers the capability of determining how much the productive effort was divided, relates man hours against machine hours, and facilitates systematic workload control and scheduling.

In **Exhibits 1 and 2**, respectively, are examples of a punched card used to record data on employee-machine utilization, and a form for recording vital information about work orders.

However, before setting up an elaborate system, it will be best to utilize the follow-up period for having a shakeout of the bugs in the proposed reporting system, as well as that of operations. Refinements in procedures are perhaps best postponed till after the follow-up period of the installation, at which time the procedures have passed their trial by fire and management has had the chance to appraise them.

RECORDING UTILIZATION

Machine utilization records document the use and expenditure of men, money, and machines. From this wealth of data, trends can be determined, products costed, effort measured, and forecasting accomplished. During the follow-up period, management must make sure that the data to be recorded for analyses and studies are not only valid, but reliable.

Standard coding systems are essential to obtaining factual and consistent data. Most organizations should have code systems showing jobs assigned, type of machines used, card files and tape records used or created, and other vital data. Corporations having large scale electronic computer systems and big staffs will most likely have coding systems to show personnel utilization. A typical system will show how much time a systems analyst, programmer, key puncher, clerk, or machine operator may have contributed to completing one job. From this kind of system, cost and time standards can eventually be established for most jobs.

As a minimum, utilization records should:

1. Pinpoint how machine time available for use is in fact used, including the amount of productive time, down time, maintenance time, and idle time occurring each work day.

Exhibit 1

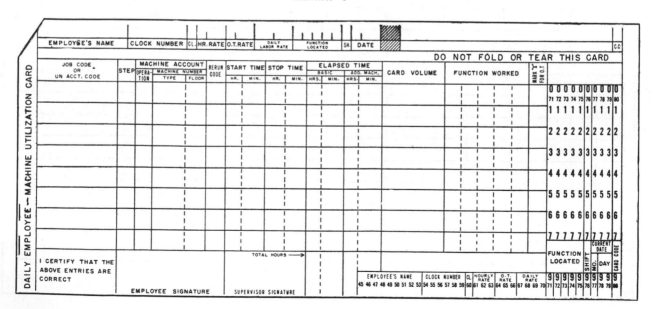

2. Show the volume of data processed and the length of time necessary to process it so as to document information for determining future requirements.

3. Provide sufficient information for billing purposes for rented equipment.

4. Be a basis for charging machine rental, personnel time, and maintenance costs to the proper user.

5. Provide sufficient information for job costing.

When making a systems analysis of a new system, or a recurring systems survey, these key questions can usually provide answers which will indicate whether or not further study is warranted in the utilization area:

1. Are there too few or too many properly trained machine operating personnel or systems designers?

2. Are there indications of excessive idleness, tardiness, and/or absenteeism among the machine operators, systems designers, or machine operation supervisors?

3. Is the same input or source data often run through the machine processing operations more than once (may indicate faulty planning, excessive machine error, or hidden time)?[4]

But be careful lest you kill the goose that laid the golden egg. A too elaborate system can cost more money than it can turn back in savings. As Robert W. Parsons, in his excellent article on the subject of utilization

[4]*Guide For Auditing Automatic Data Processing Systems*, Auditor General, Comptroller, Department of the Air Force, Washington 25, D. C.: U. S. Government Printing Office, November, 1961. 128 pp.

Exhibit 2

DATA SERVICES WORK ORDER										
1. JOB TITLE									2. JOB CODE	
3. DATE INITIATED			4. CONTROL NUMBER				5. DUE OUT DATE			
6. SOURCE DATA DUE IN			7. SOURCE DATA RECEIVED				8. DIVISION			

DATA CONT'L	KEY PUNCH	MACHINE ROOM	EDPE	TRANSCEIVER	DECOLLATING	9. TIME IN		10. TIME OUT		11. INITIATED OR COMPLETED BY
						HOUR	DAY OF YEAR	HOUR	DAY OF YEAR	

12. REMARKS

(PREVIOUS EDITIONS OF THIS FORM MAY BE USED)

reporting, writes, " . . . whether our needs are small or large, good utilization records are helpful to every manager, but the system should be short and economical."[5]

OTHER IMPORTANT ELEMENTS

Work measurement. Not limited to clerical procedures, this important management tool can be used to set machine utilization standards and to apply these standards to evaluate expected man hours per machine hours per specific job. Work sampling can be used to check reliability of machine utilization recordings to determine if they fall into statistical limits acceptable in terms of work standards.

Workload control. Production scheduling asks: What jobs must be done? How long does it take per job? When should a job be run? How does it stand in relation to another job? Who does the work? Are there adequate resources to do the job? Are schedules being met?

One business firm employs an unusual but effective device called the "Daily Newspaper" or daily operation status report to control its workload. By eight o'clock each morning a clerk prepares a listing from a machine run which shows jobs delinquent, due out that day, and due out tomorrow. Each line chief receives a copy. On it he must annotate why some jobs are behind schedule. Then he sends it back to the front office for any follow-up needed for recurring delinquencies for which the line chief has not clearly explained the reason. To date in this organization the Daily Newspaper has proven very effective in helping to reduce delinquent jobs. The Daily Newspaper looks like this:

DAILY NEWSPAPER
Delinqunt As Of Day 146

Unit	Priority	Job Code	Job Title	D/O	Remarks
Supply	1	1057	Ball Bearings	146	Follow-Up

Data processing center controls. To know what is going on in the computer center, most organizations now use management run books. These are geared to insuring management that provisions have been made for all desired information. They include narrative descriptions, flow charts, input/output tape layouts, logic diagrams, sample output print-out, and other information to describe unusual runs. Management run books are especially de-

signed to be responsive to audit and recurring survey analysis requirements.

Costing of the system. The *raison d'etre* for putting automatic data processing into an organization is to reduce operating or program costs. A complete record of costs for each project should be kept. "After" costs should be based on a period of time and a volume of records comparable to the ones used in determining "before" costs. "After" costs should be taken when the system is in full gear and measured against "before" costs for both program and administrative costs. Whenever possible, costs should be expressed as cost per unit processed.

MANAGEMENT INFORMATION SYSTEMS

Space unfortunately does not permit a more detailed discussion of some of the management tools noted in this article, nor have other important ones been mentioned. But the ones indicated demonstrate that with a careful approach to setting up an installation, reporting and controls systems can supply management with the feedback it needs to run the shop. These systems also lay the groundwork for an effective follow-up survey as well as later recurring ones, because the source data have already been prepared.

Management information systems have become fully developed by management executives of both government and industry. DuPont and United Air Lines have led industry in developing these systems. Federal Power Commission, Federal Aviation Agency, and Veterans Administration have done the same for the government areas. None yet have completely tied electronic computers into their systems to take advantage of real time computer techniques and electronic display systems to take the place of the present manually presented systems. Automated data processing can become a main bulwark of these management information systems since it meets commonly accepted criteria for management con-

[5]Robert W. Parsons, "Installation Management by Exception," *Data Processing*, December, 1961, p. 52. Also, for an interesting case example of how much an unnecessary reporting system can cost management in time and money: Maurice F. Ronayne, "How Much Does Your 'Alibi Systems' Cost You?" *Office Management*, March, 1960, pp. 15-18.

trol and reporting systems, such as those prescribed by John R. Curley:

1. It is timely.
2. It covers only the important items which are in need of review.
3. It aims in the establishment of goals and the development of yardsticks for attainment of these goals.
4. It is flexible.
5. It is a top executive tool.[6]

A FINAL COMMENTARY

A follow-up on an installation is much like a shake down cruise for a ship. It's built and christened, but it still must have its first sea run to prove its practicality under actual conditions.

With an automatic data processing installation, an effective reporting system plus good systems analysis can feed back information to management on how the system got off the ground. This follow-up serves also as a pattern for periodic recurring systems analyses of automatic data processing operations. It insures that an effective reporting system has been established to feed back continuously to management the right kind of information for decision making, both for organizational programs and for an evaluation of the automatic data processing operation itself.

In closing, it is well to note the words of one top systems man, John B. Joynt, concerning ways to appraise and improve management. Although written before computers became important management tools, it still makes thoughtful reading for today:

"A program to appraise and improve management must be carefully planned and judiciously executed. It should be established on a continuing basis and tailored to meet the particular requirements of the organization. It should be entrusted only to individuals with the perspective and objectivity to visualize broad problems without being impeded by unimportant detail; individuals with the aptitude and judgment to analyze pertinent facts and develop appropriate solutions. Furthermore, any successful management control program must be carried out with complete cognizance of the human relations so vital to its success."[7]

---

[6] John R. Curley, "A Tool for Management Control," *Harvard Business Review*, March, 1951, p. 45.

[7] John B. Joynt, "Management Controls," *Modern Management*, May, 1947, p. 9.

By Joseph Hayden
Hayden Associates

The Role of Management Consultants in Implementing Business Systems

SINCE business data processing expanded so rapidly during recent years, it is interesting to consider the part that management consultants play in automation.

The role of management consultants in automation presumes a need to know. Consultants need to know that it is necessary for them to recognize the rapid industrial development which is taking place. Consultants must increase with the rapid progress of data processing, because business automation is here to stay.

Businessmen sometimes engage consultants to make general and detailed studies and surveys, and to assist them in deciding whether automation should be implemented.

Therefore, management consultants are serving in a role in which they need to know more about the types of electronic equipment, the best use of available equipment and other related factors, such as staffing, costing, programming and systems design.

Businessmen tend to call upon management consultants soon after becoming entangled with electronic equipment manufacturers and their technical terminology bits, memory, word length, on line, off line, input, output, coding, access time, tape speed, machine logic and program commands.

It is understandable that when industry looks toward automation it also seeks information, advice, guidance and assistance. After all, electronic data processing is new, fascinating and bewildering to many businessmen. Inasmuch as industry looks to management consultants for assistance, it behooves them to recognize their role.

Most professional management consultants today are trying to keep abreast of automation, endeavoring to learn more about the equipment, its capabilities and its limitations.

In the past, management consultants performed their function by working from the core out. They proceeded as soundly as possible and worked upwards and outwards from fundamentals. Basic guideposts marked the way: Why is the work being done? How is the work being done? Who is doing the work, or who should be doing it? When looking at the questions, it was at times advisable to ask if the work could be eliminated.

But this was not the only role which management consultants played in industry. Considerable progress was also made in some industries toward integrating production control and costs.

Looking at consulting services statistically, about 30 percent of them are concerned with manufacturing and engineering, putting considerable emphasis on production control, plant layout, and machine and production design.

Another 30 percent go into the area of general management, dealing with organization, costs, pricing, budgets, financial controls, personnel areas such as recruiting, hiring, training and compensation plans.

Approximately 20 percent go into industrial relations, including job evaluation, while the remaining 20 percent may be termed miscellaneous. This group includes some of the many newly formed research and development firms, and even some of the organizations entering the difficult field of technical information retrieval.

ROUNDTABLE MATTERS

In a recent roundtable discussion concerning the role of management consultants in automation, the group focused attention on its ability to adapt to new requirements and to keep abreast of new information. Other major issues involved working cooperatively, under difficult conditions, with the clients and their personnel to obtain team effort, and at times to lead in business progress.

The group members noted they try to avoid being classified as superdexterous — simultaneously fully qualified in many technical areas — because management consultants employ specialists themselves. Specialists have also gone through the need-to-know process, consequently there is no guarantee that either consultants, or their consultants, know it all.

The members of the group agreed they have tried to provide businessmen with systematic examinations and analyses, information and assistance, tools for identifying and solving problems, and money making techniques.

Consultants approach their tasks with a backlog of facts, and they are greatly concerned with aiding industry to increase profits. The roundtable group, consisting of professional consultants generally hired for a fee on a temporary basis, felt that their views could be as follows:

We sell no one design or brand of equipment, but design integrated data processing systems and recommend various pieces of equipment to fit closely the operations of a company. We combine and coordinate the best talent available in operations research analysis, systems and forms analysis, and the selection of the components which best fit the operation specifications.

Whenever we feel that work can be systematized, mechanized, or automated, we act as impartial advisors. Our role is consulting rather than managing. We use the best qualified consulting engineers, trained to look at new problems, to analyze present processes and blueprint a better one.

We carry out a project right from the idea stage through installation, training and debugging.

Professional management consultants, as a rule, readily deny that their vocation is an outgrowth of the medicine man's technique: a cure-all for every illness. Many professional consultants use what was called the scientific method, a term applied to Frederick W. Taylor's principles of management.

Although supplied with the basic concepts of examination and analysis, and with professional precepts derived from a college education, many management consultants practice their trade under a variety of titles: systems engineer, efficiency engineer, management engineer, consulting engineer, industrial consultant, and business counselor.

Some engineering and business administration colleges use the assorted titles in their curriculum. In several of the larger cities, college instructors and professors teach specific phases of management engineering, operations research and corollary subjects during evening sessions, while working at the same time in industry as consultants.

This situation is beneficial because the education thus offered contains a considerable amount of applied research findings in the field of management science.

Management consulting is not as simple as some consultants permit it to appear. Automation alone is admittedly complex. There are facets of automation ranging from problem identity to feasibility studies, implementation, systems integration, and last but not least, dealing with relationships between consultants and businessmen.

In fact, there are possibly more facets than any one person should claim to know.

TEAMWORK ENCOURAGED

If each member of a working group is interested in his work, there can be a solid basis for teamwork. Unless cooperation is actually achieved, rather than ordered by a memo, the mainsprings of action cannot be touched. Management consultants need to know of the results they can accomplish by stimulating and integrating group thinking and interaction.

As advisors to businessmen, qualified consultants provide leadership for teamwork. The techniques of teamwork for business and for management consultants may possibly be as important as the need to know as much as possible about the technical aspects of automation, systems and integrated data processing techniques and electronic equipment.

Although planning for automation presupposes careful thinking and logical thought processes, there are many well qualified people in business who recognize that comparatively few people are dominated by reason. They see that emotion governs nearly everyone.

Automation may bring more facts and more information to top management and do it faster than ever before, but the era of "my mind is made up, don't bother me with the facts" may be with us for quite awhile.

Decision making is all too often thought of as being a top drawer function. Yet middle management and, in fact, a large portion of the people employed at all levels, participate to some extent in decision making. Decision making has been dependent upon quick mental reaction, and the attainment of this quality is considered a matter of fixed habit.

Slowness in production has often been found to be related to decision making; appreciable time has been needed for a person to decide to make a motion, especially in clerical work. While decision is a great factor in the development of speed, there is also the habit of making quick motions.

Going further, it seems that after employees have learned the correct motions and their proper sequence, they then require development of speed. It is one of the oddities of labor contracts that they usually leave undefined the amount of work expected in return for an agreed hourly or weekly rate of pay.

With the widespread implementation of automation, great changes can be expected concerning what is normal output, or what is standard. In fact, standards of what to expect in the way of volume, speed, accuracy and cost shall change completely with automation. Management consultants, when offering assistance to managers, need to realize this.

Executives and managers must be alert to new developments if they are to administer their businesses profitably. Management consultants can serve a useful purpose by helping executives and managers to keep alert to changing conditions. The many executives and firms not yet ready for automation should learn in a general way, immediately, what the machines can do.

Management consultants when called upon in the past have served executives and managers profitably. They can expect to be called upon again in the era of automation.

It is not implied that all management consultants are experts in electronics or mathematics. It has been the custom for both operating executives and management consultants to learn to deal with technical problems in business by becoming acquainted with general principles and with the capabilities and limitation of systems and methods.

When it comes to technical details, there are others who are expert. For example, coders, machine operators and programmers are not management consultants, but they are experts in their particular areas. It is the task of management consultants to serve businessmen by helping them to select experts. This is not an unsound concept; it still calls for a logical approach to problems, definitions and objective measurements.

Management consultants can be expected to become part of feasibility teams considering the practicability of implementing electronic equipment. They will join with others who endeavor to understand the application of the tools of management science in certain fields, including research and development, production control, accounting, sales, personnel, purchasing, electronics and mathematics.

Consultants can be expected to work closely with all types of businesses and to keep abreast of changing conditions and changes in the state of the electronic art. Consultants should especially recognize the need to utilize the technical skills of specialists.

Management consultants are expected to be reliable and trustworthy advisors to businessmen considering improvements and benefits aimed at increasing efficiency and profits.

Many firms are not large enough to require the services of full time management consulting men. Whether they work part time or full time, management consultants can expect to be evaluated thoroughly by potential clients.

Although the great majority of management consultants have proven themselves to be honest and reputable, management consulting firms should establish self-policing mechanisms to insure that unqualified practitioners are barred from operating.

Management consultants who adapt themselves to the changes caused by and effected by automation can meet the need-to-know challenge which is inherent in their role in automation.

By Robert E. Fendrich
The Howard Savings Institution

A Real Time System for Banking

THE FIRST combination on line (real time) and off line (back office), or total, electronic data processing system ever built for business is Howard Savings Institution's Telefile.

Linked to the Telefile by high speed communications are the Teller-Registers, the first on line or real time teller's window posting machines. These are electronic remote input/output stations which enable any teller, by random entry of the depositor's account number, to have access to all of the details necessary for processing a transaction while the customer is at the window. After the transaction has been processed these window posting machines instantaneously update the customer and the bank records.

Integration of the two firsts in savings banking permits any customer to bank at any window in any office at any time, with service heretofore unattainable.

These two innovations were recently installed in The Howard Savings Institution of Newark, New Jersey. Our entire system was designed, built and installed by The Teleregister Corporation of Stamford, Connecticut.

WORK BEGUN IN 1953

The concepts behind these developments in savings operations have been underway since early 1953. However, the great majority of bankers are still wondering what truthfully is in electronic data processing for their

A Teller-Register window machine, business end of the real time banking system, puts input/output devices at the fingertips of the tellers.

organizations and what they must do to find out now before it is too late, competitively speaking.

All of the foregoing innovations at. The Howard became possible only because, nine years ago, the president had the foresight to envision an ultimate total electronic data processing system for all of our major operations and a practical plan to effectively bring about its realization within a then anticipated 10 years. What is perhaps equally significant, he possessed the courage and the determination to do something constructive and permanent about both. With board approval he created a top management committee on electronics in banking composed of seven members of the board (today there are nine) to do the fundamental thinking about electronics and its potential.

The committee brought in a man experienced in all phases of commercial and savings banking methods and operations to direct a methods and research department which they organized to make methods studies as the first prerequisite to automation and to simultaneously conduct an electronic feasibility survey.

From the original plan, the committee evolved our electronic data processing program and spelled out in writing its framework for positive action. The program served as a guide and control for the methods and research department.

From the outset in 1953, the program was given impetus for success through its sponsorship by the president, through the full and continuing support of top management and through teamwork in the solution of management problems.

The program's first consideration was the customer and its end product was increased and improved services. The methods and research department translated committee objectives into two programs of its own. These were, first, the immediate and continuing program to determine whether the present operations or some others are best for the bank; and second, a long range program, to bring about eventually, among other things, a total electronic data processing system for all major operations if proven feasible.

TWO-PART DEPARTMENT

In early 1954, it was resolved that the department, having established itself in the preceding year, should be subdivided into two divisions: methods and services, to tackle the immediate and continuing program, through methods, systems and procedures techniques; and research and development, to conduct the automation feasibility study and other projects through pure or basic research.

It is significant to note that during the nine years in which our methods program has been in operation, our bank has grown in size by 88 percent, yet the staff required to process the work has increased by only nine percent. Methods and research has made its contribution through methods improvements that already exceed in material savings more than the cost of the entire program to date, and thereby proved to our management that methods is the first prerequisite to automation.

In our methods work we studied first the highly repetitive, voluminous operations of the banking and mortgage departments, then similar operations in other departments, because these are computer application possibilities. During the studies, we created detailed procedures manuals of all of the operations involved. These, in turn, were flow-charted so that we could have a clear picture of what we do, how we do it and why. Additionally, all activities statistics related to the operations were compiled. Preparation of the manuals, charts and statistics, as later experience revealed, constituted the second prerequisite to automation.

As the foregoing assignments neared completion, we ascertained our needs and requirements with respect to the customer, management, staff, regulatory authorities, the major operating procedures and the related accounting and auditing controls — the third and final prerequisite to automation. Then we set out to learn as much as we could about computer systems and took the path that led to our contracting, a few years ago, for the electronic data processing system that we have today.

The terms of the contract stipulated the system must be designed, manufactured and assembled to handle all of our major operations; must meet all of our major needs and requirements; must provide the maximum in dependability and reliability; and must be flexible enough to permit considerable future expansion in volume while holding the staff close to its existing level.

The Telefile is a total electronic data processing system in that it combines on line and off line data processing to handle all major operations of any business, our own included. In this respect, it differs from the other computer systems on the market today and perhaps best explains why, currently, the majority of the big electronic machine manufacturers, who scoffed at the concept when we contracted in 1956 for a system to be built around it, are developing comparable "total" data processing systems at long last.

Associated with the Teller-Registers for customer withdrawals of money are Autho-Visor tellers' readers. These verify that the right customer is withdrawing the funds by allowing the teller to immediately decode the customer's scrambled or protected signature

in the passbook or on an identification card. This is done through safeguarded prescription lenses. The purpose is to permit the teller to compare the signature on the withdrawal ticket with the temporarily decoded signature in the reader for proper identification.

FUTURE FOR SMALL BANKS

What bearing does all of this have on the operational status of smaller banking institutions in terms of today and tomorrow? The electronic data processing equipment market, today, is geared to fulfill operational needs and requirements at a substantially lower per unit processing cost. The cooperative approach to bank automation needs has been consummated in Teleregister's new Telebank Service, whose most significant advantage is that it provides all banks with an equal opportunity to share in the benefits of real time automa-

Pictured in the foreground is one of the two control consoles for the system's dual computers. The control console for the over-all system is in the center.

tion. It provides this opportunity on a feasible and realistic per unit processing cost basis, even for the smaller banks.

The organizational structure of a data processing service center takes many forms. One of the most popular types is the service bureau that is owned and operated by the equipment manufacturer. Another type of service center which has received considerable publicity lately is the data center. In this arrangement, the manufacturer provides the space and equipment. Banks then purchase time on the system and provide their own personnel to operate it. The former type seems to appeal more to the smaller banks because they do not have to provide their own trained operators or programmers.

Other types of service centers that are successful are the cooperative, prime user operated, and the separate corporate organization. In the cooperative, there is joint ownership and operation by a group of banks. The prime user operated type calls for a large bank to share its data processing system with smaller banks. In this case, the system is fully maintained and operated by the prime user. This approach, incidentally, is being pursued by The Howard in its long range plans.

The separate corporate type takes two forms. In the first, a group of banks organize a separate corporate structure to act as the service center. This is much like the cooperative with the exception of the organization's autonomy. In this approach, the board of directors is comprised of at least one representative from each of the user institutions. In the second variation of the separate corporate type, an outside group establishes, or has established, a service center. They provide all the space, equipment, manpower and technical knowledge in order to sell data processing services to banks for profit.

Another way of sharing automation is for an existing bankers' organization to acquire and operate the equipment. Clearing houses and the various state and local associations could effectively implement this approach.

Make no mistake about the fact that the combination on line, off line electronic data processing systems for the banking industry are here to stay in terms of today, and will be ready to take over, in terms of tomorrow, because they are total systems. In other words, they are geared through real time communications to handle all of the major operations of banks, individually or upon a cooperative basis, regardless of the location and size of their main and branch offices. This includes the demand deposit accounting function on line in perhaps a far superior fashion than is conceivable through any present day strictly off line computer system.

By Donald P. Chrystal, Thomas G. Guenther,
and Eldo C. Koenig

Allis-Chalmers Manufacturing Company:
Applying Control Concepts to an Organization

FROM CUSTOMER ORDER to shipped product, automatically ... a computer generated drawing and computer generated documents for complete manufacture ... cut elapsed time by three quarters ... total systems concept ...

Such comments were very abundant in the sequence of events which sought to prove that the control of an organization might be examined in terms of established control concepts. The results were not to die in the laboratory, but were to be applied to the actual organization.

The control of an organization requires the expenditure of a great deal of effort. Furthermore, as the organization grows in size and complexity at some rate, the control grows at the same or an even greater rate. It is not hard to imagine what this means to the required effort; it must increase tremendously. And effort means time and money! The paper required to help control operations must itself be controlled; this, in turn, must be controlled and soon generations of control exist with accompanying mountains of paper.

Many approaches have been pursued to remedy this. The utilization of unit record equipment in various jobs was a huge aid. Stemmed by growth of the organization and the need for more, or tighter, control, control increased, and correspondingly the amount of effort did too. The advent of electronic computers promised great help. Cards could be punched at 150 cards per minute or more, and paper reports could be generated at speeds anywhere from 75 lines per minute to 600 or 800 lines per minute or more. It was now possible to generate more paper faster than any manager could ever hope to keep up with.

Obviously, the generation of paper was more than adequate. The assembly and correlation of this information was wholly inadequate. The next step was to take certain isolated jobs and have the computer aid in handling these jobs. Payroll was one such job. Some aspects of inventory control was another.

The question now asked is, "Could the computer handle everything from customer order to product shipment?" More precisely, can some automatic system provide "customer order to product shipment" operation and also provide more effective control? The work that was done at Allis-Chalmers sought to answer these questions. Allis-Chalmers, a large and diversified company manufacturing industrial, power, farm and construction equipment, requires a complex control and should be a good test of the proposed ideas.

This article will first discuss a computer control system including some aspects of adaptive control and learning; secondly, it will discuss a computer control of a discrete process. Third, this article will investigate the segments of the computer control and the extensions of this effort that have been effected in the organization.

A COMPUTER CONTROL SYSTEM

An organization may be considered a process system consisting of three major functions: (a) in line processing, (b) daily operations control, and (c) long range planning (see **Exhibit 1**). The process might be continuous as in the processing of petroleum, or discrete as in a job shop, or even a combination of these two. These three functions are always present in any process system.

For in line processing, the input is raw

materials and preprocessed materials. Before, during, and after processing, two way communications are carried on with daily operations control; in this manner control is exerted. Output will be products, to be distributed to customers, and waste. These two broad classifications also cover by-products, reuseable scrap, non-useable waste and the like.

Some inputs for daily operations control are customer inquiries, customer orders, invoices, payments, and government and commercial data. The daily operations control function acts upon these inputs, communicates with the long range planning function, and communicates with and controls the in line processing functions. Among the many possible outputs of the daily operations control function are: purchase orders, paychecks, taxes, dividends, billings. It is important to note that the daily operations control function also controls itself.

Long range planning is the function that sets and resets long term goals and secondary

goals to accomplish the primary goals. These, of course, are very important to the daily operations control since the control uses the goals as references much like **Exhibit 2**. For example, the long range planning function may wish to have the organization enter a new market, and develop a suitable product in its research division. Subsequently it gives the daily operations control function the goal of building this product in desirable quantities in the most efficient manner.

More than just one goal is usually set so that the input is not just one goal but several. The drive mechanism drives more than one signal; more than one action results. The action measuring device must measure more than one action. The daily operations control has as its function to control inventory, work in process, machine loading, purchase orders — everything to accomplish the set operating goals, one of which obviously is maximizing profits presently or long term or both. This calls for measuring of action so that the error,

Exhibit 1
DIGITAL CONTROLLED PROCESS SYSTEM

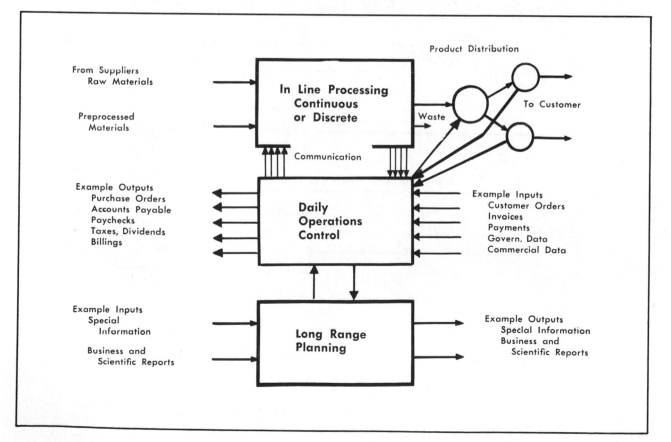

which is the difference between goal and action, becomes a minimum.

The long range planning function is, as has been said, responsible for setting the primary and operating goals of the organization. Hence, it is necessary that the long range planning function itself function as a control system, but more in the manner of **Exhibit 3**. Hence, utilizing the daily operations control reports as one input to the receptor, new goals may be set or present goals revised. When receiving information, the receptor transmits the information to the evaluator and to memory for some possible future use. The evaluator searches through memory, sifts and combines information, and finally determines a suggested goal. This suggested goal is transmitted to the governing authority and to memory. Now the governing authority communicates with memory and decides if the suggested goal meets some certain criteria. If it does not, the reasons for the rejection go back to the evaluator, which now uses this additional information to assist in forming a new suggested goal. When the governing authority decides a goal meets the criteria, the transmitter sends it to the daily operations control function which now uses this as a reference goal. Because the long range planning function has the ability to remember previous decisions and observe the effect of these decisions, it has some of the characteristics of a learner. This ability to acquire experience is obviously desirable whether the function is performed by a human, a machine, or a combination of the two.

The above, then, indicates that the daily operations control function has definite goals to achieve as determined by the long range planning function. Once these goals have been determined, the daily operations control has a fair amount of freedom in the manner of accomplishing them.

Exhibit 2
BASIC CONTROL LOOP

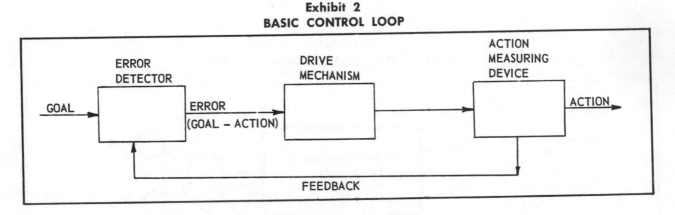

Exhibit 3
LONG RANGE PLANNING FUNCTION

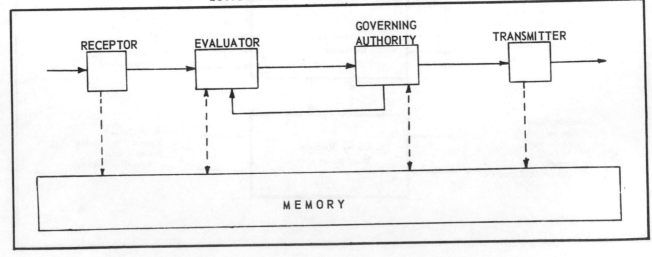

PARAMETERS AFFECTING
DAILY OPERATIONS

Success or failure in achieving the set goals by the daily operations control function is determined to a large extent by its reaction to changes in the affecting parameters. These parameters are controllable or non-controllable. Some controllable parameters include inventory levels, available manpower, number of machines, and facilities. Such parameters as raw material prices, vendor supply times and customers' orders are uncontrollable, or at best partially controllable through long range planning.

To understand how changes in the system parameters affect the goals of the daily operations control function, consider the parameter, inventory level. In **Exhibit 4,** inventory level is plotted as a controllable parameter (also the independent variable) against profit per unit. This plot indicates that a certain inventory level results in a maximum net profit per unit. If inventory levels are low, net profit per unit will be low due to the penalty costs of running short. Having a high inventory level means that carrying costs are high, reducing the net profit per unit. It seems desirable to keep the

inventory level at its optimum point; that is, where the profit per unit is greatest. This is true, but is this optimum inventory level a static thing? No. It depends on other parameters, controllable and non-controllable.

Exhibit 5 shows the characteristic curve of profit per unit versus inventory level changing as a third parameter, number of customer orders for example, is introduced. Since the number of customer orders is at best a partially controllable parameter, there is little or no control of where the optimum inventory level is, because it is affected by the number of customer orders. Use of some method that changes the inventory level to be coincident with the optimum inventory level, even as it continually changes due to the number of customer orders, would insure that the greatest profit per unit is being experienced as far as inventory level is concerned.

Now consideration should be given to determine the optimum inventory level with some number of customer orders affected by raw material prices. This last parameter, and many others such as the available manpower level, very dramatically affect the inventory level which will give the greatest profit per unit

Exhibit 4
RELATIONSHIP OF CONTROLLABLE PARAMETER TO PROFIT

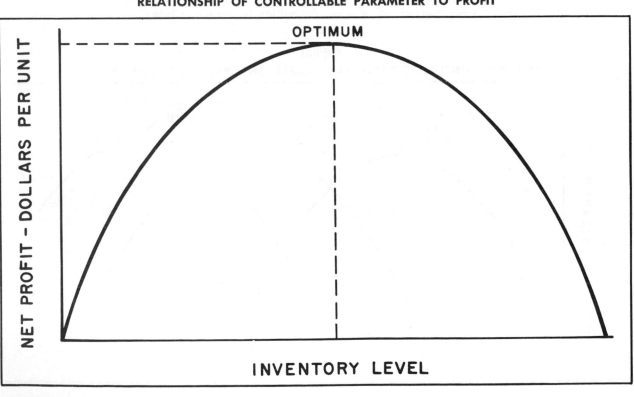

for the entire operation (called optimal system inventory level). This means that **Exhibit 5** would grow to a multidimensional plot. This is not only difficult to draw, but it is also difficult to describe mathematically or otherwise. If a method were developed to seek the overall system optimization, the probability of success in achieving the goals would increase greatly.

With so many controllable and uncontrollable parameters in existence, how can optimal operation as reflected in maximum profit be realized? It is not feasible in many physical operations to subject the system to many combinations of parameters to find out which set of values of controllable parameters will yield the maximum profit operation. This is true because: (1) It would disrupt the system. For example, in a manufacturing operation it is not feasible to expect to try one schedule of operations, then another, and so on and at the same time different inventory levels, manpower levels plus all the other controllable parameters. This would completely disrupt the operation. (2) It would be too costly. In the same example, no good physical output is gained from all this trial and error. (3) It would take too long. Shipping dates would be hopelessly extended. (4) It would not be possible to try all combinations since items (2) and (3) would really become prohibitive. (5) The uncontrollable parameters would be changing during this long period of time.

Hence, an optimum or near optimum might never be found with the limited number of trials made.

A MODEL AND ADAPTER SYSTEM

One way to achieve optimal system operation is through the use of a method which will allow many combinations and variations of controllable parameters with speed and economy *without* disrupting the physical system. One aspect of such an approach is a model of the system. The model is a description of the physical system. If the model is in terms of a digital computer program, then the operation of the model approaches the necessary speed and economy. Using the model it is possible to try a large number of combinations and variations of controllable parameters, obtaining results with great speed and economy, without ever tampering with the physical system.

These results may then be analyzed in detail by the computer to determine which set of values of the controllable parameters will yield an optimum operation. There is no doubt, as shown before, that the uncontrollable parameters will affect the optimum level of operation. Therefore, if the model is to be really reflective of the physical system, it must always know the current status of the real system. This is accomplished by sampling, which is reviewed later.

Exhibit 5
EFFECT OF UNCONTROLLABLE PARAMETERS ON ORIGINAL RELATIONSHIP

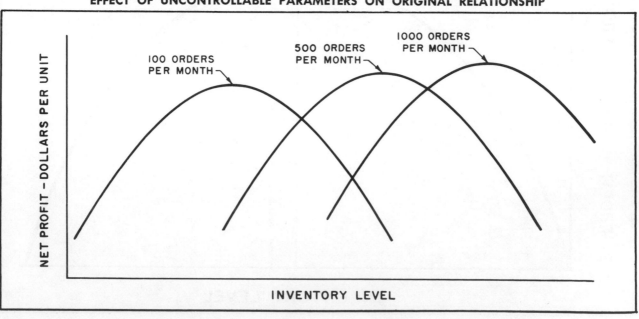

Depending on system characteristics (is it very dynamic, or almost static?) and on the computer control system, it may be possible to omit trying values on the model once an optimum level is reached. In a system where the uncontrollable parameters do not affect the operation to any great degree, the system should be operated near the optimum level that was discovered by the cut and try model method; obviously then the model will no longer be required.

Exhibit 6, block A is the real physical system, while block B represents the digital computer control. The system adapter in block A will be the management of the daily operations control function utilizing a digital computer to assist them. In certain process systems having highly advanced computer control, the adapter would be entirely a computer operation.

Consider in **Exhibit 6** that a signal f which, for example, might have been caused by introducing an additional customer order into the system, is emitted from the adapter and goes to a model of the system. The model output f_1 then goes to the model adapter, and its output f_5 goes back to the model. The flow continues around this loop until a signal f_2 is given as the output of this path. This signal f_2 is sent back to the system adapter which subsequently emits a signal f_3 which at junction K reinforces the original signal f, detained at lag L. Then signal $(f+f_3)$ goes through the physical system which has as its output f_4.

Signal f_4 is then the output of the system and is sampled (fed back) to the system adapter. The system adapter examines the error $e=(f_4-f_2)$ and may change a parameter in the system to attempt to minimize e. The system adapter may sample f_4 to know what has been accomplished by the parameter change, and to see if the e signal is being decreased. At any time the system adapter may send a signal to the model path to obtain a signal f_2 which it can sample.

In this manner, the system adapter can "try out" different possibilities before injecting any changes in the physical system. For example, as f_4 is sampled, if a bottleneck develops the system adapter would become aware of this and try to correct it, meanwhile sending a signal to the model path to develop a revised schedule. Then the system adapter would sample f_2 for the revised schedule and

Exhibit 6

AN ADAPTIVE CONTROL SYSTEM

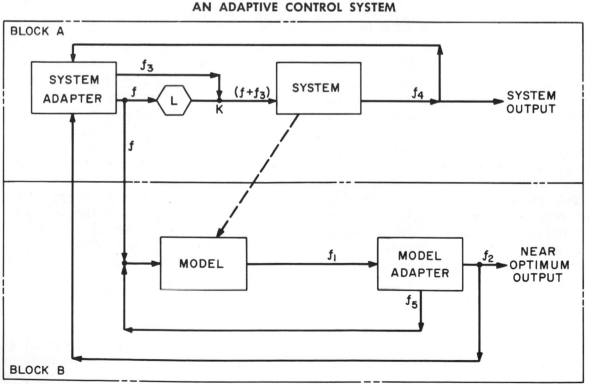

send this revised schedule as f_3 to the physical system.

The model is a description of the system. When it receives the signal f it simulates what the system will do with this signal. The model adapter examines output f_1 with the updated conditions which initially may be the same as the real system, since the model path samples the physical system and hence can know what conditions exist in the system. The model adapter then may increase the inventory level of the model and feed this signal f_5 back to the model. The model adapter examines the new f_1 signal and determines if it is better than the original f_1, representing an improvement in system performance. If an improvement is noted, inventory level might again be increased, while some other controllable parameters are changed. Again the model operates with the new parameters and the model adapter examines the new output.

This cycle continues until a change in the controllable parameters reflects little or no improvement in the model's performance for the present values of uncontrollable parameters. It is possible to go through this cycle of model, model adapter, changing controllable parameters in the model and back to simulating the system in the model, many times in the time interval it takes the real system to react to f to obtain f_4. That is to say, the real system might take days or months to react, but the model utilizing a digital computer can react in seconds, minutes, or hours.

Once the model has arrived at its optimum operation, it emits the signal f_2 which indicates the system's optimal operation to the system adapter. It examines this signal and will implement immediate operational directives (such as a scheduling program or a material useage program). The system adapter deals differently with some controllable parameters such as manpower level, overtime work and plant expansion, which are not always put into effect immediately. The system adapter would search its memory for past suggested parameter values and actual operating parameter values, combine these with the present suggested values to establish trends using forecasting techniques, and finally move to adjust parameter levels according to these studies. This would lead to continually improving the system operation.

ADAPTER OPERATION

Model adapters may be of three types: (1) with no ability to learn, (2) having the ability to learn, (3) mathematically defined, such as an adapter utilizing linear programming. Of the first two types, each may have two variations: one having initial information about the system it is to work with, and the other not having this information. The first type has no learning ability and consequently will not profit from experience. When it seeks to improve the model after some disturbance it cannot "recall" that changing some controllable parameters will do no good in optimizing the model.

The one variation of this type adapter changes parameters blindly, while the other knows it must remain within certain ranges of the parameters. These ranges are established by analyses of the system. It might be said that one knows almost nothing about the system whereas the other does.

The second type of model adapter has learning ability. It will "learn" from experience about the system. Again there are two variations. One model adapter does *not* have initial knowledge of the system; the other does. Both variations of the "learning" type model adapters will eventually learn the system to the point that the changes they make will likely improve the system. The advantage of providing the model adapter with initial system knowledge is that it will arrive at the optimum operating level much sooner than without that knowledge. On the other hand, the model adapter without initial system knowledge has the advantage that it does not require a previous analysis of the system. In fact, this model adapter is "general purpose" in that it can be used for different systems.

A learning adapter increases its knowledge by relating variations in input, operating conditions, and output. If only the normal variations are allowed to take place, it may be a relatively long time before the adapter has experienced the full range of each variable. A technique is used in which the model adapter itself introduces various operating conditions into the model and observes the results of these variations.

To illustrate adapting, consider an event everyone is familiar with — the tuning of a radio. If the dial were marked for station

XYZ it would be surprising if the best reception were always at that mark. Aging of tubes and changing humidity conditions, among others, are circumstances which will tend to change the best reception point.

What will a person ordinarily do? He will turn the dial to the mark and listen; next he will turn the dial to the right and listen. If the clarity has increased he will again turn right and listen. Again if the clarity increased a further turn to the right would be in order. Eventually a right turn will cause less clarity. Then a move to the left is made which was probably too far to the left (overshoot). A slight turn to the right will find the best reception point. If the first right turn, after listening to the reception at the mark, resulted in lesser clarity, then the sequence of events would be as above except that the dial turning would be in the left direction.

Notice that the optimum system operation point (dial setting for best reception) changes due to uncontrollable parameters (aging of tubes, humidity conditions). The optimum system operation point is found for the particular parameter values (values of tube age, percent humidity) in existence at a particular point in time by imposing several operating points (different settings of the dial) and evaluating (listening for greatest clarity) system performance at these operating points. Finally, the best point is picked and the system is operated at this point.

Now, suppose that the man tuning the radio did not have even a rough idea of where the dial should be set for reception of station XYZ in a one station community. He can either have someone tell him about where to set the dial and work around this, or make his own trys which would be wider swings and take him longer to "home in" on the optimum point. But once he has found approximately where to operate he knows the optimum at any time is around this point. That is, he would only have to make changes around the mark he made and would not have to try the whole dial range.

A control system considered here has some aspects of the above example. (In the above the man was the control system.) The control system will attempt to find the optimum system performance level. Now it may be told that the optimum point is near a particular

point or is in a certain range. This would be the case where the control system was given initial knowledge of the system it was to control. If it did not have this initial knowledge it would need to swing through a wide range of values of the controllable parameters to find the approximate range. Operation then is about this point. Many systems are more complex than the radio control example in that they have more controllable parameters (the radio has one — the dial setting) and more uncontrollable parameters.

ACTUAL RESULTS USING AN ELEMENTARY LEARNING ADAPTER

Some investigation was conducted into a very elementary learning system. A simple manufacturing system was described to the IBM 704 computer. It was assumed that a certain number of products were ordered from the in line processing function when some reorder level was reached, then stored in product storage, and shipped from product store as required. The controllable parameters are then: raw material reorder level, raw material order size, product reorder level, and product order size. The adapter seeks by varying the controllable parameters to maximize profit per unit shipped.

Exhibit 7 is a graph of actual variations and results plotted against time. Curve one shows variations in raw material reorder level; curve two shows the variations in raw material order size; curve three, the product reorder level; curve four, the product order size; and curve five shows the actual profit per unit shipped. It must be stressed that the adapter providing these variations and resulting system performance was really a learning adapter of a very elementary type. Nevertheless, the results it produced are noteworthy.

All controllable parameters are started at one on the per unit scale. The first random variation is introduced by increasing product reorder level (curve three). This caused profit per unit to go down (curve five). This was not really a good variation since profit decreased. The product reorder level then was left at this value, but the adapter remembered that it should decrease the reorder level the next time it varied this parameter.

The adapter then increased raw material order size (curve two). This change results in a large decrease in profit (curve five). Now the adapter randomly chooses product reorder level (curve three), remembers to decrease it, and the profit rises greatly (curve five). The adapter happens to choose the product reorder level (curve three), and again reduces it. This again increases the profit. Now the adapter increases product order size (curve four). This decreases profits (curve five). The next move is decreasing product reorder level (curve three). This increases profit per unit (curve five). The whole analysis continues in this fashion, randomly choosing parameters to be varied.

Note that the adapter makes many "wrong" moves. This is very noticeable at the start, but as time passes and the adapter gains experience it becomes better. At the far right of the curves, the adapter has the system operating at a much better profit point than at the start of the processing. This illustrates how learning ability in the adapter can help direct the system to a near optimum operation point.

ASPECTS OF SAMPLING

Previously it was seen (Exhibit 6) to be necessary to measure the output of the system and of the model, so that the two might be compared. The method by which this measuring is accomplished is sampling. At some specific times the output is sampled (sampling is not continuous). Questions such as, "How often should sampling be done?" and, "How much will it cost?" are asked in relation to sampling.

Sampling is the means by which the control knows what the actual output is, so that it can be compared with the desired output. In addition, sampling at different points in the system will allow knowing what status exists at that system point. To keep track of the progress of a particular order, it is necessary to know at certain time intervals where the product is and how much work has been done to it. This might be accomplished by having automatic tools transmit the work accomplished directly to a central data collecting system, or by having the workers punch in on a data collecting system when they are starting and finishing a particular operation or series of operations on a customer order. This information is made available to the controller. At a particular time the controller could know that at last report operation 16 was completed, meaning that the product for

customer Jones was in shop 1081 on January 5 with all work through operation 16 completed.

The equipment necessary for sampling (the data collection equipment) costs money. How many "punch in" boxes should there be? This requires answers to such questions as, "How often will the workers be required to 'punch in'?" and, "How far should they have to go to this data collecting box?" These questions will have different answers depending on circumstances. However, a rather general rule concerning the interval between samples is that it not be less than the time it takes for the adapter to react to changes, nor should this interval be much less than the elapsed time of the operation being sampled. (It would not be practical to see the progress of job operations every minute on a job that will take several hours to complete.)

Exhibit 8 shows the economics of sampling. Curve A shows that the more sampling that takes place the greater the savings (because of closer control, ability to react quickly). Curve B shows that the more sampling that takes place, the greater is the cost (for equipment, time). Curve C is the sum of these curves and shows that there is an optimum point of sampling maximum savings (point x) beyond which a higher sampling rate costs more than the savings achieved.

The above has been an attempt to describe how an automatically controlled organization could function. The analysis applies whether the company is large or small and regardless of the product or service it makes available.

COMPUTER CONTROL OF AN EXISTING DISCRETE PROCESS

With the intention of utilizing some of the above ideas, a research project was initiated to have an IBM 704 digital computer perform the daily operations control function in an existing discrete process. The objective was to have the computer accept a customer's specifications for a product, perform all the necessary control functions, and enable the manufacturing process to begin within a few hours of the receipt of the order.

The designers of the research project performed the function of long range planning having as their goal to show that application of the control concept utilizing a digital computer was practical and would reduce costs and required times. The products chosen for

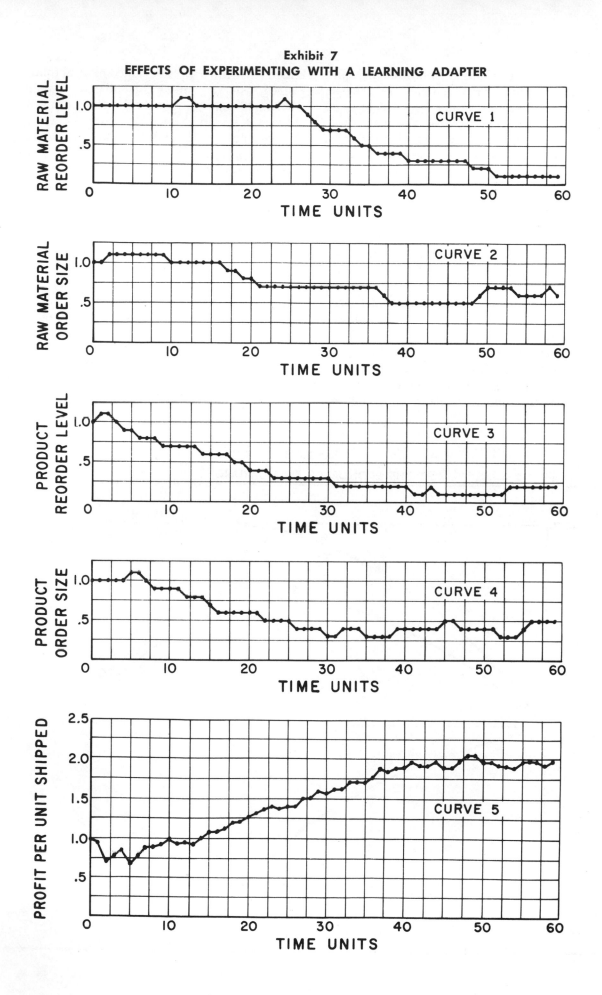

Exhibit 7
EFFECTS OF EXPERIMENTING WITH A LEARNING ADAPTER

CURVE 1

CURVE 2

CURVE 3

CURVE 4

CURVE 5

this project were electric motors, and in particular the coils for those motors. These products were chosen mainly because of the availability of data and because the manufacturing process is relatively straightforward.

Since the motors are built to customer specifications, design is an important function of daily operations control. When the design is complete, it must be sent along with associated information to the manufacturing function (the in line process). Ideally, this information could be sent by wire to an output printer in the shop office, or even to numerically controlled machine tools. However, for the purpose of this project it was decided that these instructions would be put out in a form similar to the existing manual form.

This superposition of an automatic control system over the existing system would allow that: (1) eventually the automatic control could replace the manual control, and then be modified into the kind of control actually desired, but (2) until this ultimate system is achieved many benefits in the form of reduced costs and times, greater efficiency, and experience in the applications would result.

Design was the first area of the daily operations control function which was considered by the project. Computer programs were written to perform the electrical design of motors and of coils and were combined by having the coil program get its input data from the output of the motor program. The input data to the motor design program are: (1) HP, (2) RPM, (3) voltage, (4) number of phases, (5) frequency, (6) temperature rise, (7) WK², (8) required breakdown torque, (9) required starting torque, and (10) Y or delta connection. Other information may be given as optional data if the designer so desires.

A supervisory program causes these input

Exhibit 8
THE ECONOMICS OF SAMPLING

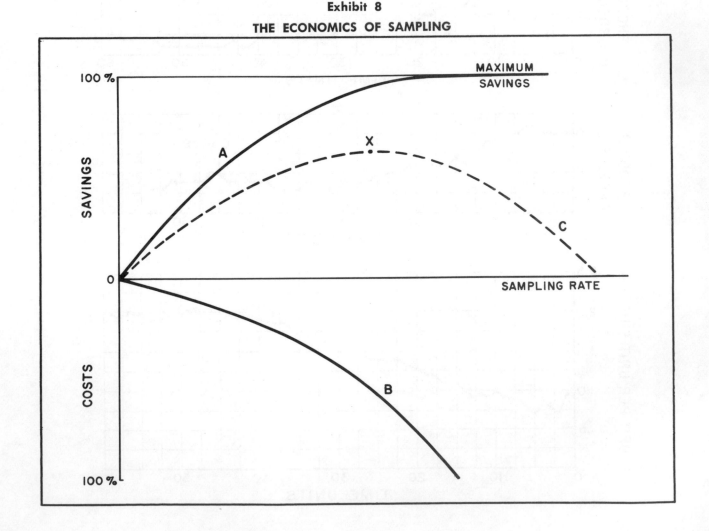

data to be read into the computer, at which time the motor design program is called into the computer and allowed to operate. Upon completion of this design, output is written on magnetic tape and selected output is written on another magnetic tape. Control is passed back to the supervisory program which arranges the selected output of the motor design program into an input format suitable to the coil design and manufacture program. This program operates on the selected data and computes required number of coils and the physical dimensions of these coils, and the sizes, types, and amounts of copper and insulation necessary to make them.

The next portion of the program was written to produce a coil drawing complete with dimensions and annotations. Next, a specifications sheet of necessary materials is produced by the program. At this same time material requirements are prepared for off line punching. The entire output is put on magnetic tape, selected output is put on another tape, and control is again passed to the supervisory program.

This selected output is readied for the next program, the labor ticket program, which computes standard time rates and decides which series of operations are necessary to make these coils according to their physical characteristics and planning department directives. Labor tickets are prepared which contain the specific operation to be accomplished with times, rates, shop areas, machine or hand designation and identifying data. Move tickets telling what should be moved where, and inspection tickets, are prepared where necessary. Likewise, a shipping order which instructs the Shipping Department to send the manufactured product is prepared.

The need for a supervisory program to control the sequencing of programs, readying of input, editing of output and other tasks arises from the fact that most of the programs strain available computer storage. The IBM 704 used has 8,000 words of core storage, 8,000 words of drum storage and six tape units. Even if this were not the case, this type of operation allows each individual program to grow in size as more types of input are accommodated. It also easily allows more programs to be added as more products or more inclusive operation on present products become incorporated.

Exhibit 9

AUTOMATIC DIGITAL CONTROL OF THE MANUFACTURE OF ELECTRIC COILS

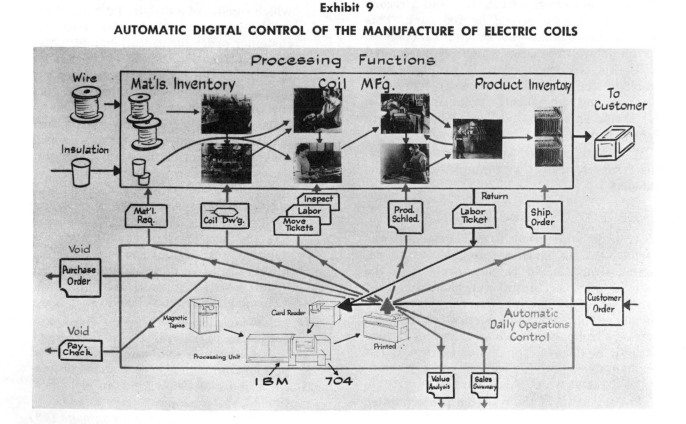

Finally, use of the supervisory program allows great flexibility in that different sequencing of programs is easy; that is, the motor design program alone may be run, or the coil design program may be run with a new motor design program instead of the original one, and so on. The whole operation of this computer system is thus intimately bound up with the supervisory program.

An inventory control program was completed which had information as to the amount of copper and insulating material in stock. It would deduct the materials required from the inventory and, if the inventory dropped below the minimum requirements, it issued a purchase order. It also added receipts of material to the amount on hand.

Next, a scheduling program was written which would accept information on the motor to be manufactured, and would schedule the movement of its parts through the shop.

The documents mentioned are the controls exerted upon the processing function by the daily operations control. This is the information needed to manufacture and ship the product ordered; the processing function in turn can feed information back to the daily operations control. Labor tickets containing the time for each specified job, the name of the worker who performed this job, and a record of materials used, would be fed back. This information enables the control function to accumulate all the costs which are associated with this customer order. It can also keep track of the total work done by individual workers and subsequently prepare paychecks for them. This is the feedback loop shown in **Exhibit 1.**

With data collected and programs finished, the research project was completed. (Review **Exhibit 9.**)

EFFECT ON THE ORGANIZATION

After demonstrations to management it was decided that as much as possible of this research effort should be put into use in the daily operations control function, and that continued effort be applied to fully developing the above concepts. Some portions of the project were complete enough so that they needed little or no changes for immediate use. Other segments were only indications of very extensive programs which would have to be written.

The segments of the research project which were put into effect initially cause the computer to receive the input indicated previously and produce as output the following documents (see **Exhibit 10**) which, except for (5), are prepared on ditto master forms with correct duplication quantities indicated.

1. *Motor design information* which lists the specified input data and all calculated information for the motor. This is useful to the Product Department and can be a production run (customer order) or can be for development purposes.

2. *Coil design information* which lists quantities that were input to it (output from motor design program or data given to the program from an engineer's calculations). Intermediate design values and final design values are listed.

3. *An annotated coil drawing* which has all dimensions and supplementary information on it. This drawing in its entirety is prepared on the computer. Page two of the drawing is also prepared and is a consolidation of some of the information needed by the manufacturing function.

4. *A specification sheet* which specifies types and quantities of materials.

5. *Punched material requirement cards* which consist of a disbursing code (feet, rolls, etc.), some other codes, quantity, customer order identification, and material identification. These cards can go directly to the material control section and, either manually or by machine, post the requirements for the affected materials. Ultimately, of course, this information will be passed on to the material control program in the same computer, and will be posted by that program.

6. *Move ticket masters* which direct and authorize movement of items from one designated area to another. These masters are ditto masters which are sent to a duplicating section. The computer program also determines and prints the quantities that should be duplicated. (This applies also to (7) and (8) below.)

7. *Labor ticket masters* which direct and authorize operations to be performed. Standard times and rates are included plus an indication of a manual or machine job and, if machine, an identification of the machine.

(continued on page 128)

EXHIBIT 10

SOME OF THE COMPUTER OUTPUT USED IN DAILY OPERATIONS

```
INPUT DATA

        HORSEPOWER =      700.000    VOLTAGE    =     4000.000
        FREQUENCY  =       60.000    SPEED      =     1200.000
        TEMP. RISE =       60.000    PHASES     =        3.000
        WK2        =     8500.000    B.D. TORQUE=        0.
        ST. TORQUE =        0.       CODES      =        0.   0.   3.

SPECIFIED DESIGN QUANTITIES

        STATOR O.D.          37.500
        STATOR I.D.          26.000
        FRAME LENGTH         10.000
        STATOR SLOTS         90.000
        SLOT WIDTH            0.470
        SLOT DEPTH           2.750
        CONDUCTORS/SLOT      14.000
        NO. OF CIRCUITS       1.000
        COIL PITCH  1 TO     14.000
        AIR GAP LENGTH        0.060
        ROTOR I. D.          17.000
        ROTOR SLOTS          76.000
        ROTOR SLOT NC.        3.000
        SLOT-C-DIMENSION      0.050
        BAR RESISTIVITY       1.000
        DEPTH OF RING         1.000
        WIDTH OF RING         2.000
        AREA OF RING          2.000
        RING RESISTIVITY      2.780
        CORE LOSS             6.500
        W.+F. LOSS            4.500

STATOR DESIGN           ORDER NO.

FRAME  6.- 26.0-10.0    37.50 O.D.

W/S NO.                    POLE PITCH    13.614   COND/SLOT      14.000
NO. OF SLOTS    90.000     SLOT PITCH     0.908   CONNECTION 1.CKT Y
SLOTS/POLE      15.000     TOOTH WIDTH    0.438   PITCH     1- 14.000
SLOT SIZE  0.470X2.750     SLOT/TOOTH     1.074   KP/KD      0.978/.957
SEGMENTS         0.        CORE DEPTH     3.000   CONDR-  1.WIDE X1.DEEP
SLOTS/SEG        0.        TOOTH AREA    52.426   0.   X.    -0.130X.270
L.B.HDS.        11.000     CORE AREA     23.962   0.   X.    -0.   X.
GROSS IRON       8.875     GAP AREA     120.820   0.   X.    -0.   X.
NET IRON         7.987     COIL M.T.     66.395   0.   X.    -0.   X.
VENTS END    2 - 0.500     LE1            6.059   0.   X.    -0.   X.
VENTS CTR    3.- 0.375     LE2            1.250   COIL SIZE  0.460X1.190
PACKAGES     4.- 2.219     SKEW IN/IN ST ID 0.    STR INS.  FDDG   0.015
CORE WT.      1022.555     COPPER WT.   455.729   INS.SP. 05-086-650-175

PROPOSED ROTOR DESIGN (ALL DIMENSIONS IN INCHES)

WINDING SPEC.

        EXTERNAL DIAMETER    25.880    NUMBER OF SLOTS     76.000
        INTERNAL DIAMETER    17.000    SLOTS PER POLE      12.667
        FRAME LENGTH         10.000    SLOT -C- DIM.        0.050
        DUCTS-CENTER          3.000    SLOT NUMBER          3.000
        DUCTS-END                      BAR NUMBER           3.000
        TOTAL IRON            8.875    BAR RESISTIVITY      1.000
        PACKAGES             4.000     MIN. SLOT PITCH      0.967
        WIDTH OF PACKAGE     2.219     MAX. SLOT PITCH      1.070
```

```
NET IRON                    7.987        MIN. TOOTH WIDTH           0.613
SEGMENTS PER CIRCLE         0.           MAX. TOOTHWIDTH            0.970
SLOTS PER SEGMENT           0.           MEAN TOOTH WIDTH           0.
FASTENING                                MIN. CORE DEPTH            3.015
DIE                                      TOOTH AREA                61.982
M. D. END RING             23.030        CORE AREA                 24.082
DEPTH END RING              1.000        EFF. BAR LENGTH           16.000
WIDTH END RING              2.000        TOTAL BAR LENGTH          18.000
RESISTIVITY ENDRING         2.780        AIR GAP LENGTH             0.060
WEIGHT RT.LAM.            594.058
WEIGHT RT. COPPER        192.614
WEIGHT END RING           92.609

FLUX DENSITIES-KLINES/SQ. INCH

FLUX/POLE-MLINES            4.411        CART. COEF. STATOR         1.462
ST. TOOTH DENSITY        132.159        CART. COEF. ROTOR          1.024
ST. CORE DENSITY          92.037
RT. TOOTH DENSITY        111.785        MLT STATOR                66.395
RT. CORE DENSITY          91.580
AIR GAP DENSITY           36.508

GAP AMP-TURNS           1610.782         STAT. TOOTH AMP-TURNS   217.942
STAT. CORE AMP-TURNS     101.083         ROTOR TOOTH AMP-TURNS    34.132
ROTOR CORE AMP-TURNS      56.664         TOTAL AMP-TURNS        2020.603
EFFECTIVE TURNS           88.506         MAGNETIZING AMPS         22.830

STARTING PERFORMANCE

P U B.D. TORQUE            2.153         KA/IN2 START ST COND      13.333
P U START TORQUE          0.826         C RISE/MIN START ST.     156.438
P U START AMPS            4.994         KA/IN2 F.L. ST.            2.670
LOAD WK2               8500.000         WATTS/IN2 F.L. ST.         0.471
MOTOR WK2                 0.            SKEW                       0.
TOTAL WK2             8500.000         KAC/INCH ST.               1.402
KW-SEC, 1 START       2827.440         KAC/SLOT ST.               1.273
KW-SEC BAR,CORE       1199.983
KW-SEC BAR,END         419.536
KW-SEC END RING       1207.921         F.L. AMPS PER BAR       1313.334
WT.LBS BAR,CORE        107.008         F.L. AMPS END RING      5295.265
WT.LBS BAR,END          85.606         START. AMPS,BAR         6874.090
WT.LBS END RING         92.609         START. AMPS,END RING   27715.818
KWSEC/LB BAR,CORE       11.214         KA/IN2 F.L.,BAR            2.985
KWSEC/LB END RING       13.043         KA/IN2 START,BAR          15.623
DEG C RISE BAR,CORE     63.920         KA/IN2 START,END RING     13.858
DEG C RISE BAR,END      27.934         C RISE/MIN START BAR     921.143
DEG C RISE END RING     74.346         C RISE/M START END RG    544.553
KWSEC/LB BAR,END         4.901
STALLED 10 SEC,BAR     133.            STALLED 10 SEC,RING       83.

PERFORMANCE DATA

STATOR I2R 5/4 LOAD     14.362         EFFICIENCY 5/4 LOAD       92.519
STATOR I2R 4/4 LOAD      8.884         EFFICIENCY 4/4 LOAD       93.413
STATOR I2R 3/4 LOAD      5.063         EFFICIENCY 3/4 LOAD       93.918
STATOR I2R 2/4 LOAD      2.532         EFFICIENCY 2/4 LOAD       93.685
IDLE I2R                0.560
                                       POWERFACTOR 5/4 LOAD       0.880
ROTOR I2R 5/4 LOAD      15.154         POWER FACTOR 4/4 LOAD      0.887
ROTOR I2R 4/4 LOAD       9.097         POWER FACTOR 3/4 LOAD      0.876
ROTOR I2R 3/4 LOAD       4.885         POWER FACTOR 2/4 LOAD      0.828
```

```
ROTOR I2R 2/4 LOAD        2.110
                                          P U SLIP 5/4 LOAD    0.0221
STRAY KW 5/4 LOAD        12.242           P U SLIP 4/4 LOAD    0.0167
STRAY KW 4/4 LOAD         7.835           P U SLIP 3/4 LOAD    0.0121
STRAY KW 3/4 LOAD         4.407           P U SLIP 2/4 LOAD    0.0078
STRAY KW 2/4 LOAD         1.959

CORE LOSS                 6.500
W. F. LOSS KW             4.500           LOCKED ROTOR P. F.   0.208

EQUIVALENT CIRCUIT PARAMETERS

R1                        0.358           R2                   0.423
X1                        3.325           X2                   3.081
GM                        0.000           BM                  -0.010

NAMEPLATE DATA

HORSEPOWER              700.000
SYNCHRONOUS RPM        1200.000
FULL LOAD RPM          1179.917
VOLTS                  4000.000
AMPERES                  90.905
PHASES                    3.000
FREQUENCY                60.000
DEGREES CENT RISE        60.000
OUTPUT FACTOR             8.629
```

SLIP	RPM	AMPERES		PU CURRENT		PU TORQUE		P.F.	
		UNSAT.	SAT.	UNSAT.	SAT.	UNSAT.	SAT.	UNSAT.	SAT.
1.00	0.	403.5	451.3	4.44	4.96	0.64	0.81	0.185	0.207
0.70	360.0	395.4	439.7	4.35	4.84	0.79	0.98	0.215	0.240
0.50	600.0	386.0	428.3	4.25	4.71	0.95	1.18	0.250	0.278
0.40	720.0	378.8	417.7	4.17	4.60	1.08	1.32	0.277	0.307
0.30	840.0	367.1	403.4	4.04	4.44	1.27	1.54	0.323	0.356
0.20	960.0	348.3	377.4	3.83	4.15	1.55	1.83	0.395	0.430
0.15	1020.0	330.4	354.4	3.64	3.90	1.78	2.05	0.464	0.500
0.10	1080.0	296.4	311.2	3.26	3.42	2.06	2.28	0.580	0.611
0.05	1140.0	212.6	213.3	2.34	2.35	2.04	2.05	0.771	0.774
0.01	1188.0	58.8	58.8	0.65	0.65	0.64	0.64	0.861	0.861

```
ORDER NO 2-0510-31000


                        STATOR COIL PROGRAM
DESIGN DIMENSIONS IN INCHES
INPUT DATA
COIL DWG. NO.      2-0510-31000GR0206W/S NO.            05-030-200
   INSUL. SPEC.    05-086-650          MK. NO.                 175
INDICATOR               3.0     FRAME          6.00-26.00-10.00
VOLTS                4000.0     L.B. HEADS               11.00
NO. OF SLOTS           90.0     L.B. F.PL.               0.
SLOT WIDTH            0.470     SLOT DEPTH               2.75
PITCH 1-              14.0      CIRCUITS                 1.0
Y-1. OR DELTA 0.       1.0      TURNS PER COIL           7.0
STRANDS IN WIDTH       1.0      STRANDS IN DEPTH         1.0
STRAND WIDTH         0.270      STRAND DEPTH             0.130
STRAND COVERING      0.015      SL.STICK THCKNS.         0.095
INSUL.BET.STRANDS      0.        SKEW      0.  IN  1.000 AT  26.000


DESIGN OUTPUT
   BOTTOM            TOP
    6.573    CP     6.005    WCE   0.460    UR  1.102  SL.DEP.  2.776
    1.011    SP     0.924    BHFP 11.000    UF  0.957  ANGLE   52.000
    0.575    SW     0.563    LOOP 30.445    RC  1.000  CHORD   11.398
   34.636    PHI   37.537    MT   65.250    RU  1.000  PD       1.000
    2.305    D      2.305    DROP  1.000    H   3.412
    4.541    Z      4.614    LS    1.089    F  24.000
    1.209    2Y     1.136    ODR   4.205    A   0.146
    5.750    G      5.750    ODF   4.380    B   0.234
    0.750    EXT    0.750    CLB   0.115    D1  1.398
   12.500    E     12.500    CLT   0.103    E1  1.190
  SKEW  0.        OFFSET  0.        QMIN 3.000    LEAD CLEARANCE      0.134

COIL DRAWING DIMENSIONS
SBJ    8.97    RC      0.75    FX    0.           J    13.17
REQ   18.00    J      13.17    B     3.50
REQ   54.00    A       3.50    B     3.50
REQ   18.00    A       3.50    K    13.17
REQ    0.      J       0.      K     0.
D     12.50    A       3.50    RX    0.           TOT  90.00
LS     0.54    SKW     0.      IN   11.00         ON   26.00
L     30.45    RU      0.75    MT   65.25         PIT  14.00
B      3.50    K      13.17    SIA   1.71         SIJ   8.78
SIK    8.78    E      12.50    RC    0.75         BB    0.23
AA     0.15    UBT     1.00    SPT   0.56         XT    0.75
XT     0.75    WCE     0.46    XB    0.75         C    11.00
XB     0.75    CHD    11.40    DKP   1.00         INC  52.00
UK     1.10    RSO     6.50    FSO   6.50         UF    0.96
STB   26.00    F      24.00    G    26.06         SPB   0.57
E1     1.19    D1      1.40    FSL   9.91         ODF   4.38
ODR    4.20    PD      1.00    DGC   1.65         SGC   3.70
H      3.41    LGC     1.00    FPE   0.

COPPER WT.    480.0


COIL DWG IS DESIRED
CHANGE PRINTER TO 8 LINES PER INCH
DISCONNECT CARRIAGE CONTROL TAPE
PRESS START WHEN READY
```

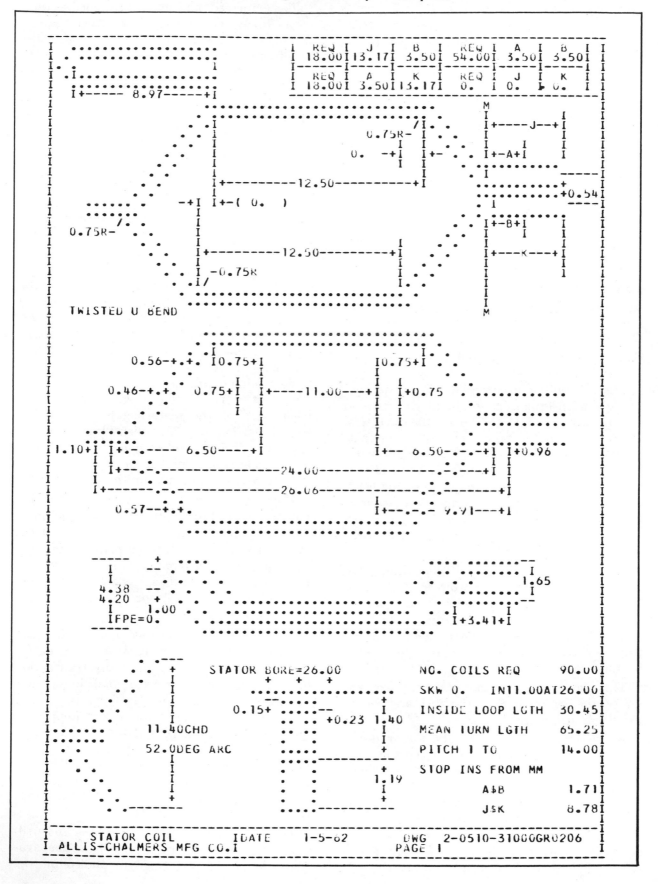

8. *Inspection ticket masters* which direct and authorize inspections.
9. Optionally, *a master operations list*, which lists all the specific operations required to build this product, along with standard times and prices.

At this point it was concluded that the scheduling program written for the research project was too abbreviataed and simplified to be completely useful in the daily operations control function. Hence, an extensive scheduling program was initiated.

The resultant scheduling program requires a description of available facilities in terms of a facility identification, number of shifts of operation, number of man hours available in the area, and an efficiency factor. Next, each order must be described in terms of order identification, an indentification of each job to be performed to complete the order including the facility on which each job will be done, the number of men required, number of hours this job takes, and an indication of the next job to be performed.

The scheduling program then operates on the given information either to calculate a day to day schedule for all of the facilities involved, or to determine the daily load that would exst on each facility if every job were started on the latest possible date. In either case, the program needs to compute for each order the path which requires the longest time, that is, the critical path. One option of the program is to have this critical path printed.

The normal output of the scheduling program is a tabulation of the work load for each facility. This tabulation shows when particular jobs on each customer order should be started and completed. The number of time periods which will be scheduled are determined by the user.

This program is of such size that it requires all of the equipment on the 704 and could profitably use more.

As was mentioned previously, material requirements cards are punched at the time the specification sheet is prepared. This allows the posting of material requirements. Now the question arises, when should these materials actually be disbursed. The obvious answer is that disbursement should be such that the correct materials can be at the right place at the time needed. This means that at the time at which the schedule calls for an operation to be performed, any material needed is there so as to avoid idle time for either man or machine. A program has been written called "projected material requirements" to accomplish this determination of disbursing dates.

Restating, the purpose of the projected material requirements program is to know when and how much material should be disbursed to meet the required shipping date. This aim is completely compatible with the aims of the scheduling program which in part are to schedule the operations necessary for complete manufacture so that the shipping date will be met. Although these are presently two separate programs, it is conceivable that they be combined into one.

Input data for the projected material requirements program are: customer order number for identification purposes, number of units in the order, shipping date, frame size, horsepower rating, type (synchronous, induction, d.c.), specified bearings, brass and copper designations. A search is made through a file to determine quantities of materials required. The next part of the program determines when each of the materials is needed. The output consists of order identification, materials by code and number, quantities, and date to be disbursed. This program uses all the storage and components of the computer.

From a material control standpoint, the posting of requirements and disbursing of materials are very important, but are not the only functions of controlling material. A computer program designated "material control," records all transactions, reports errors, reports shortages, and keeps a detailed history of material useage.

Transactions are matched against the master file and the affected records are updated. Besides the master file and daily transaction files, there are files for error conditions, order shortage conditions, and history. It is now possible to know the status of any item from the master file as kept updated by this material control program, and further to have a history of activity. This history may be important in determining whether a particular item should be stocked or its reorder level changed due to its activity.

The actual program is run on the 704 utilizing tape oriented procedures. Tape preparation and output printing is handled on the

IBM 1401 which is more economically suited for these operations. This is another program which stretches the capacity of the 704.

Many of the programs now in operation can be used alone or in conjunction with the other programs. This allows the greatest flexibility, since this type of operation recognizes that manual methods still exist to varying degrees. Hence, in some areas a series of programs are used and the operation approaches a computer control system. In other areas, the programs are used more as aids than as complete systems. Nevertheless, it is important to realize that savings and benefits are being experienced by all users. This allows the investments in the programs to be recaptured and allows real savings to be increasingly evident.

This type of operation also allows the programs to be "sold" completely on merit to unenthusiastic groups. Further, the organization benefits over-all much sooner and more readily accepts plans for future accomplishments.

CONCLUSION

A manufacturing company may be considered a process system consisting of: (a) in line processing, (b) daily operations control, and (c) long range planning. A computer control system may be suitably applied to such a process system. A research project did apply the concepts of such a control system to a discrete process, showing that the application was practical and could result in great benefits. Then application of segments of the research project was made to actual operations with satisfactory results. Further, large extensions of the aspects covered in the research project were made. The resulting system is particularly practical because it allows total or partial use of the computer system with direct benefits resulting from this use. Nevertheless, the total system concept is encouraged and expected to grow. For example, motor coils are completely automatic and approach the "customer order to product shipment operation with more effective control" concept.

Costs have been halved since the computer system took over the motor coil operation from the old method. Elapsed time (customer order to product shipment) was cut by three quarters. This means it takes only one fourth the time it previously took for complete processing.

Partial use of the computer system has shown great time and money savings, too. In all areas the intangible benefits have been felt. "Never had such consistent results before — much more accurate." "Facilitates closer control, and better utilization of resources." "Never had this information before. Wish we had!" These are some of the comments describing the computer control system.

Hardly noticed (a very good sign) but very important was the elimination of paper. Master operations lists, though mentioned as optional output, in practice are never called for because the computer control system supplies all documents necessary for control and manufacture. With the old method, these lists were required since the labor tickets were derived from them. Furthermore, instead of six or seven drawing types, one computer originated drawing with correct dimensions is provided. There is the savings of drawing tracings. This is not at all the complete list of eliminated paper.

The trend of closer control requiring more paper has been reversed. The computer control system provides closer control with less paper. This new trend will contine as the computer control system handles more operations.

The ideas behind the computer control system are sound. Many of them have been proven out in laboratory circumstances and the real system daily operations function. Time and economic considerations, which in a competitive society many times determine success or failure, seem to smile success on the computer system from the indications up to now.

But not all ideas have been tried and put to the rigorous tests of real competition. Nevertheless, future success may well hinge on the use of these other ideas and application of the computer control system to the entire operation.

By William A. Clark

Monsanto Chemical Company:
A Total Systems Approach to Marketing

LIKE SO MANY other large companies, Monsanto initially applied computers to accounting problems. The goals were speed, improved accuracy, greater detail and economy. The company's first large scale computer, an IBM 702 designed with accounting problems in mind, accepted massive amounts of input data, subjected them to relatively straightforward arithmetic treatment and spewed output at a pleasing rate.

The payoff, of course, was the availability of timely information and the more efficient use of human resources as accountants learned to command the machine. An important fact to note is that the computer at this point was regarded as an Egyptian slave of sorts, better suited to relieve the master of physical work than to take on problems involving sophisticated mathematics.

It was inevitable, however, that someone should begin thinking about the Grecian slave potentialities of the machine; for example, to consider its use in activities which are normally thought of as being largely mental rather than physical. A single mathematician was assigned an office, given a small amount

IBM 702 installation at Monsanto Chemical Co.

of machine time each day and asked to determine what mathematics could do for the company. He ferreted out problems and helped in their formulation, thereby making better use of the computer's potential. He added three mathematicians, unearthed more problems, made increasing demands on computer time and, most important, began showing a clear payoff.

Soon there arose, in a rather inconspicuous way, a new notion about computers. Our justification for getting a computer in the first place had been on the basis of accounting applications. Now, ironically, we were hard put to measure the savings we were realizing on those applications since no one really knew what it was worth to get income statements or balance sheets a few days earlier.

In contrast, the application of mathematical techniques, which had begun as an afterthought, was showing demonstrable (and measurable) savings. Before long, an IBM 704 was acquired and turned over to the mathematicians.

FOUR CATALYSTS

In retrospect, there were at least four basic policies which catalyzed the rapid application of the computer to the mathematical solution of business problems:

1. The mathematicians chosen for the group were of a rare, English speaking, practical thinking breed. Only when talking to one another did they prattle about the "ith row" or the "jtn column" or "n-dimensional space."

2. People with problems were put at ease. They were taught that the computer, despite its complexities, was no better than the human being who, with practiced patience, gave it unbelievably detailed instructions. Potential users were

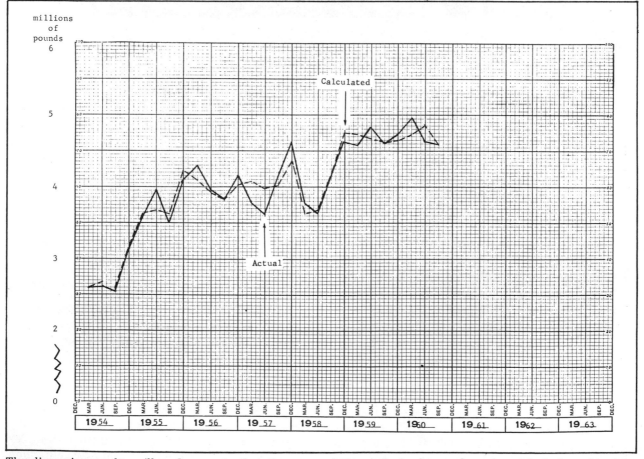

SALES OF DIMETHYL DOORKNOB

The discerning reader will perhaps note that the name of the product whose sales are graphed above has been changed. The coordinates of the dotted curve in this graph come from the computer which has been taught to study the relationship between actual sales of a product and various economic goings-on.

IBM 704 installation at Monsanto Chemical Co.

further encouraged by not being charged for the use of the computer or for the services of the mathematicians; problems were justified on the basis of the potential payoff to the company.

3. Through short courses of instruction, the people with problems learned enough about the workings of the machine and and the job of the programmer to present their problems and data in proper form. Their knowledge ensured quick flow through the programmer to the computer.

4. **Mathematicians** accepted the fact that they could not simply take existing mathematical techniques and search for possible applications for those techniques. It was also imperative that they find economically important problems and, if necessary, come up with new, untried ways to solve those problems.

From the marketing man's viewpoint, then, there have been these resources: two computers, one an accounting machine, the other a mathematical machine; separate organizations for each of the two functions; cooperation, encouragement, adequate help and an above average understanding of computers and computer programming.

With such resources, marketing has been able to undertake what might fairly be termed a total computer effort. It is this effort which will be discussed throughout the rest of this paper, in terms of three types of activity which admittedly are not mutually exclusive: (1) mining the information in existing accounting records, (2) creating a complementary data processing system for marketing and (3) applying mathematical techniques.

MINING THE EXISTING ACCOUNTS

Although the accounting records of most companies are designed to serve financial needs, they are a prime source of marketing information. To overlook using them would be analogous to abandoning a productive oil well to start drilling a new one. The preferred strategy is to continue making the most of the productive well *and* to start drilling a new one.

It is the nature of the input information for accounting records which makes them such attractive sources of marketing knowledge.

Thus, the fact of completion of a sale is of marketing interest; while the fact that sales revenue is generated is of sufficient financial interest to guarantee inclusion of the event in accounting records.

When a product is manufactured, certain costs are incurred and these are of interest, not only to the financial man, but to the marketing man who must decide on a selling price. Money spent on technical service or on entertaining customers represents both an outflow of cash and a marketing effort.

At Monsanto, accounting records are mined rather seriously. The information needs of marketing people are made known to a group called Accounting Research who determine whether the accounts have the requisite data and if so, how difficult it will be to extract them. Often this is done on a custom scale, to provide a basis for a single decision. Often it is done to take care of a continuing, widespread need.

Sales figures, for example, may be reconstituted and reported routinely in a number of ways to show how they are divided between geographic areas, types of products, classes of industries making the purchases, salesmen receiving credit, individual customers and the times at which sales were made. Because the records have been kept for some time, there is no great problem in analyzing the seasonality of demand on a product by product basis. There is also no problem to discover how vulnerable a particular product is to a cyclical downturn in the economy or to find out which products have strong long term growth characteristics. Sales performance against the forecast can be measured quickly, easily and in detail by products, by salesmen and by territory.

On the expense side, too, there is oil in the accounting shale. The company for some time has embraced the popular philosophy that each market requires a particular balance of marketing effort. The market for a commodity type product may require more personal selling effort, less advertising, less technical service, more uniform product quality and greater assurance of swift delivery than, for example, might be required by customers for a relatively new, non-commodity product.

Existing accounting records, when properly culled by the right combination of men and machines, can provide valuable insight into this balance of effort for particular markets. With manufacturing costs, too, there are opportunities for disaggregation and regrouping so as to provide a basis for better marketing decisions. Rather than list a number of specific examples, let us consider the hazards involved in becoming too preoccupied with the notion that further processing of accounting data is the only answer for the marketing man.

HAZARDS NOTED

1. There is the very real danger that the accounting data may be irrelevant for the marketing decision at hand. For example, in the chemical industry a manufacturing process may yield two products, one that is truly wanted and one for which there may be little or no demand. When the accountant looks at such a process, he assigns costs to each product on some arbitrary basis, such as the apparent market value of each. If the marketing man accepts either of these arbitrarily assigned costs as a basis for pricing, he may be abdicating his responsibility to engage in the profitable sales of products.

   In a situation of this sort, his job is to price both products in a way which will maximize profit from the whole process. One might argue that the accounts do have the information and they could be reconstituted to give relevant information. This may be true, but the point here is these accounts present an apparently relevant piece of information which might be used incorrectly by a marketing man who was unskilled in the subject of economic costs versus accounting costs.

   A second example is a salesman calling on a customer in hopes of selling five different products. Perhaps his real reason for being there is to sell one product, but there is no harm in asking about the other four, so he does. The accountant might evenly split the expense of the call between the five products. If he does, will the marketing man understand when he tries to determine the total amount of selling effort being expended on a particular product?

2. There is the danger that the accounts will contain insufficient detail. The chemical industry spends large sums for technical service, but this has been a growing expenditure and not until rather recently has there been sufficient interest in it to justify a breakdown into specific kinds of technical service or even into the particular kinds of customers for whom the service was rendered. Consequently, the basic input data are not in the accounts and time spent trying to synthesize them will lead either to wasted effort or to the acceptance of meaningless figures.

3. There is the danger that the cost of extracting worthwhile data from the accounts will militate against going ahead. A corollary to this is the danger that information will not be available in time to be of any use, possibly because the computer will be tied up with accounting problems at the very time marketing needs answers.

The accountant records history with Cratchit-like care, listing every transaction, every allocation and creating googol sets of numbers which must be both complete and internally consistent from an arithmetic viewpoint. By such practices he has contributed — perhaps more than he realizes — to the development of hardware to handle his numbers. But the marketing man often has a greater need for speed than for the ultimate in arithmetic precision or completeness. His important decisions can tolerate a one percent error, but he does need timely information. Unfortunately, even today's computers may be impractical sieves for a bale of accounting data which was assembled for financial, rather than marketing, needs.

In summary, Monsanto devotes a substantial amount of effort to the mining of accounting data in support of the marketing effort. There are personnel in accounting who are ready to help in the effort and their help is used, both on a custom basis and on the basis of recurring needs.

At the same time, though, there is widespread awareness that the accounts were not designed primarily for marketing use and may therefore yield information which is

U.S. PRODUCTION ASPIRIN

$Y = K*A**(B**X)$ K = 0.11265555E 08 A = 0.83276872E-04 B = 0.99018227E 00

SQUARE OF CORRELATION COEFFICIENT = 0.96214113E 00

YEAR	X		Y	Y(CALC.)	Y — Y(CALC.)	CONFIDENCE LIMITS	
						LOWER	UPPER
1918	1	0	961.	938.	23.	608.	1447.
1919	1	1	1777.	1029.	748.	672.	1575.
1920	1	2	1708.	1127.	581.	741.	1715.
1921	1	3	734.	1234.	-500.	815.	1868.
1922	1	4	1483.	1349.	134.	895.	2035.
1923	1	5	1526.	1474.	52.	980.	2218.
	1	6	1367.	1610.	-243.	1073.	2416.
		7	1499.	1756.	-257.	1172.	2631.
			1824.	1914.		1279.	2865.
						1393.	
	1	41	1789.		-3459.		
1960	1	42		22712.		14721.	3503.
1961	1	43		24139.		15541.	37492.
1962	1	44		25640.		16384.	40125.
1963	1	45		27218.		17248.	42953.
1964	1	46		28877.		18131.	45992.
1965	1	47		30619.		19033.	49259.
1966	1	48		32448.		19951.	52773.
1967	1	49		34366.		20883.	56554.
1968	1	50		36377.		21828.	60622.
1969	1	51		38484.		22785.	65001.
1970	1	52		40691.		23750.	69715.

This is a print-out from the trend-fitting program. The table shows calculated and actual U. S. Production of Aspirin, 1918-1959, and a projection to 1970. Values of the Gompertz parameters (k, a, and b) are printed out so that aspirin production for other years could be calculated. Confidence limits and the coefficient of determination give some idea of the goodness of fit.

irrelevant, insufficiently detailed or too difficult to gather. We continue to mine, in other words, but only so long as the value of the ore exceeds the costs of bringing it to the surface.

CREATING A COMPLEMENTARY SYSTEM FOR MARKETING

In discussing the program Monsanto is undertaking to improve and extend the information going into its data processing system, a few historical comments are in order.

The postwar years have taught Monsanto management a valuable lesson: the growth of information needs can indeed outpace the growth of the company itself. The reasons for this are clear in retrospect, but were not so clear in prospect.

Companies grow in many directions, not only in terms of sales volume or assets or number of employees. They grow in terms of the number of markets they serve, the number of new products spawned by research, the number of different kinds of services rendered, the number of plants, warehouses, sales offices, tank cars and salesmen, and the number of different raw materials used. There is no reason to suppose each of these forms of growth would exactly parallel the growth of company sales, for example; and even if they did, there is the added fact that people grow in terms of their ability and desire to handle more information in an effective way.

For Monsanto, recognition of the problem came early (we like to think) and a task force was created to cope with it. Marketing men from each of the divisions and from the central office studied what happened when an order was placed with a sales office. They determined who received each piece of information from the order and who wished that he could get more from that order. They found out what people did with the information they received. They studied the mechanics of the information flow from the incoming order to the outgoing bill; they noted time cycles and estimated costs.

STUDY PRODUCES FOUR OBJECTIVES

Soon they were able to outline a program whose first phase had these objectives:

1. To introduce more types of information and more detail into the system.

2. To improve the accuracy of the data entering the system.

3. To improve the timeliness of information by narrowing the gap between recording and reporting from days or weeks to hours.

4. To reduce the expense of data processing, despite the larger volume, by making sure problems are put on the right computers.

Note: Earlier it was stated that the company had two computers, a 702 and 704, available for work on marketing problems. While these are the company's major computers, there are also smaller machines such as 650s and a 1401. Others are on order.

This phase of the work, which is concerned primarily with the input side of the problem and the generation of straightforward kinds of information, is now nearly complete. Soon the composition of the task force will change. Charter members will leave in order to help run the system they have created. New members, skilled in disciplines other than marketing, will make the computers do a complete, sophisticated job of processing the data into forms previously unavailable within Monsanto. A few of the specific areas to be covered by the reconstituted task force are these:

1. *Computer freight rating and freight cost analysis* — Since freight costs are a major part of total distribution costs, it behooves Monsanto to analyze such costs carefully, making many comparisons between the actual costs incurred and costs that might have been incurred had other forms of transportation been used. Such analyses, when carried out on a large scale, will arm the company's traffic personnel with data needed to negotiate with carriers for more equitable rates.

   To conduct such analyses, the computer will have to be instructed how to calculate freight rates; but once it has learned this rather complicated procedure, it will be ready to apply its knowledge to new incoming orders. It is but a small step from there to the point that the computer figures the rates for alternative ways of shipping and selects the lowest cost carrier, recognizing there may be constraints, such as the maximum allowable time for shipment.

2. *Automatic field warehouse inventory control and distribution point analysis* — The plan is to have the computer accept an incoming order, choose the optimum warehouse from which to ship, check the inventory level after the shipment and reorder warehouse stock if necessary. Some formidable problems are expected in this project. Even the matter of the computer selecting the correct warehouse is not simple. The computer must consider such variables as freight costs, customers' time requirements, the cost to replace inventory and the ability of the warehouse to maintain a satisfactory inventory level until restocking occurs.

3. *Analysis of rolling stock utilization* — Work in this area will be designed to answer such questions as: How many box cars and tank cars should the company own and how many should it lease? When should customers be prodded to return trip-leased cars? Where should such cars best be returned?

This might be viewed as a traffic problem rather than as a marketing problem. On the other hand, this is an integral part of marketing. The fact that accountants ordinarily do not treat freight in the same way they treat advertising or sales promotion does not alter the fact that marketing men have an obligation to narrow the spread between gross and net sales. The tank car is a container whose need arises when an order is placed. The marketing man should have a consuming interest in the containers used for his products.

4. *Product allocation* — This is an area in which computers will be of greater help to decision makers, but will not assume the decision making function. When a product is in short supply, the sales manager for that product wants to see it allocated on an equitable basis. The computer is suited to the task of examining the historical performance of

---

"You say that you have not tried reading Peyton Place aloud as a family project. May I ask why not?"

	Grandfathers No. %	Grandmothers No. %	Mothers No. %	Fathers No. %	Boys No. %	Girls No. %	Total No. %
Considered unsuitable as a family project	15 33	11 50	28 62	9 47	9 39	7 30	79 45
Have narrow-minded relatives	28 62	11 50	15 33	7 37	10 43	14 61	85 48
I've already read it	2 4	0 0	2 4	3 16	4 17	2 9	13 7
Sums	45	22	45	19	23	23	177

Results of Chi-Square Tests for Significance
T stands for the sum of all other columns

1 vs Tcs = 4.12	Sig = 0.95	2 vs Tcs = 0.03	Sig = 0.	3 vs Tcs = 6.70	Sig = 0.95
4 vs Tcs = -0	Sig = 0	5 vs Tcs = -0	Sig = -0	6 vs Tcs = -0	Sig = -0
1 vs 2cs = 1.39	Sig = 0	1 vs 3cs = 7.86	Sig = 0.95	1 vs 4cs = -0	Sig = -0
1 vs 5cs = -0	Sig = -0	1 vs 6cs = -0	Sig = -0	2 vs 3cs = 1.39	Sig = 0
2 vs 4cs = -0	Sig = -0	2 vs 5cs = -0	Sig = -0	2 vs 6cs = -0	Sig = -0
3 vs 4cs = -0	Sig = -0	3 vs 5cs = -0	Sig = -0	3 vs 6cs = -0	Sig = -0
4 vs 5cs = -0	Sig = -0	4 vs 6cs = -0	Sig = -0	5 vs 6cs = -0	Sig = -0

This is a facetious example of the print-out from Monsanto's program for handling the results of surveys. The top table shows the numbers and percents of various classes of people (grandfathers, grandmothers, etc.) giving various answers to the question. The lower table shows the results of chi-square testing. Example "1 vs Tcs = 4.12" means that answers of grandfathers are sufficiently different from those of all others to give a chi-square of 4.12 which is statistically significant at the 95% level.
One set of tables of this sort is prepared for each question in the survey.

many customers (performance against contract, for example) and producing an equitable allocation of the product, but the product sales manager will continue to make the final decision.

5. *Customer profitability analysis* — How does a company decide how profitable a particular customer is? Today, such analysis is carried out on a limited scale or not at all. Yet it is quite important to a marketing man to know whether he is directing his efforts toward truly profitable accounts. Important, too, that he know which accounts are unprofitable and why, so that he may take corrective action.

By identifying the many cost factors associated with each order received, there is at last hope of cutting through the tangle of varying price structures, packaging, selling expense, distributor discounts and the like to arrive at profitability information for each of a very large number of customers.

6. *Analysis of sales call effectiveness* — By comparing the frequency of sales calls and their costs to data on the orders placed, the task group hopes to come up with measures of sales-call effectiveness. This will be an experimental effort fraught with certain difficulties, such as the fact that some sales calls are intended to be missionary while others are not, but it is worth a try. In the chemical industry, experimentation is, understandably, looked upon with favor.

This section has presented some of the highlights of the company's organized attempt to create a complementary data processing system for marketing personnel. The task force responsible for the work has viewed the incoming order as an ideal vehicle for introducing more and improved information into the system while at the same time ensuring personnel outside the marketing area will have their data needs satisfied.

Particular attention has been paid to the needs of those concerned with shipping, warehousing, packaging and materials handling. The group has made noteworthy progress, especially toward defining information needs, in establishing procedures to have the data fed into the system accurately and completely,

and in choosing the hardware (including communication hardware to link sales offices, for example, to the computer) for the system. Future work by a reconstituted task group will be concerned with generating output information in a form well suited to the needs of the decision maker. Many of the planned projects will require sophisticated mathematical treatment. All will take time.

MATHEMATICAL TECHNIQUES SET TO MARKETING PROBLEMS

If computers are to serve marketing management well, they must ultimately do more than gather data in one form and print them in another. Marketing men are already inundated with paper. The prospect of more to come, while consoling because new information will be available, is also frightening because of the chore of finding the answers in a bale of paper from the computer. Computers must be made to do more — they must be taught to interpret the data. For this, mathematics must be used.

Monsanto's use of mathematical procedures in processing marketing information covers a number of applications, some quite simple, some complex, some original, some permissively plagiarized. Here are some examples.

SALES FORECASTING

In preparing sales forecasts for over 1,000 products, it is important to know the nature of the demand for each of them. Is the product's demand growing rapidly or has it slowed down? Is there a seasonal pattern and if so, what, specifically, is that pattern? How vulnerable is the demand to a downturn in general business conditions? As noted earlier, the accounting records contain the raw data necessary to answer these questions, but who has the time to perform the calculations for so many products?

If a Monsanto marketing man wants to look at the rate of growth of sales of his product(s), he has only to submit the historical sales data, elect the kind of curve he wants fitted, allow a short time for the data to be punched into cards plus 50 seconds or so for machine time per product, and come away with a print out showing the yearly sales (calculated and actual) for the past and a 10 year extrapolation of the trend curve. His choice of curve types is quite broad. He may have any or all of the following: straight line, semi-log line, logistic, Gompertz and quadratic. Since this is a single computer program, there is no need to pass the data cards through the computer's card reader more than once. One simply decides which curves are to be fit and the machine proceeds on its own.

For seasonal index calculations there are three computer programs, two of which use calculations quite similar to those found in elementary statistics texts. The other is a modification of the now famous Shiskin program which determines not only the seasonal pattern of demand, but also the cyclical behavior and impact of such random forces as strikes.

Monsanto's sales forecasting problem has undergone a significant change in recent years. Immediately after World War I, the company's major problem was one of determining a way to build enough capacity to take care of the demand. Sales were growing so rapidly the effect of changes in economic activity was hardly noticeable.

Today, however, the industry is so well developed, so large and so entwined with other industries that we can no longer count on being invulnerable to economic change. As a result, the company must learn how to anticipate economic change and how to translate that change into its impact on the sales of particular products.

To understand the relationship between product sales and economic conditions, marketing personnel have tracked the flow of major products through the economy to the point of final consumption; for example, to such consumer goods as automobiles, refrigerators or rugs whose demand ultimately shapes the demand for the Monsanto product. For each product, the list of ultimate end uses has formed a basis for deciding which measures of economic activity should bear a logical relationship to the sales of the product. By feeding the computer historical data on product sales and for the various appropriate economic indices, such as automobile production or refrigerator production, and by using a standard multiple regression program, equations have been generated. These equations show what should have happened to sales of the product in view of the levels of automobile and refrigerator production.

The computer examines, stepwise, the relationships between sales of a single product and each of over fifty economic indices. First, the machine finds that single index which does the best job of explaining variations in sales of the product. Then a second index is selected as the one which, in combination with the first, does the best job of explaining variations. The process is repeated again and again until the addition of one more index adds little to the equation.

The final equation is tested by the machine and by people who study a graph showing calculated and actual sales over a fairly long period of time. With two or three good equations in hand for a product, Monsanto either purchases or develops economic forecasts for the appropriate indices, substitutes the forecast values into the equation and comes up with a forecast of sales for the product. This forecast is, of course, refined to reflect the marketing man's knowledge of unusual situations that are expected to prevail during the forecast period — such as a shortage of material or a major price change.

PRICING

For specific pricing problems the computer can be of material help. The development of long term contracts involving escalation clauses as an inflation hedge is one such problem. Sometimes the clauses are tied to a single price index, such as the cost of living index, but it is not uncommon to find contracts which embody several appropriate measures of price fluctuation. If Monsanto were selling a product on a long term contract, its price might be tied to some measure of the cost of raw materials, some measure of the cost of labor and perhaps a third general index, such as the cost of living index.

Before signing such a contract, it would be prudent to know what would happen to the price under a wide variety of changes in the various indices. It takes but a little understanding of the algebra of permutations and combinations to realize that a very large number of price calculations might have to be made if each of the three indices were allowed to take on as many as five or six values. The computer is well suited to this kind of problem.

Since the marketing man would, in all likelihood, be interested only in very high or low prices, he would ask the computer to report only those extreme cases. Thus he could focus attention on the prime problem (the probability that the economic indices in the escalation might take on values which would lead to extreme prices) without having to pore over needlessly complete tables.

POLLS AND SURVEYS

Poll taking is a popular and expensive pastime in many U. S. corporations. Employes are polled to find out whether they are happy. Potential customers are polled to see what they think of a company's products or to find out whether they have read company ads. Financial analysts are polled to find out what they think about the stock. Shareholders are polled to see whether they like the annual reports being sent them.

The procedures for getting at these audiences vary. The method may be by a mailed questionnaire, personal interview or telephone interview. Once the questions have been asked and the answers gathered, there remains the rather formidable task of compiling the information and interpreting it in a way that is both practical and statistically sound.

Since this was a general problem at Monsanto, a computer program was developed to handle the results of any survey or poll. The computer helped to reduce the clerical costs involved in using non-computer procedures. It guaranteed that results were available quickly and assured rigorous statistical analysis of the answers.

As an example, consider a tea merchant who wishes to see whether an advertising campaign, when tried in three cities, can change people's attitudes toward his product. He hires an outside firm to conduct 2,000 interviews before the campaign and an equal number after it has ended, in both cases covering six cities — three experimental cities and three controls.

The interviews last 30 minutes and include such questions as "How many times was tea served in your home during the last week?" or "Which do you think contains more caffeine: a cup of tea or a cup of coffee?" or "What are your three favorite non-alcoholic beverages in the order of your preference?"

When the interviewing is complete, the answers must be tabulated and interpreted. Comparisons must be drawn between the pat-

67. 0. 1. 0. 1. 0. 1. 1. 0. 0. 0. 0. 0. 0. 1. 0. 0. 0. 0. 1. 0. 0. 0. 0. 0. 0. 0. 0. 0. 0. 1. 0. 0. 0. 0. 0. 1. 0. 0. 0.
1. 0. 0. 0. 1. 0. 0. 0. 0. 1. 0. 0. 0. 1. 0. 12.
70. 0. 1. 0. 1. 0. 1. 0. 1. 0. 1. 0. 0. 0. 0. 0. 0. 0. 0. 0. 1. 0. 0. 0. 1. 0. 0. 1. 0. 0. 0. 0. 0. 1. 0. 0. 0.
0. 0. 0. 1. 0. 0. 0. 0. 1. 0. 0. 1. 0. 0. 0. 1. 8.
74. 1. 1. 0. 1. 0. 1. 0. 1. 0. 0. 0. 1. 0. 0. 0. 0. 1. 0. 0. 0. 0. 0. 0. 0. 0. 1. 1. 0. 1. 0. 0. 0. 1. 0. 1. 0.
0. 0. 1. 0. 0. 0. 0. 1. 0. 0. 0. 1. 0. 8.
76. 1. 1. 0. 1. 0. 1. 1. 0. 0. 1. 0. 0. 0. 0. 1. 0. 0. 0. 0. 0. 0. 0. 0. 0. 1. 1. 0. 1. 0. 0. 0. 0. 1. 0. 0. 0.
1. 0. 0. 1. 0. 0. 0. 1. 0. 0. 1. 0. 0. 1. 5.
78. 1. 1. 0. 1. 0. 1. 0. 1. 0. 1. 0. 1. 0. 0. 0. 0. 1. 0. 0. 1. 1. 0. 0. 0. 0. 0. 1. 0. 0. 0.
1. 0. 0. 1. 0. 0. 0. 0. 1. 0. 1. 0. 0. 1. 8.
80. 1. 1. 0. 1. 0. 1. 1. 1. 0. 0. 0. 0. 1. 0. 0. 0. 0. 1. 1. 0. 0. 0. 1. 0. 0. 1. 0.
0. 0. 0. 1. 0. 0. 0. 0. 0. 1. 0. 0. 1. 14.
85. 1. 1. 0. 0. 0. 0. 0. 0. 1. 0. 1. 0. 0. 0. 1. 0. 0. 0. 1. 1. 1. 0. 0. 0. 0. 1. 1. 0. 0.
0. 0. 0. 1. 0. 0. 0. 0. 1. 0. 0. 1. 6.
86. 1. 1. 0. 0. 0. ... 0. 1. 0. 0. 1. 0. 0. 1. 0. 0. 0. 0. 0. 0. 1. 1. 0. 0. 0. 0. 0. 1. 0. 0. 1.
0. 1. 1. 8. ... 0. 0. 0. 0. 0. 0. ... 0. 1. 0. 0. 0. 0.

110. ... 0. 1. 0. ... 1. 0. 0. 0. 1. 0. 1. 0. 0. 0.
1. 0. 0. 0. 1. ... 0. 5.
111. 1. 1. 0. 0. 0. 0. 0. 0. 1. 0. 0. 0. 0. 0. 0. 0. 0. 0. 1. 0. 0. 0. 0. 0. 0. 0. 0. 0.
0. 0. 0. 0. 0. 1. 0. 1. 0. 0. 0. 1. 4.
112. 1. 1. 0. 0. 0. 0. 0. 0. 1. 0. 1. 0. 0. 0. 0. 0. 0. 0. 0. 0. 0. 0. 1. 0. 0. 0. 1. 0. 0. 1. 0. 0. 0.
0. 0. 0. 1. 0. 0. 0. 0. 1. 0. 0. 0. 1. 16.
114. 1. 1. 0. 0. 0. 0. 0. 0. 1. 0. 0. 0. 0. 0. 1. 0. 0. 0. 1. 0. 0. 0. 0. 0. 0. 1. 1. 1. 0. 0. 0. 1. 0. 0. 0.
0. 0. 1. 0. 0. 0. 1. 0. 0. 0. 1. 0. 0. 4.
115. 1. 1. 0. 0. 0. 1. 0. 1. 0. 1. 0. 1. 0. 1. 0. 0. 0. 0. 1. 0. 0. 0. 0. 0. 1. 0. 0. 0.
1. 1. 0. 0. 1. 1. 0. 0. 0. 0. 0. 1. 0. 0. 4.
116. 1. 1. 0. 0. 0. 0. 0. 0. 1. 1. 0. 0. 1. 0. 0. 0. 0. 1. 0. 0. 0. 0. 1. 0. 0. 0. 1. 0. 0. 0.
1. 1. 0. 0. 1. 0. 0. 0. 1. 0. 0. 7.
117. 1. 1. 0. 0. 0. 0. 0. 1. 0. 1. 0. 1. 1. 0. 0. 1. 0. 0. 0. 0. 1. 0. 0. 0. 1. 0. 0. 0.
0. 0. 0. 1. 0. 0. 0. 0. 1. 0. 0. 0. 1. 1. 9.

This is not wallpaper but a print-out of the input data for the problem concerned with designing well-read advertisements. Beginning in the upper left hand corner, the "67" refers to the number of the ad, the series of "0's" and "1's" describe that ad and the "12" refers to the actual readership score for that ad. Throughout the series of "0's" and "1's", a "1" means that an ad shows a certain characteristic such as a long headline or particular position in the magazine and a "0" indicates that the ad does not possess some other characteristic such as a rectangular illustration or a right hand page position.

SUMMARY FOR QUARTER 4.	Firm 1	Firm 2	Firm 3	Firm 4	Firm 5
SALES (UNITS)	91940.	98200.	89327.	90939.	98200.
SALES ($)	1043523.	1104750.	1027256.	1045799.	1138138.
PRICE	11.3500	11.2500	11.5000	11.5000	11.5000
MARKET SHARE (PCT.)	19.62	20.96	19.06	19.41	20.96
COST OF GOODS SOLD	720389.	765390.	701509.	706345.	746369.
UNIT COST	7.8354	7.7942	7.8533	7.7496	7.6005
GROSS PROFIT	323134.	339360.	325747.	339454.	391769.
GROSS PROFIT (PCT.)	30.97	30.72	31.71	32.46	34.42
MARKETING	60000.	70000.	40000.	50000.	80000.
R. + D.	45000.	60000.	30000.	40000.	55000.
MARKET RESEARCH	2000.	6000.	6000.	6000.	6000.
INVENTORY CARRYING CHARGE					
INTEREST - SHORT TERM LOANS	225.	1250.	744.	500.	675.
INTEREST - LONG TERM LOANS	3750.	0.	0.	750.	4259.
OPERATING EXPENSES	110975.	137250.	76744.	108749.	145934.
OPER.EXP./SALES (PCT.)	10.63	12.42	7.47	10.40	12.82
UNIT OPER. EXP.	1.2070	1.3977	0.8591	1.1958	1.4861
OPERATING PROFIT	212159.	202110.	249003.	230705.	245835.
OPER.PROFIT/SALES (PCT.)	20.33	18.29	24.24	22.06	21.60
UNIT OPER. PROFIT	2.3076	2.0581	2.7876	2.5369	2.5034
TAXES	106079.	101055.	124502.	115353.	122918.
NET INCOME	106079.	101055.	124502.	115353.	122918.
NET INCOME/SALES (PCT.)	10.17	9.15	12.12	11.03	10.80
DIVIDENDS	20000.	15000.	50000.	15000.	70000.
RETAINED AS CASH	86079.	86055.	74502.	100353.	52918.
DIVIDENDS/NET INCOME (PCT.)	18.85	14.84	40.16	13.00	56.95
CASH	958281.	1013877.	1101021.	945193.	1015262.
DEPRECIATION	60720.	58920.	55920.	58920.	61920.
AVAILABLE CASH	1019001.	1072797.	1156951.	1004113.	1077182.
SHORT TERM CREDIT	151460.	153395.	154122.	155005.	150394.
SHORT TERM LOANS	22500.	125000.	74400.	50000.	67500.
AVAILABLE FOR INCREASE	128960.	28395.	79722.	105005.	82893.
LONG TERM CREDIT	302920.	306790.	308244.	310009.	300787.
LONG TERM LOANS	250000.	0.	0.	50000.	283920.
AVAILABLE FOR INCREASE	52920.	306790.	308244.	260009.	16867.
BEGINNING INVENTORY	100200.	98200.	93200.	94272.	98200.
PRODUCTION	91940.	98200.	89327.	90939.	98200.
SALES					
ENDING INVENTORY	8260.	0.	3873.	10829.	0.
INVENTORY/SALES	0.09	0.	0.04	0.12	0.
PLANT CAPACITY AT START	101200.	98200.	93200.	98200.	103200.
PLANT CAPACITY AT END					
ASSETS	3786499.	3834877.	3853050.	3875116.	3759842.
RES. AND DEV. EFFECTIVENESS	3	2	5	4	1
RELATIVE ATTRACTIVENESS	3	2	4	5	1
STOCK PRICE	58.13	56.54	59.93	57.96	62.61

After each quarter of play in the management game the referee gets a sheet such as this showing how each of the five teams is performing.

terns of answers given by people before and after the campaign, and between the patterns of answers given by people in different cities, and perhaps between the patterns of answers given by men as opposed to women. With the Monsanto computer program, a table is generated by the machine for each question — a table giving the numbers and per cents of each class of respondent giving each kind of answer to the question. Next, the computer studies the answer patterns. By chi-square testing, answer patterns (between those who have been exposed to the campaign, for example, and those who have not) are compared to see whether the differences are real or are statistically inadequate because of the sample size.

The entire analysis requires about 20 minutes of 704 time for a study of the type just described.

TRAINING OF MARKETING PERSONNEL

Another of Monsanto's computer uses in the marketing area involves the training of marketing personnel by means of management games or management simulations. Thus far, only total management games have been used rather than marketing games because the marketing department feels strongly that its personnel should become familiar with the functions of other departments within the company.

As in similar games, marketing men have been divided into teams (or companies), each of which begins with a pre-determined set of assets, which it tries to employ to greatest advantage. Decisions are made by each team. They concern such areas as quantity of the product to manufacture and what price to charge. The results are calculated in the light of the decisions made by other competing firm. The process is repeated many times with each repetition representing a simulated month or quarter of business operation.

To teach the importance of planning, each team is required to set forth definite objectives before play is begun, and performance is measured against those objectives. If a team says that it wishes to maximize return on investment, for example, referees will be quite interested in seeing whether the team concentrates on just the numerator (the return) or whether they also reduce the denominator (investment) by paying out dividends when profitable reinvestment of earnings is unlikely.

At the completion of play, there is a critique which is sometimes ruthless and always thorough. Also, there is a session in which players (who are knowledgeable marketing men) disclose any lack of realism in the game's response to such marketing decisions as price changes. When they do, the mathematics behind the game is changed to approximate reality more closely. Thus an evolution has occurred which we think has led to an accurate simulation of real life.

ADVERTISING

An important facet of Monsanto's total data processing approach to marketing is the work which has been done in advertising. The problem of measuring advertising effectiveness is by no means a simple one since most advertising is designed to increase sales in some way, but not to carry the entire burden or even, necessarily, a major part of it.

When an ad man buys space in a trade journal, his notion of what that ad will accomplish is sometimes recondite, so anyone wanting to check the success of the ad will have to turn to such indirect measures as readership scores. Scores of this sort are developed routinely by various advertising research firms whose interviewers sit down with readers of a particular issue of a journal and determine the percent of those readers who read various ads in the journal. Although the validity of the tests has been debated zestfully for many years, advertising men and marketing men generally agree that a high readership score is good.

There has long been the feeling that if certain mechanical aspects of an ad could be taken care of properly, a reasonably good readership score might be achieved more or less automatically. In fact, many people have tried to arrive at an intuitive solution of the problem by gazing at great collections of ads hoping to discover whether the size of the illustration, the location of the ad in the journal, the length of the headline, the length of the copy, the kind of illustration used, the presence of certain kinds of words in the headline, the style of type and other factors really determine how good a readership score an ad will have.

Monsanto, being interested in learning how to design well read ads, and being skeptical of some of the published findings on the subject, contacted the Industrial Advertising Research Institute of Princeton, New Jersey, which had amassed data covering many thousands of ads. For each ad there was a readership score and a description of the ad in terms of more than 70 variables. Early attempts to deal with these data had amounted to sortings and tabulations in which the researcher sought to let one variable be altered while holding all others constant.

It takes little imagination to realize when one wants to study the effect of illustration size, for instance, by studying a group of otherwise identical ads, an original sample of thousands of ads can be pared to a handful. Furthermore, by trying to hold so many variables constant, researchers were ignoring the possibility of interaction. Maybe the effect of shortening a headline is enhanced by the presence of a large illustration. Who can tell without considering the possibility?

Using Monsanto's program and machine, the Industrial Advertising Research Institute's data were put through regression calculations which have told the advertising people which mechanical features of the ad should be taken care of and in what way. The results of these calculations have been used in designing certain ad campaigns with results that have been most encouraging.

CUSTOMER SERVICE

Occasionally the computer can be used by marketing people to process customer data, either on a fee basis or in the hope of a better relationship between Monsanto and the customer. An example concerns the customer who blends various chemicals into fertilizer formulations.

Each of his formulations may contain plant nutrients, such as nitrogen, phosphorus and potash, but in varying concentrations. The raw materials which he may buy are many. They differ in price, in physical form and in the amounts of plant nutrient they contain.

The customer's problem is an easy one, providing he knows someone with a computer trained to do linear programming. He simply wants to know which raw materials to buy and how to blend them in order to produce his many fertilizer mixtures at minimal cost.

The final section has dealt with a number of specific instances in which mathematics has played a dominant role in data processing. In Monsanto, mathematical activity goes on quite independently of Accounting and of the task group previously mentioned. Occasionally, someone muses about the coalescence of the three types of effort into a single data processing organization. So far, though, the spirit of competition between the three groups, their cooperation on matters of mutual concern and their records of achievement augur strongly against coalescence in the near future.

By A. B. Curchin

Lumbermens Mutual Insurance Company: Conversion to Data Processing

THE LUMBERMENS Mutual Insurance Company was founded in 1895 by a group of lumber dealers. Fire insurance premiums for saw mills, planing mills and lumber yard stock were excessive, so they undertook to provide themselves mutual protection at a reasonable cost.

The company was operated successfully as a lumber insurance specialist until 1928, when an expansion was begun through the American Agency System. At present, approximately 1,500 local agents represent our company.

Until 1955, when the state of Ohio authorized domestic companies to write both fire and casualty insurance, Lumbermens wrote only the fire and allied lines coverages.

As of today, we annually write $17,000,-000.00 fire and allied lines, inland marine, homeowners, automobile liability, automobile physical damage, general liability, burglary, and plate glass coverages.

In 1960, Lumbermens innovated five package policies, providing all necessary protection in one policy to motel owners, apartment house owners, retail store owners, laundry and dry cleaners and office building owners at competitive prices.

Charles E. Nail is chief executive officer of the company. The policy making function is the responsibility of a three man management committee, consisting of the president, secretary, and treasurer. Each of the latter two are also vice presidents. The vice president and treasurer is also responsible for internal operations, which consist of methods, procedures and personnel. All line authority flows from the chief executive officer.

The vice president and treasurer maintains a staff relationship with the line executives on internal operational matters.

FIRST MACHINE IN 1916

Lumbermens has been a user of punched card equipment since August, 1916, when we received the first machine in the Mansfield eight county territory. Practically the same equipment was used until 1940, at which time we received the first IBM 405 alphabetic printer in this territory. In 1952, the 405 tabulators were converted to 402 tabulators. The 402s were continued until our 1401 electronic equipment was received in May, 1961.

In the period from 1952 to 1959, when the 1401 was announced, many changes were effected in the data processing and computer field. A number of interim studies on new types of equipment were made, but none that we studied satisfied our requirements. We recognized, however, the potentiality of the 1401 for our situation as soon as it was announced in October, 1959. An order was placed for the 4,000 K card equipment within a week after the announcement. Upon the announcement of increased capacity, our order was changed to an 8,000 K machine.

Programming began early in 1960. We tested our first completed program in December, 1960. Upon delivery of our equipment in May, 1961, we had completed and tested about 75 percent of our programs, which comprised about 85 percent of our total card volume.

The final responsibility for our studies and the decisions affecting our data processing had been delegated by management to the treasurer. In cooperation with the manager of our data processing department, and our IBM representative, a complete written recommendation was prepared and submitted to the then existing management committee. Approval to order the equipment was granted a day after the report was submitted. The report covered:

1. 1401 data processing system anticipated load.
2. Comparison of present rental to projected rental.
3. Comparison of rental and purchase prices.
4. Personnel present and future.
5. Cut-over plans.
6. Estimate of additional applications.
7. Training requirements.
8. Education of management and other company personnel.
9. Publicity.
10. Installation planning with schedule.
11. Physical installation requirements.

PROGRAMMING

After approval, we employed one experienced programmer, who reported to the manager of our data processing department. Together, they became the spearheads for the analysis work required prior to programming. In addition, each department head appointed one person in his department as liaison to the programming team, so that a real working relationship developed with a minimum of formality.

The balance of the programming staff was composed of two men who were formerly in our tabulating department. They were employed originally as tabulating operators, but were selected on the basis of their potentiality for programming.

In retrospect, we feel a creditable job was done in preparing to convert our operations to the electronic equipment, but if we had it to do again, our approach would be different. We began with programming and testing our large volume jobs. We were anxious to have under lock and key tested programs for our bread and butter operations. These required considerable time in checking, testing and making necessary investigations and analyses for programming.

Our results would have been achieved faster and at less cost if we had given preference to the smaller operations first. This would have given our staff very valuable programming experience and the necessary training in machine logic and capabilities before they had to tackle the larger, complicated routines.

We also believe our phase out of personnel and equipment could have been accomplished faster because the larger jobs may be scheduled to be performed by a fewer number of operators, whereas a great number of smaller jobs require more operators due to identical deadlines.

This is contrary to general opinion, but worthy of study by anyone considering the conversion from mechanical equipment to a card computer system. Whether this same concept would apply to a conversion to a tape system, we do not know.

Our installation at this writing has been operating at varying levels of utilization for

Exhibit 1

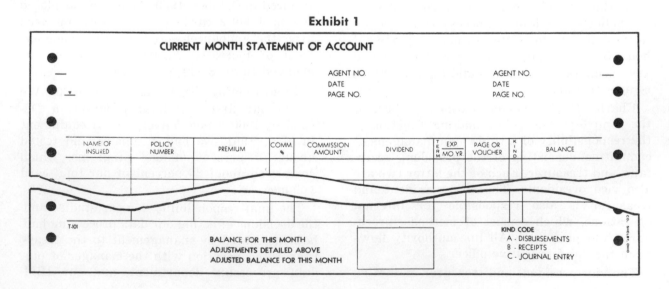

one year. We had planned to allow 6 months to achieve a break even point with our mechanical operation. We have not quite reached our anticipated goal, but it is within sight.

IMPACT ON COMPANY

What impact has the conversion to electronic equipment had upon our total company operation?

I believe the first, most evident effect was the speed up of reports to management. This, in spite of the increased speed of the equipment, did not materialize as an automatic result. Scheduling is an area which requires large doses of constant supervision to insure proper flow of input data and checking of output results to maintain satisfactory machine utilization. The 1401 system produces most complete jobs in about one-sixth the total elapsed time compared with the electro-mechanical equipment.

Another major advantage has been the ability of the equipment to produce from one program a combination of similar results that were formerly separate jobs. For example, we produce a listing for each agent of each transaction for the month. This is a large volume, time consuming job. We also produced as a separate job for each agent his ledger account, which began with the prior balance, recorded journal entries, cash entries and charges. This also was a large volume, time consuming job. The combined time required approximately 25 hours each month. They were programmed as one job (**Exhibit 1**), which now requires seven hours.

The result was the acceleration of our whole accounting department schedule and rendering an account to our agents about 10 days faster each month. Of course, from this we have gained an advantage in an over-all cleaner accounts receivable operation.

Another major improvement has been effected in our agents' experience reports, which show for each agent the dollars of premiums written and the losses incurred for the current month and cumulative year to date segregated by each type of policy written — for example, fire and automobile.

This report (**Exhibit 2**) has been extended to include for each agent some significant statistical data, such as number of new policies, number of renewal policies, the number of endorsements or changes required, the number of policies canceled and the average premium for each type. This will aid in our evaluation of an agent's performance and the cost of maintaining his account as compared with others.

There have been some side effects, in that one of the great advantages to any major change in procedures is the opportunity to review current methods. One saving, which was programmed as a by-product into the agent's account operation, was the automatic calculation of the commission earned by each agent. Formerly, this was calculated by our account clerks. We estimated that this saved about 50 hours per month in clerical time.

MORE WORK FOR EQUIPMENT

Other jobs have been added to the equipment, which we did not have the ability to do

Exhibit 2

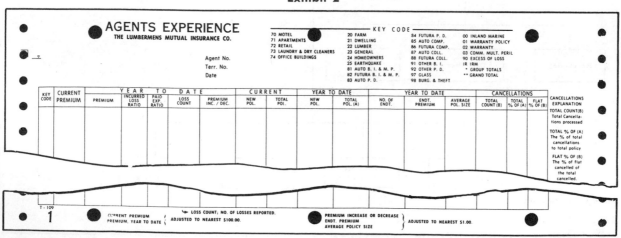

before. One major task, which began operation with policies effective January 1, 1962, was the automatic preparation of private passenger automobile policies and automatic premium billing of the policies every six months. We have high hopes for automatic writing of other types of personal lines policies and conversion to an automatic preparation of invoices for billing the premiums to insureds.

A by-product of automatic policy writing will be the elimination of rate checking, which presently is quite an extensive operation. In order to be certain that policies presently rated and typed by the agents have been prepared correctly, each one received is checked for proper classification and premium amount. This will no longer be necessary. The saving in personnel cost when this is eliminated will achieve our break even point.

Generally, the electronic equipment has provided us with a cleaner, more compact data processing operation. Fewer, more highly specialized personnel, operating higher speed, more versatile equipment, in a more concentrated area with a reduced number of individual requirements, lend themselves to a better controlled, more efficient operation.

When reviewing our operation in preparation for the equipment, we listed 116 separate jobs completed, either monthly or quarterly. By combination or elimination, this was reduced to 46 separate programs. The net result of the reduction in numbers has been more information produced faster.

FUTURE PLANS

We will continue to re-program and refine our operations. In addition, we have plans for the future which will keep our programming

Exhibit 3
ORGANIZATION CHART

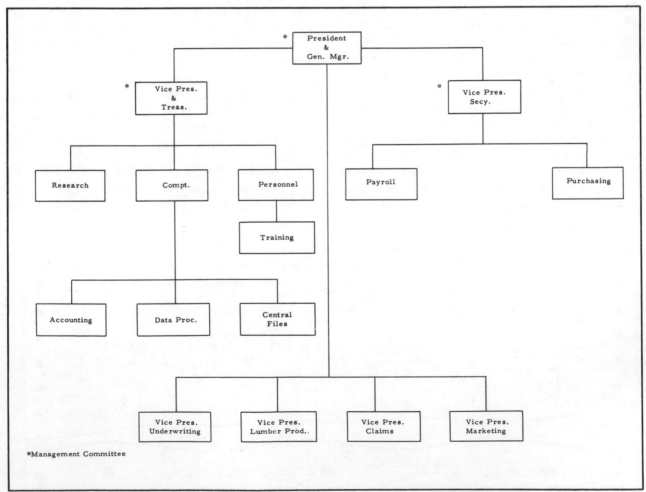

*Management Committee

staff occupied for a long time to come.

We plan:

1. More detailed agency experience reports.

2. More detailed expense distributions.

3. More detailed profit and loss data by cost centers, which will provide a basis for closer management control by spotlighting accountability.

4. More detailed analyses of our loss statistics, as respects severity and frequency of occurrence.

5. More automation of our claims clerical operations.

Each company planning to convert to an electronic system must be guided by its own set of circumstances. However, it is our opinion that too much valuable time has been spent in so called feasibility studies. We have known of some companies and heard of others devoting from three to more than 20 man years, trying to determine whether the equipment should be ordered at all and if so, what type. Determining whether the equipment is within the realm of possibility depends upon whether you can at least break even in cost and in additional advantages.

Having been operating on a card system, it was decided early that, although a tape system offered many interesting areas of exploration, the complete conversion would be much more difficult. We preferred to make the transition in two phases: first, to a card input computer; later to a tape system, after necessary over-all corporate systems planning.

A TOTAL SYSTEM?

As we look even further into the future, a most interesting possibility appears which might become a third phase of our transition to electronic data processing. It was not our intention, when we installed our computer, to attempt a complete overhaul of all of our systems, much less to attempt to integrate them into a single information processing system. But this total systems concept, remote as it was from our thoughts at the beginning, does not seem quite so impossible to attain from our present position.

We now have some valuable experience with a computer. In gaining that experience, we have seen the inevitability of an integration of formerly separate procedures in order to better utilize our electronic equipment. We know, too, that no one has yet fully achieved this ultimate goal of a totally planned and automated business information processing system. Without intending to do so, we have found ourselves heading in the general direction of such a goal.

As do other managements, we periodically review past operations, assess current conditions and attempt to look into the future so that we can modify policy to ensure the best possible operation of our company. We are watching others as they experiment with the total systems concept and try to fit together into one mosaic the myriad policies, methods and procedures of generating, communicating and using corporate information. If at some future time we decide to move further toward the goal of a total system, we are confident that our experience to date will enable us to do a creditable job.

Martin-Marietta Corporation:
Centralized Operations Control

MARTIN MARIETTA CORPORATION'S AEROSPACE DIVISION is comprised of the personnel and facilities of the former Martin Company which consolidated with American-Marietta Company in 1961. The division's operations and products were changed little by the move. Originally an aircraft manufacturer, Martin foresaw the coming importance of space as long ago as World War II. The company produced its last airplane in 1959 after becoming deeply entrenched in this nation's missile and space effort. The aerospace division now devotes all its energies to missiles, space vehicles, space exploration, electronics and nucleonics.

During the past decade, the division has grown from a single plant near Baltimore, Maryland, to an industrial complex with operating divisions in Baltimore, in Denver, Colorado, and in Orlando and Cocoa Beach, Florida. Representatives are located in most major United States cities and many foreign countries.

The demands such a highly technical, diversified and scattered industry place on its management are many. Martin Marietta's Aerospace Division now is in the process of developing and implementing a uniform integrated data processing system which will bring management up to the minute and comparable information on all operating divisions. Thus, through an integrated data processing system, top management will be provided with the tools necessary for measuring performance and for reaching overall decisions on the future goals of the Aerospace Division.

EARLY EXPERIENCE

The first step toward major use of data processing equipment was taken in 1942 when electric accounting machines were installed by the finance department. Since the primary application of this equipment was financial in nature, the finance department for many years retained control of the company's electric and later electronic calculating machines. Additional equipment to control elements of production, engineering release and personnel was added in 1945, still under control of the finance department.

In 1949, the engineering department began extensive use of analog equipment for scientific calculations, but not until 1951 did the department take advantage of services offered by digital equipment made available by the finance department. A computing section separate from finance and other business-type calculating was established by engineering in 1953.

By this time, the former Martin Company rapidly was becoming one of the country's major missile manufacturers and was taking part in some of the initial steps by the military services toward space exploration. The MATADOR, forerunner of a series of Air Force tactical missiles, was in production. The VIKING high altitude research rocket built by the company already had made some major contributions toward better understanding of the upper atmosphere in Navy supported flight tests over New Mexico. The need these and other programs created for more sophisticated equipment resulted in installation of electronic data processing equipment for engineering use in 1955. Since then, the engineering department has kept abreast of the advances made in the field of data processing and currently uses IBM 7090 equipment for all calculations, with analog equipment for special applications such as space flight simulators.

Exhibit 1

SYSTEMS INTEGRATION FLOW CHART

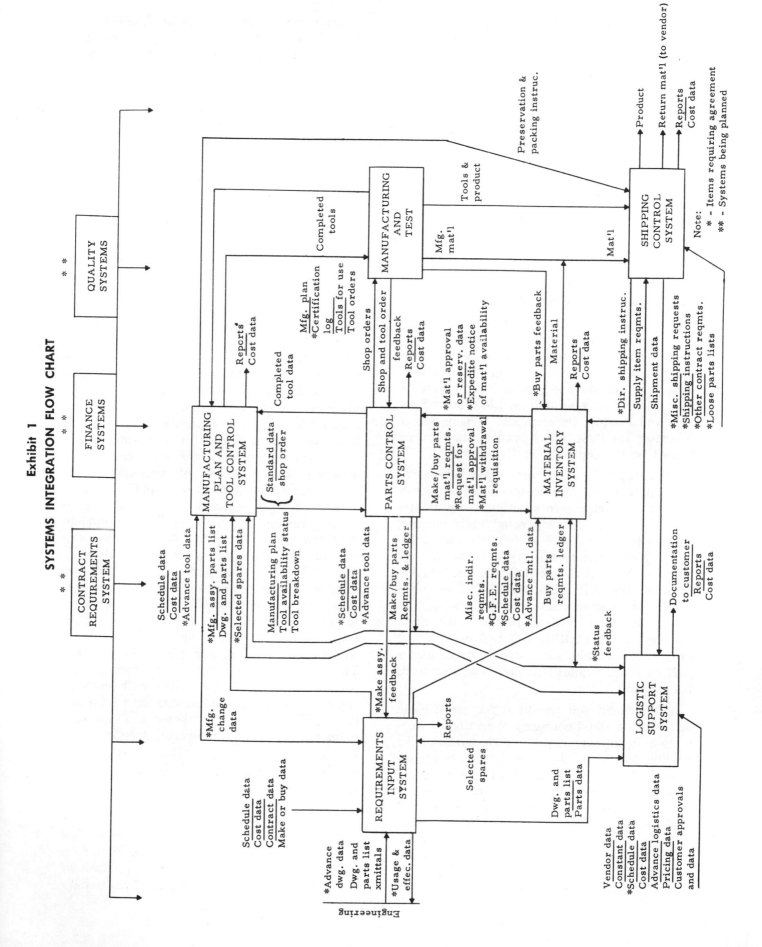

Note:
* - Items requiring agreement
** - Systems being planned

Business data processing took on new importance in 1955. A new division of the company was being established in Denver to build the Air Force TITAN ICBM, a separate nuclear division was opened in Baltimore to place the company in position to build reactors and nuclear generators for use by the military services, and electronics was achieving new importance at Baltimore as its application became necessary to all company products. Management needed increasingly greater controls over operations of the company to be able to make intelligent policy decisions. Electronic data processing equipment was installed primarily for finance, material inventory and production control. A separate service organization was established in 1956 to handle all business data processing for the company.

Inventory management, logistic support, production control and finance computations were applied to the equipment. In addition to Denver, new company divisions were established in Orlando and Cocoa Beach, Florida near Cape Canaveral, and an Electronics Systems and Product Development division and a Research Institute for Advance Study were opened by the company in Baltimore.

To adequately serve the expanded operations, data processing centers were set up in Denver and Orlando in addition to Baltimore. Each of the centers operated more or less independently in choice of methods and equipment. The company now was producing the BULLPUP, MACE, LACROSSE and TITAN missiles, the MISSILE MASTER, an electronic air defense missile control system, and SNAP auxiliary nuclear power units. Such missiles as the PERSHING and many other programs including extensive study of man's part in space exploration had begun or were just ahead.

Management felt the need for more basic information about company operations, information in greater depth which would make possible intelligent decisions on future expansion. Difficult questions about the company could not be answered because of the decentralized nature of the organization, a result of rapid expansion. Management could not determine without considerable guesswork whether it would be best to expand one or more of the existing facilities or create a new division if expansion appeared necessary; which of the existing plants could be most efficiently enlarged; whether materials and accumulated skills within the divisions could be considered expandable or perhaps temporarily interchangeable.

Aerospace Division President W. B. Bergen in August 1960 issued a directive creating an administrative staff headed by a vice president for administration. This group is charged with responsibility for division organization and the initiation, coordination, publication and audit surveillance of all systems, procedures and reporting techniques in areas of internal administration.

Data processing was seen as the most efficient tool for realizing centralized control of internal operations at all company operating divisions. However, standardization of equipment and integration of systems and language at each of the Aerospace computing centers was necessary before complete administrative centralization would be possible. The first step was installation in 1961 of IBM 7070 and 1401 machines in Denver, Orlando and Baltimore centers. Development of integrated data systems then was initiated for uniform application by the various divisions to increase speed, accuracy and economy of processing and maintaining management information. Teams of experts were organized representing each of the three centers and charged with complete development of one system such as inventory control. The individual team thoroughly analyzes a major system and with participation of operating personnel, designs the best possible system. Once established by the team, the system is subject to further review both by representatives of divisions who will use the system and by the Aerospace division staff. The goal of the program is to produce data processing systems compatible with each of the divisions and providing required information for use by top Aerospace division management in making overall decisions.

A basic flow chart was drawn setting down the major systems — requirements, manufacturing planning and tool control, parts control, material inventory, manufacturing and test, shipping, and logistic support — needed to place all aspects of production, from sale of the product to delivery to the customer, under an integrated control system. Each of the major systems was designed to satisfy

Exhibit 2

SYSTEMS INTEGRATION FLOW CHART

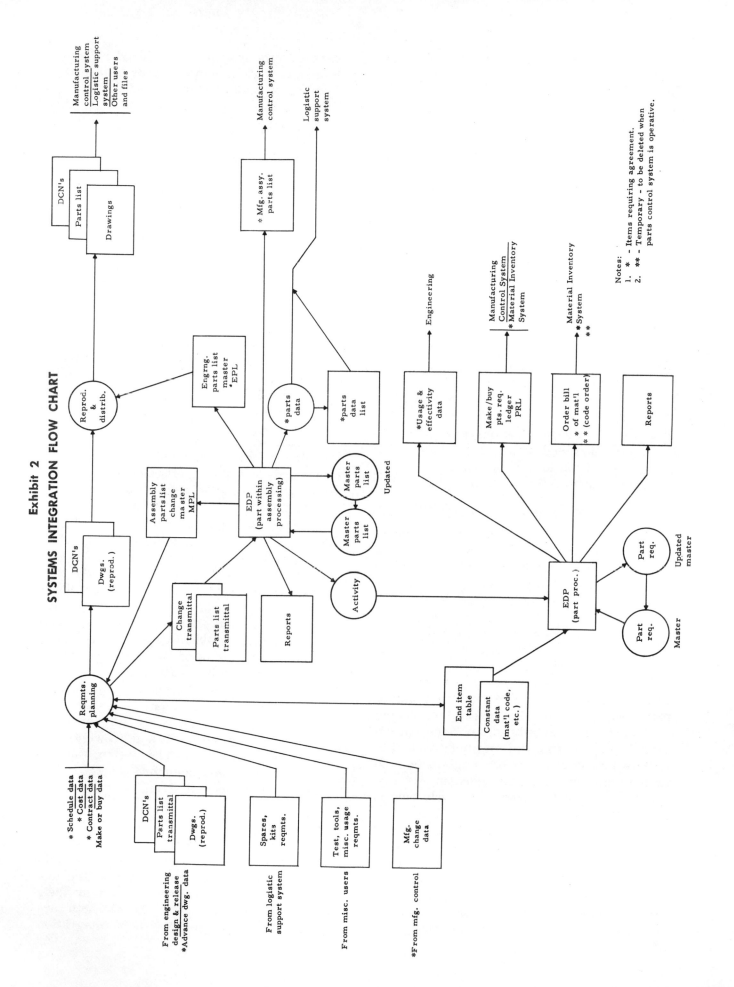

management objectives and needs while making use of the most efficient combination of manual and mechanized methods. Data in the systems ultimately will reflect financial as well as engineering and other company activities, with a minimum of duplicated effort in record keeping, data processing and reporting.

Certain guidelines and goals were established for the teams preparing the major systems:

1. Original data should be recorded in mechanical form at the point of origin.

2. Subsequent processing of this data should be performed mechanically without manual recording.

3. Original data in mechanical form and that generated by mechanical processing is to be re-used whenever required.

4. Data transmitted from one major system to another is to be only that which is necessary for the second system to operate.

5. Advance sophistications and other unnecessary additions which might delay implementation of a system or even cause it to fail were to be eliminated.

SYSTEMS INTEGRATION (EXHIBIT 1)

The integrated system begins with advance engineering data, drawings and parts lists which constitute input to contract requirements, the first of the major individual systems. From requirements, information flows through scheduling to the parts control system to develop orders either to make parts within the company or to buy them from outside suppliers, and to the manufacturing plan and tool control system, which has been combined with parts control, to develop standard manufacturing data and process plans, and tool control data. Scheduled buy requirements then flow to the material inventory system to initiate procurement action if necessary and to maintain material management records. The first half of the production cycle then is completed.

The necessary information generated by these systems, including engineering, is then transmitted to manufacturing and test which must meet the contract requirements under the circumstances established by manufacturing planning and tool control and with the parts and material made available through the parts control system and material inventory. Shipping control, supported by information supplied by logistic support and contract delivery requirements system, controls final transmittal of the product to the customer and later support of the product in operation, such as with spare parts.

Flow charts prepared for each major system further break down the production cycle to show the input information required to successfully generate data needed by other systems and for management control.

REQUIREMENTS (EXHIBIT 2)

Inputs to the requirements system include schedule data cost data, contract data, and make or buy data (whether an item will be made in the plant or purchased from a vendor). These inputs generally are decided in advance as part of the contract negotiation with the customer. In addition, the system receives design change notices, parts lists, and drawings generated by engineering. Needs for spares or special kits to be furnished with the final product are supplied to the system from logistic support. Miscellaneous requirements including tests and tools also are inputs to the system.

During the course of manufacture, manufacturing change data becomes an input to the system and must be compatible with drawing data issued by engineering. The data is used to generate a master parts list file in assembly sequence and a master parts requirement file in part number sequence. These master files are used to generate the various output requirements of the system including parts requirements, parts usage and effectivity data, material ordering requirements (active until the parts control system takes over), group assembly parts lists, manufacturing assembly parts list, and drawings with associated parts lists. The system supplies inputs to the manufacturing control system and logistic support system.

MANUFACTURING CONTROL SYSTEM (EXHIBIT 3)

The manufacturing control system encompasses both manufacturing planning and tool control and parts control, because of their interrelated nature, even though both are broken out on the overall systems integration

Exhibit 3

MANUFACTURING CONTROL SYSTEM

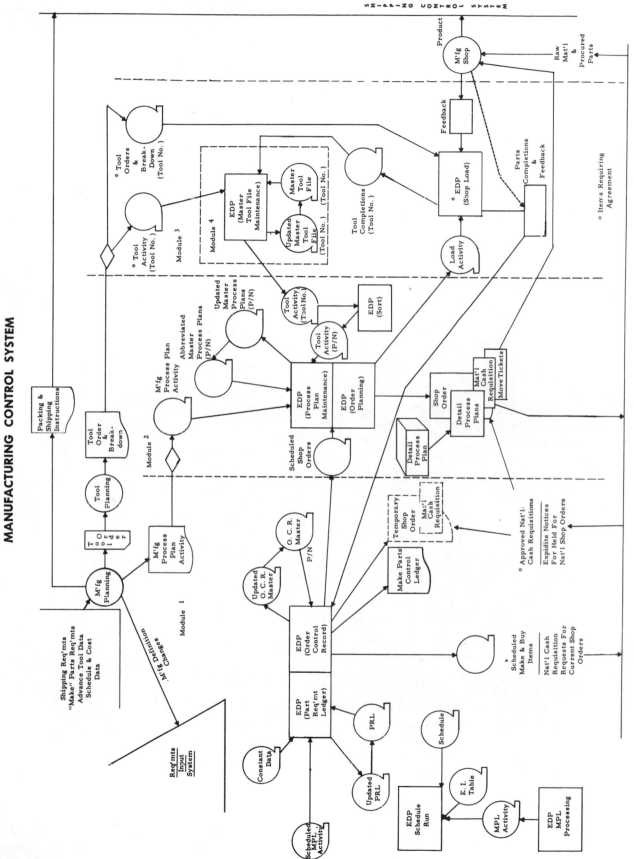

chart. Eventually, separate systems plans will be drawn.

Inputs to the manufacturing planning and tool control system include drawings and parts lists for components of the end product to be made in the plant, schedule data, cost data, advance tool information, shipping requirements and tool completion data. The information is used to generate a master process plan file showing tool availability, and a master tool record indicating necessary time needed on each machine, the term "tools" covering all items used in manufacture. Outputs of the system include manufacturing process plans, tool orders and tool breakdowns, packing instructions, assembly manufacturing plans and certification logs, and the master process plan file used in the parts control system to assist in creating shop orders.

In the parts control phase, inputs include schedule data, cost data, advance parts information, parts requirements, manufacturing plan and tool availability status, tool order and tool breakdown, assembly manufacturing plan and certification logs, material approval data, notices of material availability, and physical material necessary to make the product. The data are used to generate and maintain a master part requirement and inventory file, and a manufacturing activity and load file, plus shop orders for activating manufacturing on parts production. Outputs of the system include tool completion data, material requirements requests for material approval, material withdrawal requisitions for obtaining material for manufacturing, and transmittal of the product to shipping control.

MATERIAL INVENTORY (EXHIBIT 4)

The material inventory control system includes all of the activities involved in procurement and control of all direct and indirect materials procured for stock. Direct materials are those specified on an engineering release for production or other contractual requirement. Indirect materials are not specified by engineering, but may be needed to support the contract. Accounting functions associated with the system will be incorporated into a combined material control and financial record. The system also includes government furnished equipment. Outputs from the system include purchase requests for all inventory materials, buyers' notices, notices of im-

pending shortages, supply item status, material budgets, commitments and a listing of transactions affecting inventory balance.

LOGISTIC SUPPORT (EXHIBIT 5)

The logistic support system encompasses parts listings, supply item selection and supply item status, for support of the finished product in the customer's hands through supply of information and direction manuals, parts and equipment, materials, and status and accountability of these items.

SHIPPING CONTROL (EXHIBIT 6)

The shipping control system is the final checkpoint between the company and the customer. All contract delivery, including the end item, manuals, reports, spares and other equipment is included. Shipment of any items to other company divisions, vendors, subcontractors or any other destination, as well as to the customers, is included in the system control. The two principal sections of shipping control are contract delivery control and shipping. Contract delivery control contains the master record and maintains status of all contract requirements. The shipping portion of the system is concerned with the documentation and actual shipment of the items, with control over document writing, the preshipping stores area, quality control, preservation and packing, and loading. Inputs to the system include contract requirements, supply item authorizations, miscellaneous requirements, preservation and packing instructions, shipping instructions, shipping lists for disassembly, purchase orders, and receiving documents. Included in the shipping control system where applicable are inventories controlled by the company, such as support depots maintained by the contractor for the customer at operational sites.

OPERATION

The seven major systems operate on all requirements released by engineering. General input to the systems includes schedules, contract information, cost data, make or buy data, advance material requirements, drawing and parts data, spares requirements, pricing information, approval by the customer of purchases, and government furnished equipment requirements. Information other than that

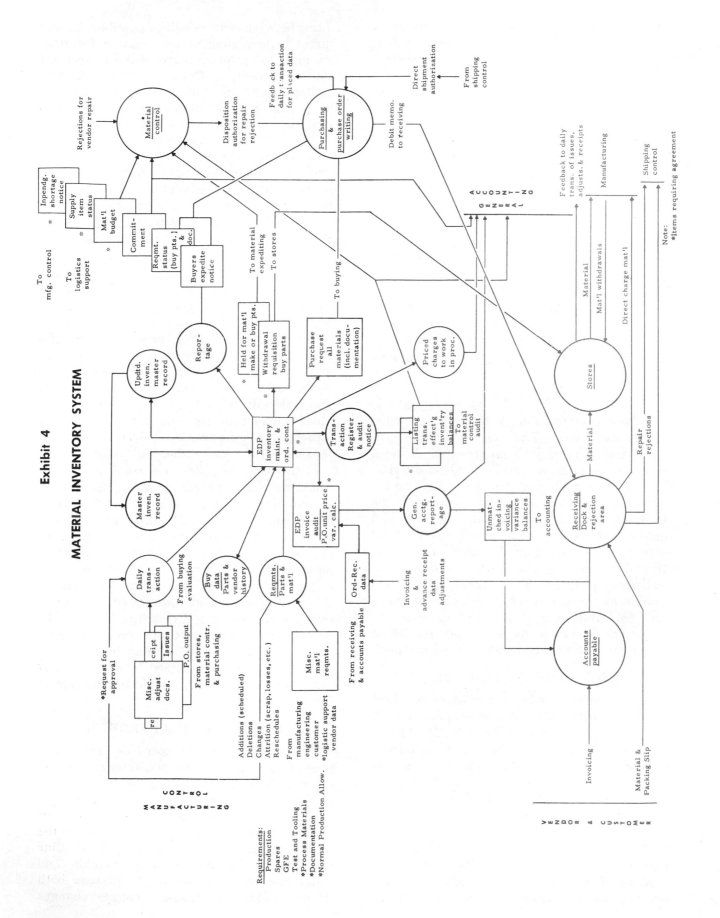

Exhibit 4

MATERIAL INVENTORY SYSTEM

directly related to the product can be processed within the system only as long as system development is not delayed or the system integrity impaired. Output of the systems includes operating reports, management information reports, illustrated parts breakdown and provisioning parts breakdown, and delinquency reports when necessary for the customer. Additional outputs for labor and material costs are integrated with product cost and payroll. Each system is required to produce labor and material cost.

Additional systems coverage planned for the integrated system includes equipment and facilities; manpower and personnel; proposals, simulations and management analyses; and additional management information. These systems will be planned at a later date. The current systems include design release, material acquisition, support requirements, manufacture, delivery of hardware and associated controls.

FEEDBACK

Information feeds back through the cycle as well as forward. Thus, as engineering supplies the necessary requirements, it also receives reports on usage and effectivity. Manufacturing change data flows back to requirements so that necessary changes can be made throughout the program. Finance and quality control have an overall effect on all aspects of the integrated system because of the vital part they play in the success of an individual program. They include such information as work authorizations, bills of material, performance controls, payroll, labor distribution, accounts payable and receivable which must be worked into each major system.

NETWORK OF CONTROL

As the major systems are developed and reach final form, they will be adopted at each of the computing centers. The effect will be to tie each division to the other by uniform integration of data processing. The systems will provide a network of control over all company operations — whether in Denver, Baltimore or Orlando — which can be interpreted on a top Aerospace management level in a far more comprehensive, accurate and current manner than was possible in the past.

Many of the advantages of such a program are obvious. Interchange of work and procedures between centers will be possible. Already direct transmission of information for processing is being tested between the Denver and Baltimore centers. Once perfected, all three centers could be linked with transmission equipment so that overloads at one center could be transmitted to another which is not so busy, the output returned by transmission, and the results available at the initial division with much greater speed than ever before possible. Such interchange of work currently is impossible because of major and many minor differences between the systems and the language used at each of the centers.

The common Aerospace division computer language will eliminate duplication of recording source input data by re-using information. In many instances, the operating divisions support each other with manufacturing or engineering effort. For example, parts for both the BULLPUP built at Orlando and the TITAN built at Denver are produced by the Space Systems division in Baltimore. The Electronic Systems & Products division provides support in its field for all divisions. although both Denver and Orlando have extensive electronics production facilities.

In the past, an order generated in Orlando would have been processed at the data center there and transmitted to Baltimore for fulfillment. But at Baltimore, different computer language made necessary re-recording of the identical information so that it could be processed by the computers and the necessary action taken within the operating division. When fully instituted, integrated data processing will provide a direct link between the two centers, providing basic records in high speed form which can be read by personnel at both centers or processed by data processing equipment without any basic changes in format or language.

BENEFITS OF APPROVAL

By making teams composed of representatives from each center responsible for the new systems, the best of existing systems can be combined, accelerating development of the new systems and producing a better end result than had been used in any of the centers in the past. The experience of many persons familiar with Aerospace division requirements and policy also can be combined to prepare both the new major systems and to suggest changes

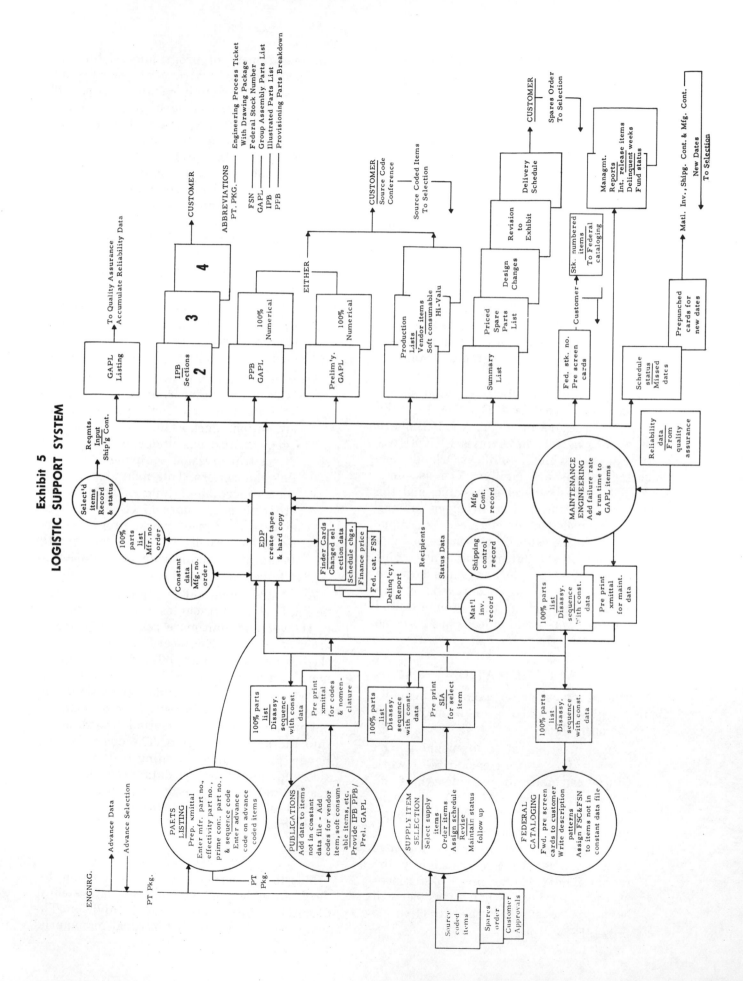

Exhibit 5

LOGISTIC SUPPORT SYSTEM

ABBREVIATIONS

PT. PKG. —— Engineering Process Ticket With Drawing Package
FSN —— Federal Stock Number
GAPL —— Group Assembly Parts List
IPB —— Illustrated Parts List
PFB —— Provisioning Parts Breakdown

157

as the systems are put to use at the three centers. These same persons also will be available for employment at any of the three centers with a minimum of training, since one center will be as identical to the next as possible. The personnel at each center will have understanding of all systems in use at Denver, Baltimore or Orlando centers.

Similarly, a program to standardize engineering computations carried out at the three centers has been initiated. Because of the very nature of engineering computation, which encompasses many varied problems depending upon project and individual, standardization will not be possible to the same extent as in business computations. However, many problems and much of the language used in engineering data processing are similar and at times identical, so a fair degree of standardization is possible.

Computation of the effects of wind shears or cross winds over Cape Canaveral on the flight and structure of a TITAN ICBM are not the same as for the Army's PERSHING tactical missile, which is built at Orlando, but the computations are similar. The use of a common language wherever possible, and the interchange of ideas and problems among personnel responsible for engineering computation at the three centers, will make possible a fair degree of standardization. Thus, joint meetings of these people and visits between the centers have been encouraged by top Aerospace engineering management and exchange of work and ideas has become possible.

STANDARDIZATION

Additional steps undertaken by management to achieve standardization in engineering computation include:

1. Standardization of equipment at the three centers so that exchange of work will be mechanically possible. All of the centers are using IBM 7090 equipment now, which are compatible even though some detail differences still exist.

2. Language and programming methods used at the centers also are slightly different. The elimination of differences in these methods where feasible will be a major step in the direction of integration.

3. Assignment of programmers, for engineering computation at each center, trained in as similar manner as possible and using the same methods and tools is the next step toward integration. Management already has taken this approach to the problem to secure programmers at each center who will, by training and background, naturally take a similar method toward the solution of similar questions. To aid them, program abstracts devised at the three centers have been collected and made available to programmer and engineers.

4. Steps also have been taken to develop a library of standard programs, so that the programmer will be able to draw on past experience and will not have to devise a new approach to each problem.

5. Interconnection between the centers also is seen by engineering management as an important tool for achieving standardization, much as administrative management also has undertaken to install direct transmission equipment to solidly link the centers. This final step will become increasingly important as the other plans are more effectively realized, since exchange of work, programs and experience will be possible, greatly facilitating engineering computation at all operating divisions.

As an additional aid in engineering computation, IBM 1620 machines have been installed in Denver and Baltimore centers and are on order at Orlando. Engineers, through training classes and assistance offered by programmers, are learning to make use of these machines for small, one time calculations and also for preliminary investigation or roughing out of a problem for eventual programming into the larger machines. The engineers will have a greater understanding of the capabilities and limitations of data processing as a result, and will be better equipped to work with the programmers toward solution of problems.

MANAGEMENT TOOL

Martin Marietta's Aerospace division believes an integrated data processing system is essential to future growth of the division. The computer will become an integral managerial

Exhibit 6

SHIPPING CONTROL SYSTEM

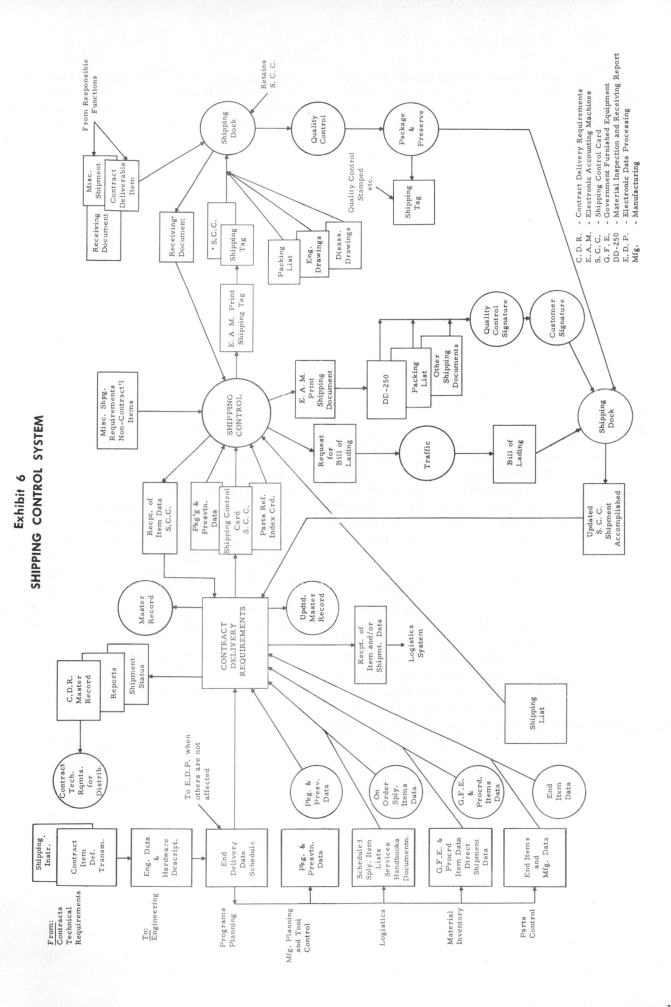

tool, while performing the basic business and scientific computations common to its application by most of industry. Aerospace, which is one of the first companies to undertake total integration on such a large scale, believes the program also will become an essential prerequisite in future contractor-customer relations within the defense industry.

Already, the military services have undertaken ambitious programs aimed at placing as much of their accounting and records maintenance under data processing systems as possible. They also have taken initial steps to bring the contractor into their various systems. Aerospace has been affected in logistic support of the Air Force TITAN and MACE missiles which it builds.

In each case, the company and other prime suppliers of parts for the missiles are linked in an intricate network with the various Air Force Air Material Areas and the actual bases where the missiles are stationed. The system provides the Air Force with current information on inventory, location of spares and needs of the installations. Various changes in status of parts are transmitted over a combination teletype-punched card communications system which links the installation, the responsible Air Force procurement agency and the contractor together.

Crude as this system might be when compared with electronic data processing links now possible, the program nevertheless represents a bold step forward and a tremendous advance over military service procurement of only a few years ago, which was primarily dependent upon manual accounting. The system almost surely will be extended in the future so that computers at all participating offices can automatically order a part, provide for shipping or initiate other action at all levels of both customer and contractor. As weapon systems become more complicated and thus need many more parts, an integrated, computer-controlled program linking both the producer and purchaser becomes increasingly important.

FUTURE EXPECTATIONS

Aerospace division management expects its integrated program to be well along the way by 1963 or 1964. Within a few more years, the division will be able to claim a truly integrated data processing system, linking all aspects of company business and all plants and offices through direct transmission tape to tape equipment, identical computer machinery and identical programs. The division, despite its diversified operations, will have readily available for management the vital information needed for coordinated functioning of all its operating facilities and for centralized direction of the Aerospace division based on the concise and accurate managerial information it will realize from an integrated computing program.

Management will be able to take best advantage of capabilities of all its divisions on a broad scale with confidence in the information it has available. The division expects to participate in many of the nation's most ambitious projects in space in future years, projects which will demand the utmost of engineering talent and managerial strength. By taking steps now toward centralized control of its operations through integrated data processing, the division expects to be in a position to better meet the challenge of the coming years.

Canadian Pacific Railway Company: Integrated Data Processing

CANADIAN PACIFIC is a pioneer in integrated data processing among transportation companies, and is a leading example of the total systems concept applied in a corporation which includes many diverse enterprises.

THE COMPANY

The Canadian Pacific is described as "the world's most complete transportation system." The company operates some 17,000 miles of its own railway line; nearly 5,000 additional miles of line are operated by its controlled companies. Rolling stock inventory includes more than 80,000 freight cars, 1,200 locomotives, and 1,600 passenger cars. There are often 10,000 units of other ownership on its rails. The rail lines serve Canada from Halifax and Saint John on the Atlantic to Vancouver and Victoria on the Pacific, plus nine of the 50 states.

The corporate complex includes Canadian Pacific Airlines, serving Canada and five continents; Canadian Pacific Steamships, in passenger and freight service on the North Atlantic and St. Lawrence Seaway and in the cruise business; Canadian Pacific Express; Canadian Pacific Communications, which operates a nationwide commercial communications system as well as the normal complement of transportation communication facilities; hotel, coastal steamship, bus, truck, and piggyback services; and oil, gas, land, mining and other enterprises. All told, these activities involve some 75,000 employees.

DATA PROCESSING AND MANAGEMENT INFORMATION PRIOR TO IDP

Canadian Pacific first installed punched card equipment for accounting purposes in 1912. Over the years, as new processing equipment became available, improvements in methods and machines were introduced. By 1954, mechanization of paperwork in the accounting field had been carried to the limits of the technology of that date, and accounting department installations in Montreal and Calgary were the largest in Canada. Since 1949, the transportation department, based on a machine room in Montreal, and with IBM installations at 10 major yards on the line between Windsor, Ontario, and Farnham, Quebec, connected by teletype, provided train and car movement information on a current basis for operating and traffic purposes. By 1954, plans were under review for extension of this mechanization elsewhere on the system.

Canadian Pacific Express, with headquarters in Toronto, and Canadian Pacific Air Lines, with headquarters in Vancouver, had punched card installations for accounting purposes. There were additional punched card applications in other segments of the complex. When the integrated data processing program began, there was an organizational nucleus and some body of experience in data processing equipment and methods work. Subsequent developments were to show that this constituted only modest preparation for the grand scale of change that was to come. Data processing was organized essentially on a departmental basis, with each department often developing its own information from the same source documents, and frequently developing substantially the same information either manually or by machines.

INTEGRATED DATA PROCESSING INCEPTION, AUTHORITY, CONCEPT

By mid-March, 1954, Canadian Pacific officers, who had been maintaining a watching

7080 Installation — Canadian Pacific's Montreal Computer Center.

Heart of the Canadian Pacific IDP complex; the IBM 7080 computer, with eight high speed and five low speed tape drives, is supported by three 1401 computer systems and 1405 disc storage, and by a Digitronics tri-directional tape converter.

brief on developments in the high speed computer field, had become interested in the possibilities as a corporate tool instead of exclusive accounting or single departmental use, and in the then new idea of integrated data processing. In the fall, preliminary studies on an extensive scale for application to the Canadian Pacific began. These studies included consultation with other roads and with professional consultants. They indicated that the installation of a high speed electronic computer for Canadian Pacific would be economical if incorporated in a full scale program of integrated data processing.

Authority for detailed planning and the development and implementation of a program was accordingly granted with full responsibility assigned to the vice president, accounting, reporting to the president.

The terms of reference provided for eventual review of all company paperwork. The comprehensive or integrated approach was adopted to cover data processing and the development of a system of business intelligence for all Canadian Pacific services within the concept of total systems.

HISTORICAL

After review, including reference to outside consultants, the IBM 705 computer was selected. By March, 1955, an order was placed for its delivery early in 1957, thus establishing a target date for planning. Although all facets were examined, the extensive existing installations and long corporate experience with IBM equipment had considerable weight in the decision.

From among the major fields in which the survey and follow up studies had indicated potential applications, five were selected for intensive planning. These were freight, labor, materials, statistics, and accounting consolidations. They represented the areas which promised the largest returns, and which, in any event, were the base from which it would be possible to move into others.

The organizational pattern that had emerged by March, 1955, called for mechanical recording at source, or as close to source as possible. Because of the nationwide extent of operations, it also called for collection and relay points across the country, which would collect data and relay them for processing on the high speed computer in Montreal and, in return flow, distribute processed data.

The task was to determine where source recording would be done, where the collection points, or data centers, should be located, how they should be constituted, and what functions they would perform. The answers were not quite as obvious as they may seem. The Canadian Pacific organization then consisted of system headquarters in Montreal, three railway operating regions, apart from some subsidiaries, divided into eight operating districts, further subdivided into 28 divisions.

As already mentioned, headquarters of the Express Company is in Toronto, Air Lines in Vancouver, and western road transport in Winnipeg. All of these, as well as 1,500 freight offices and stations, 75 yard offices, 66 shops, 78 stores, the communications system, steamships, hotels, and foreign agencies originated data affecting one or more of the first five applications. To complicate matters further, the geographical boundaries of the subdivisions established by different departments could not, in all cases, be uniform.

The task also involved, as preface, the selection and training of staff in the new techniques of computer programming, and orientation of systems analysts into the new directions which paperwork planning was to take. Then we had to move on to the examination of present input and processing, with determination of desired output. Given the new horizons of a computer based, integrated data processing program, it was then necessary to redesign the input information and forms to conform, and to chart the new proc-

essing procedures, including the highly complicated and time consuming task of computer programming. The paperwork planning also had to cover staging the move, step by step, from present procedures, through improved procedures, to ultimate 705 procedures.

From March, 1955, to March, 1957, progress was steady. Organizational changes to provide for staffing the new project without any increase in expense were initiated during the first half of 1955. Recruiting of a full time planning staff began both inside and outside the accounting department. The existing conventional tabulating equipment of the accounting department and the transportation department was consolidated to form the nucleus of the new computer center, and to serve as the central mechanized processing agency for the system.

District data centers, using the district accounting staffs as nuclei, were established. The existing conventional tabulating equipment of Canadian Pacific Express in Toronto and of Canadian Pacific Air Lines in Vancouver was assigned to the new data centers as the nuclei of the data center machine installations at these points.

The mechanized system for car tracing and car accounting which the operating department had pioneered between Windsor and

Transmission Section — Canadian Pacific's Montreal Computer Center.

This office has direct teletype connection to 36 yards in the eastern and atlantic regions of the railway and to Canadian Pacific agents in Boston, New York, Detroit and Chicago; also Dial-O-Verter connection to Data Centers in Winnipeg and Vancouver.

Exhibit 1

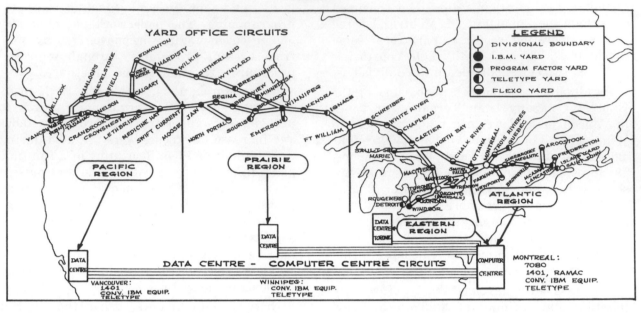

Farnham was modified and extended from coast to coast. During 1956, terminal and circuit equipment was installed and yard to yard processing of train consists was progressively placed in operation. The 705 model I computer was installed early in January, 1957, and by mid-February the system car tracing data and return flow to on line and off line points were placed in regular production. For all practical purposes, all essential physical links for the new mechanized system were then in operation. Concurrently with the freight applications, the first labor applications were brought into operation on the computer early in 1957 and implementation has since proceeded on an expanding scale to reach the present status, which is described later.

PHYSICAL ORGANIZATION

A schematic of the physical system for flow of data is shown in **Exhibit 1**. There are 65 mechanized field offices, which function both for source recording of input information and for local dissemination of wired output information. The information from the field offices is channelled into four regional data centers. A fifth data center services the extensive railway shops in Montreal.

The regional data centers, in addition to serving as collection points, perform certain local processing, relay data for computer processing in Montreal and distribute proc-

essed information received from the computer in return flow to regional offices. They also perform initial mechanized recording.

The computer center, as the central processing office for the system, serves all departments. There is direct wire connection to Canadian Pacific traffic offices in the United States to provide car tracing and car supply information.

Not shown on the schematic is the provision, now in process of installation, for mechanized recording in London, England, to serve Canadian Pacific steamships and other European or European based operations.

The administration of integrated data processing, under the direct jurisdiction of the vice president and comptroller, is shown in **Exhibit 2**.

EQUIPMENT

The field office — data center — computer center complex just described is served by circuits provided by Canadian Pacific Communications operating on a 24 hours a day, seven days a week basis.

On-line equipment in each yard office consists of a transmitter distributor for the reading and transmission of paper tape, a reperforator or typing reperforator for the production of paper tape from incoming transmissions, and in some offices an on line

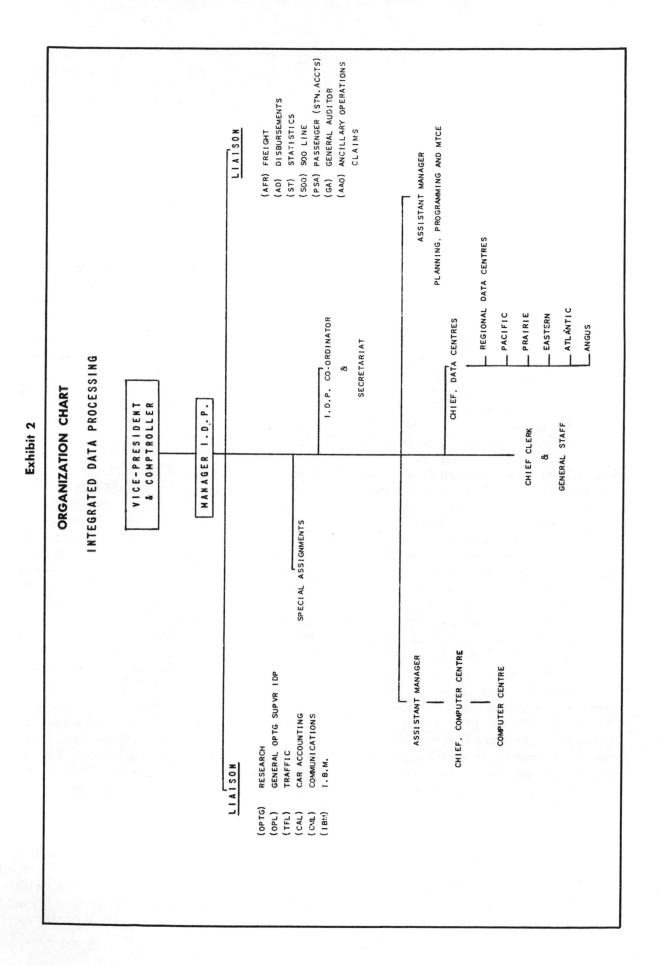

Exhibit 2

ORGANIZATION CHART

INTEGRATED DATA PROCESSING

VICE-PRESIDENT & COMPTROLLER

MANAGER I.D.P.

SPECIAL ASSIGNMENTS

I.D.P. CO-ORDINATOR & SECRETARIAT

CHIEF, DATA CENTRES

ASSISTANT MANAGER
PLANNING, PROGRAMMING AND MTCE.

REGIONAL DATA CENTRES
- PACIFIC
- PRAIRIE
- EASTERN
- ATLANTIC
- ANGUS

CHIEF CLERK & GENERAL STAFF

ASSISTANT MANAGER

CHIEF, COMPUTER CENTRE

COMPUTER CENTRE

LIAISON

- (OPTG) RESEARCH
- (OPL) GENERAL OPTG SUPVR IDP
- (TFL) TRAFFIC
- (CAL) CAR ACCOUNTING
- (CML) COMMUNICATIONS
- (IBM) I.B.M.

LIAISON

- (AFR) FREIGHT
- (AD) DISBURSEMENTS
- (ST) STATISTICS
- (SOO) SOO LINE
- (PSA) PASSENGER (STN. ACCTS)
- (GA) GENERAL AUDITOR
- (AAO) ANCILLARY OPERATIONS
- CLAIMS

165

teleprinter for the monitoring of inward and outward transmissions.

In 1956, IBM transceivers operating over telephone circuits were installed to connect the computer center with data centers in Vancouver, Winnipeg and Toronto. These provided for the sending and receiving of information on punched cards at a speed of 150 words a minute. In 1961, a further advance came with the installation of a Dial-O-Verter to provide transmission of information on punched paper tape at rated speeds of 1,000 words a minute. One such unit is operating between Montreal and Winnipeg, and a second between Montreal and Vancouver.

There are four main types of off line equipment at field offices:

1. Nineteen yard offices are now equipped with Western Union 209 switching systems, commonly called program factors. These consist of two paper tape readers, one model 28 teleprinter, two typing reperforators, and one switching system cabinet which provides the programmed control. By means of it, constant information and functional codes can be inserted into data, and automatic registration of information into the proper fields of proper length can be controlled. Output tapes of two different formats can be produced, and tear spaces (that is, a space for separating records one from the other) can be automatically inserted or deleted. For different kinds of recording, eleven different programs are wired in one panel, and an additional program is set up to permit operation without automatic control.

2. Sixteen yard offices are equipped with flexowriters. A typical unit consists of one flexowriter, which is a typing and control unit, one paper tape reader, and one or two paper tape punches. The unit reads tape and prints page copy providing all or selected information in paper tape output from the punches, controlled by codes in the tape being read. The flexowriter can also be operated by means of a program tape inserted in the reader, which will provide control similar to the program factor but somewhat more limited in scope.

3. Twenty yard offices are equipped with

teletype kits. These are smaller yards with less traffic, and the preparation and processing of data records are done on a model 15 or model 19 teletype, plus transmitter distributor (tape reader), and typing reperforator (tape punch).

4. The 10 largest yard offices are equipped with punched card machines, to provide 80 column cards as the basis for mechanized recording and handling.

In addition to the transmission equipment already described, regional data centers have a complement of keypunches and of conventional IBM machines. The installations differ as each data center handles the processing requirements of an important Canadian Pacific subsidiary or other special work.

The 705 model I, installed in January, 1957, was the first high speed computer in Canada and the first of its kind to be installed outside the United States. It was replaced later in the same year by a 705 model II, which, in turn, gave place in 1959 to an 80K 705 model III with data synchronized tape system, then described as the largest and fastest in use by any transportation company in the world.

It was replaced in October, 1961, by an IBM 7080, a much more powerful commercial computer and the first 7080 to be installed by any transportation company. Six times faster internally than our model III, it has an 80K memory capacity and is equipped with eight high speed and five low speed tape drives. These tape drives record at a density of 556 characters per inch. Scheduled for installation towards the end of this year in replacement of these are tape drives whose recording density will be 800 characters per inch. These will give an increase in overall processing speed of approximately 15 percent.

Also installed in the computer center at Montreal are three 1401 systems, which replaced the less flexible and more limited former peripheral computer room equipment — printers, card readers and magnetic tape card punches. These 1401s, as well as being satellites to the 7080 for the handling of input and output functions, are also computers in their own right and are proving a very useful part of the machine complex.

Canadian Pacific's first experience with random access data processing is now being gained through the use of a 1405 disc storage

Exhibit 3

INTEGRATED DATA PROCESSING MASTER CHART

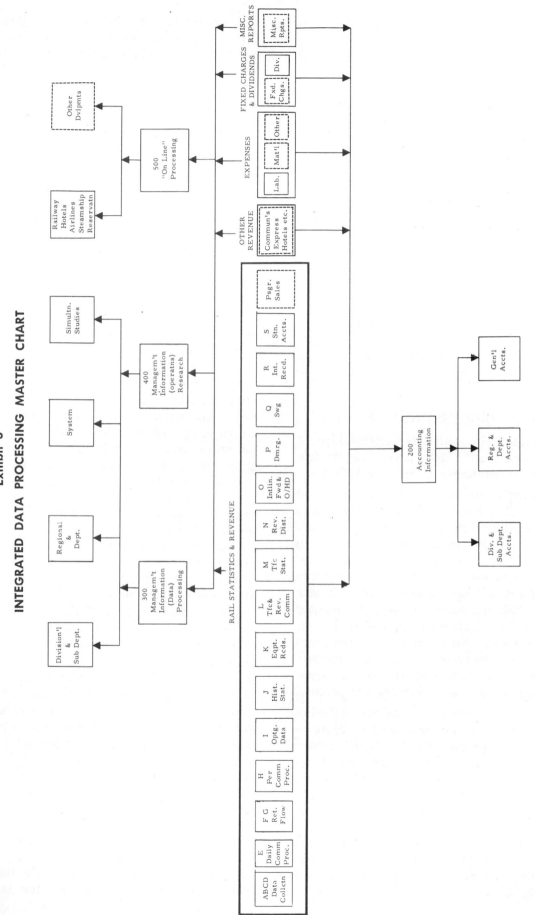

file presently installed in conjunction with one of the 1401 systems. On order for later delivery is a 1301 disc file of 56,000,000 character capacity.

In 1960, a breakthrough was achieved with installation of a D-106 converter, for high speed conversion of paper to magnetic tape (5,000 words a minute), magnetic to paper tape (1,000 words a minute) and magnetic to magnetic tape (150,000 words a minute) on a selective basis. It is now the main avenue of entry into the computer for all freight programs, converting paper tape as received from yard offices or data centers to magnetic tape for computer processing. Equally important is its function as an output medium, converting magnetic tape records to paper tape for transmission as return flow.

The computer center also has a large keypunch section and a complement of conventional punched card equipment which is being gradually released as work is transferred to new equipment.

DATA PROCESSING SYSTEM

The organization and interrelationships of the Canadian Pacific data processing system are shown in summary form in **Exhibit 3**.

The largest component is Rail Statistics and Revenue, a further expansion of which, to show processing interrelationships, is given in **Exhibit 4**. Integrated processing begins with data collection, involving the mechanical recording and reporting of source information in field offices and the movement through data centers to the computer center for computer processing. This includes complete waybill information, consist information covering train and car movements organized as departure and arrival reports, bad order, and other car status reports and passenger train reporting.

The first mechanized outputs for operating and traffic purposes are produced en route to the computer. For example, an objective yard is interested in the make up and contents of cars in trains coming towards it. This is met by the teletyped copy of the consist of the train as marshalled for departure. This serves as an advance switching list to enable the yardmaster at the objective yard to plan his work. The same information, received in the data center, is organized to produce regional car tracing lists.

A system car tracing list and regional return flow tracing lists are produced in the first computer runs each day. Regional return flow is a list in car number sequence giving the last reported movement up to a 2:30 a.m. cutoff of all loaded cars on Canadian Pacific lines destined to points on the region. It is transmitted to regional data centers to be available to regional offices at the opening of business each day. Coupled with locally prepared regional car tracing lists, it provides complete car tracing coverage. Divisional car tracing lists, and lists for off line agents in the United States, are also provided.

Indicative of the utility and speed of the data processing system is the daily freight situation report, produced for Canadian Pacific System and for each region, which is available at the opening of business each day and reflects the previous day's business. It gives the daily average for the week ending day of record (this year, last year, percent change) and reported data, month to date (this year, last year, percent change), for 35 items. These include revenue cars loaded, dollar revenues, train miles, train hours, gross ton miles, gross ton miles per train hour, car miles, etc. Under former manual procedures, some of the information on this daily statement was available only on a monthly basis and, in certain cases, as long as 45 days after the end of the month.

From the daily input in successive computer runs, are produced daily regional and divisional car count statements; semi monthly and monthly car counts for internal use and for submission to the Railway Association of Canada and the Association of American Railroads; monthly cumulative car loading and revenue analysis by origin, type of traffic, commodity, etc.; comparative statements of cars loaded and received in interchange by commodity groups; basic statistics of passenger and freight train operations and locomotive and car movement in all services; equipment records extended beyond standard car accounting to cover all units of equipment moving in trains; comparative data on customers, commodities and earnings by territorial areas; distribution of revenue tons and ton miles by commodities and revenue by type of traffic by regions and subsidiary lines; processing of interline traffic including completely mechanized accounting for interline

Exhibit 4

MASTER INDEX CHART — FREIGHT

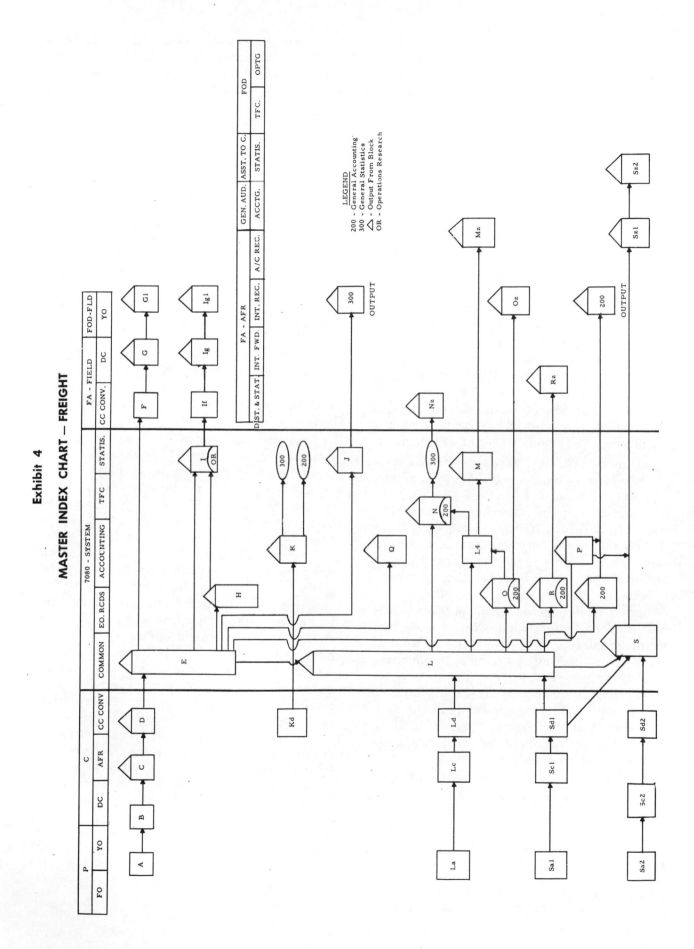

transactions; customer billing and station accounting at agents' level; and other reports.

In the rail statistics and revenue component, current emphasis is on refinements in the presentation of information, and the development of completely new presentations from the massive reservoirs of information now available on magnetic tape. Examples include statements showing empty car supply and sources of empty cars; forecasts of traffic volume through selected points and tests of traffic flow through selected areas after the event; and information on rolling stock usage, repairs and earnings, and performance of loaded cars en route to destination.

Other components of the data processing system shown in example 3 are other revenue, expenses, fixed charges and dividends, and miscellaneous reports. Of these the labor portion of expenses, including payroll and distribution to accounts, is completely mechanized, as are dividends, which include monthly statements for directors, shareholders' ledgers, dividend checks, and tax reports. The remainder are in various stages of development.

Installation of the 7080 computer and peripherals permits implementation of programs, already written and tested, to provide fully mechanized corporate accounting, shown as Accounting Information in **Exhibit 3**. Under the plan, journal entries captured mechanically near source are processed through multiple steps for all accounting purposes, culminating in mechanical preparation of comparative statements for management. This will displace many manual calculations and manual recording of the same information at many levels, making it practical to eliminate manual registers and ledgers. The changeover to a fully mechanized accounting system started with 1962 accounts for the main railway departments. The same system will be extended to all departments and subsidiaries as rapidly as possible.

The mechanization of accounting information, appropriately geared with mechanized statistical data, opens the door to electronic preparation of further sophisticated information for management. The use of disk storage greatly facilitates assembly and tabulation of such data without elaborate programming. Projects in various stages of development to prove out the new techniques include revenues

and expenses by individual track sections, divisions, regions and departments; rough variable and over all costs of handling individual commodities between origin and destination to test rates; responsibility accounting and budget control; and forecasting revenues, expenses and cash flow.

The comprehensive, accurate and timely information now available, joined with the capacity of the large computer, has made possible more extensive use of advanced techniques of statistical and cost analysis in areas where this was not heretofore practical. For example, evidence on the cost of handling grain, which represents 26 percent of Canadian Pacific traffic, required for presentation to a Royal Commission on Transportation in 1960, was based on the most intensive analysis of railway costs that has ever been made. Calculations, which could not have been done economically and within time limits without the computer, involved multiple regression analyses on both a cross section and time series basis.

Simulation techniques have been used successfully in simulation of train performance, using data for different types of motive power as a basis for setting tonnage ratings and determining schedules which would give the best relationship between speed and fuel consumption; also in the design of hump yards and centralized traffic control layouts. Work has been done in critical path planning. The study list in the operations research area includes models to determine: the minimum number of cars required for a fixed allocation situation such as might occur with covered hoppers, refrigerators or piggyback flats; the regulation of train movements to prevent unnecessary congestion and consequent poor use of motive power and crews; projected plant requirements for telex switching equipment and communications trunk circuits; future maintenance requirements for particular areas; schedules of repairs to motive power and the converse problem of locating and staffing the repair facilities to meet projected requirements; scheduling of trains for optimum use of road and yard facilities; and work scheduling through a shop or machine room.

STAFF — THE HUMAN ELEMENT

(a) *Staff development — technical personnel*

The integrated data processing program presented three major and immediate new technical training requirements. First, the training of programmers; second, the development of systems analysts, competent to work with programmers in the development of specifications; third, the development of analysts competent in the new field of common language machines and integration of processing from source to computer.

The first group of programmers, seven in number, received their training in IBM courses at Poughkeepsie, New York. All subsequent programmer training has been done in company courses. Full programmer training, supplemented by console operation instruction, has also been provided for all console operators.

System analyst and machine analyst development has been conducted on the job and in staff seminars, some formal and some informal, based on indoctrination in the use of methods procedures, control procedures, file procedures, etc., prepared for the program. Over the years there have also been a number of courses of varying duration.

Programmers, systems analysts and machine analysts together constituted a planning staff which numbered about 50.

It is noteworthy that some technical training was also taken by the supervisory and officer groups in the computer center, data center and some departmental offices, as well as planning staff. It was, in effect, basic training in integrated data processing that was the preface to positions of increasing responsibility in the accounting department.

(b) *Staff development — line personnel*

Beginning in 1955 and continuing since, a vigorous program has been conducted to meet requirements of all officers and employees who were either directly of indirectly affected by integrated data processing. Its purpose was to familiarize personnel with integrated data processing concepts and the progress of the Canadian Pacific program, to prepare for and implement changes in procedures and methods, to promote effective use of integrated data processing outputs, and to explain the integrated data processing potential for providing new and speedy management information. It was developed through briefing sessions, demonstrations and exhibits, courses, and on the job, supplemented by procedural manuals and instructions.

A feature has been use of traveling exhibits set up in a railway car which made stops at principal points across the system and served as background for seminar type training sessions. There have been four such exhibits.

Courses have of necessity been restricted to those who were involved in planning and, to a limited extent, to officers who supervise planning or use outputs. For the majority of those affected, at system and regional level and at field offices, course instruction was not practical and dependence was on on the job training, supplemented by written instructions. An instructing team went from yard office to yard office at the time new equipment and new procedures were introduced in 1956. Supervisors of the operating department and regional data centers provide continuous training liaison.

(c) *Staff — information and publicity*

A general information and publicity effort has been directed to the employees as a whole and to the general public. Its purpose is to allay any fears about job security or personal downgrading that employees might have by providing frank, full, accurate information; to prepare employees in advance for changes affecting their own department and work; and to secure the prestige, traffic, recruitment, good will and morale benefits accruing from being first in the field in an important technological advance.

The media used are a continuous flow of articles and information items in the company organ, "Spanner," press releases, magazine articles, case studies for publication, speeches by integrated data processing officers at conferences and to various organizations, conducted tours of integrated data processing installations at system, regional and field levels, radio and television interviews, movies, demonstrations and exhibits.

(d) *Staff impacts*

The integrated data processing program has changed the nature of several hundred jobs, and the process continues. It has involved the abolition of certain jobs altogether and the creation of entirely new positions.

In short range terms, during the period in which a new method involving a reduction in the labor force is planned, tested, and introduced, the experience has been that normal attrition during the same period exceeds the release rate. Again, the number likely to be affected by any one project is small in terms of the staff replacement requirements of a clerical force of over 8,000. In practice, changes have been carefully planned in advance, and each individual affected has been treated on an individual basis.

Rather than a problem of layoff, the problem has been to find staff of the proper calibrer to meet vacancies. An important by-product of the integrated data processing program is the upgrading or opportunities for upgrading that it has opened up for the staff. Among the programmers and in the junior supervisory and officer ranks, many today are at salary levels that might have taken them ten or fifteen years to achieve. Creation of the new organization has also accelerated promotions in the offices from which its members were recruited.

ECONOMICS

For obvious reasons, no dollar figures on the economics of the integrated data processing system have been published. The following statements are, however indicative:

1957: "In the matter of economy, the indications are that the direct savings will permit us to do better than break even on the overall expense of the installation. The indirect savings which depend on our ability to use the new and more prompt information to better advantage should be substantial."

1958: "The breakeven point for the systems in operation has been passed; further worthwhile economies are being real-

ized from projects now being brought into operation."

1960: "The indirect benefits now appear to be even more important than we had conceived. These benefits are much greater dollarwise than the direct cost savings possible from the new processing."

1961: "The economics of the project are working out more favorably than anticipated. The end value of the new methods, for which a solid foundation has now been laid, is confidently expected to dwarf the benefits already obtained, substantial as they are."

ASSESSMENTS

Canadian Pacific now has a complete information system which has been in operation for several years. It is regarded as well suited for adoption by other large carriers for internal as well as inter-road information. For competitive reasons, working details have been kept confidential, although the company has indicated that it would be prepared to discuss terms with other railways, or with a group of railways, on which the forms, charts, programs and know-how could be made available.

Technicians with a knowledge of other projects, who have visited the installation, have described the progress as outstanding. One American observer reported as follows:

"It is apparent that your company has developed a working integration of transportation data collection and processing to a much higher degree than has been attained in the United States . . . you have been able to make greater progress in the application of your large scale computer."

Bibliography

Permission to use this material granted by the Systems and Procedures Association, publishers of AN ANNOTATED BIBLIOGRAPHY FOR THE SYSTEMS PROFESSIONAL, edited by Maurice F. Ronayne.

I. Automatic Data Processing

ADJUSTMENTS TO THE INTRODUCTION OF OFFICE AUTOMATION. Bulletin #1276. Bureau of Labor Statistics, U. S. Department of Labor, Washington, D. C.: U. S. Government Printing Office. May 1960. 87 pp. ($0.50)

This handy study, directed and written by Edgar Weinberg, is part of BLS Research on the economic and social implication of important technological development. It analyzes some of the implications of electronic data processing in 20 offices in private industry. Most interesting is its analysis of older worker problems and labor-management negotiations. Can be gotten from the Superintendent of Documents, Government Printing Office, Washington 25, D. C.

Adler, Irving, **THINKING MACHINES**; A Layman's Introduction to Logic, Boolean Algebra, and Computers; New York: The John Day Company. 1961. 189 pp.

The book explains what a "thinking machine" is, and the nature of the routine thinking we turn over to it. Selected chapter titles include: Hardware brains; Tools with self-control; Calculating machines; Switching circuits; and, Electronic computers. Topics discussed are Turing machines, Venn diagrams, and various numbering systems. The book will also facilitate the reader's introduction into the logic and application of Boolean Algebra, and how this kind of mathematics relates to computer machine logic. Challenge is presented to the reader who must use his newfound method of logical reasoning to solve a tricky problem developed by Lewis Carrol, and the brain twister well known to puzzle fans, "Who is the Engineer?" Final chapters deal with Truth Tables and their relationships to machine switching circuits. A challenge in depth for the thinking systems or management man.

Alt, Franz L., A. D. Booth, and R. E. Meagher, editors, **ADVANCES IN COMPUTERS**, New York and London: Academic Press, 1960. 316 pp.

First Volume in a new series, *Advances in Computers*, on different aspects of design of electronic computing system, programming, and business and scientific applications. Six sections by different contributing authors on: 1. General-Purpose Programming for Business Applications; 2. Numerical Weather Prediction; 3. The Present Status of Automatic Translation of Languages; 4. Programming Computers to Play Games; 5. Machine Recognition of Spoken Works; and, 6. Binary Arithmetic.

American Management Association, **ADVANCES IN EDP AND INFORMATION SYSTEMS**, AMA Management Report No. 62, New York, 1961. 187 pp.

Based on papers originally presented at AMA's 7th Annual Data Processing Conference in March, 1961. Part 1 — Some Critical Evaluations, consists of four papers on data processing and management information systems, and on economic realities of EDP. Part 2 — EDP: Capabilities and Applications, consists of 10 papers on data communications, information storage and retrieval, data collection, video displays, advances in hardware and software off line and on line applications, and applications to manufacturing and inventory control. Part 3 — Information Systems: Theory and Practice consists of seven papers on total systems concepts and applications at a number of firms.

American Management Association, **ELECTRONIC DATA PROCESSING IN INDUSTRY — A CASE BOOK OF MANAGEMENT EXPERIENCE**, Special Report No. 3, New York, 1955. 257 pp.

A report consisting of 20 papers and supplementary material presented by different company representatives at AMA's special Electronics Conference in March, 1955. The papers are grouped into three sections — The Evolution of Data Processing, The Planning Stage, and The Equipment and Its Uses. Various examples of different company applications are included, as is a glossary of programming terminology.

American Management Association, **ELECTRONICS IN ACTION — THE CURRENT PRACTICALITY OF ELECTRONIC DATA PROCESSING**, Special Report No. 22, New York, 1957.

A report consisting of 13 papers presented by different company representatives at AMA's 3rd Annual Electronics Conference and Exhibit in February, 1957. The report consists of three sections — Feasibility Studies, Electronics at Work, and New Frontiers. Covered are different applications on small, medium, and large computers and one company's decision against a computer. Also covered are selection and training problems and Operations Research type computer applications.

American Management Association, **ESTABLISHING AN INTEGRATED DATA PROCESSING SYSTEM BLUEPRINT FOR A COMPANY PROGRAM.** Special Report No. 11, New York, 1956. 183 pp.

A series of 16 articles and four case studies

presented at an AMA Orientation Seminar on "Establishing an Integrated Data-Processing System" in February and March, 1956. The report consists of six parts — The Preliminaries, Tailoring the Program, The Installation Process, IDP and the Worker, The Long View, and in Part 6, three case studies covering applications in three different companies, and one article covering 10 selected IDP applications in different companies.

American Management Association, **KEEPING PACE WITH AUTOMATION — PRACTICAL GUIDES FOR THE COMPANY EXECUTIVE**, Special Report No. 7, New York, 1956. 136 pp.

A series of 13 papers presented at a special AMA conference on Automation in October, 1955. The papers cover a general discussion of Automation including both factory automation and the role of computers. The papers are grouped into three major sections — 1. Basic Concepts and Approaches (covering the nature and techniques of factory automation), 2. Company Experiences (consisting of four case studies of different companies), and 3. New Horizons (including a discussion of the future and worker welfare).

American Management Association, **PIONEERING IN ELECTRONIC DATA PROCESSING — COMPANY EXPERIENCE WITH ELECTRONIC COMPUTERS**, Special Report No. 9, New York, 1956. 159 pp.

A series of 11 papers presented by different company representatives at AMA's special conference on "Electronics at Work" in February, 1956. The report groups these papers in four sections — Feasibility Studies, Handling the Personnel Problem, "Payout" Applications, and New Frontiers. Each author presents applications experience from his own company.

AN INTRODUCTION TO IBM PUNCHED CARD PROCESSING, 112 East Post Road, White Plains, N. Y.: Data Processing Division, International Business Machines, Inc., 1960. 20 pp.

This interesting general information manual explains the early history of EAM, its present day applications, how to code data, and what can be done by machines with the punched card input. An hour's reading will give a basic foundation in what EAM can generally do. Includes a glossary. A copy may be gotten from your local IBM salesman or by writing to the IBM office address noted in the reference heading.

Anthony, Robert N., editor, **PROCEEDINGS, AUTOMATIC DATA PROCESSING CONFERENCE**, Sept. 8 and 9, 1955, Harvard University, Graduate School of Business, 1956. 194 pp.

A technical discussion of the field of ADP, i.e., basic principles; centralization vs. decentralization; criteria for selection of equipment; case studies of applications, operations research. Contributors include T. F. Bradshaw, Dr. A. Oettinger, F. H. Muns, Dr. K. E. Iverson, Dr. R. C. Ackoff, and Dr. M. L. Hurni.

THE AUDITOR ENCOUNTERS ELECTRONIC DATA PROCESSING. New York: Price Waterhouse & Co. 24 pp.

A fairly recent study by a well known accounting firm, it analyzes and reports on the auditing aspects in electronic data processing systems. Especial attention is given to the "audit trail". The last page shows a general flow chart for a complete payroll application. Worthwhile reading for the accountant and the systems man. Write to Price Waterhouse for a free copy.

AUTOMATION AND RECENT TRENDS, Hearings before the Subcommittee on Economic Stabilization of the Joint Economic Committee, Congress of the United States. 85th Congress. First Session. November, 1957. 100 pp.

A good study of automation as it affects banking and other financial operations. Contains a good commentary on automation by Roger W. Bolz, editor, Automation Magazine. Magnetic Ink Character Recognition also discussed as a common machine language for check handling. A single copy usually can be obtained from your Congressman.

AUTOMATION AND TECHNOLOGICAL CHANGE, Hearings before the Subcommittee on Economic Stabilization of the Joint Committee on the Economic Report, Congress of the United States. 84th Congress. First Session. October, 1955. 644 pp.

One of the earliest Congressional studies on Automation. Testimony given by top union, government, university, and private industry spokesmen. A good jumping off point for those who want to begin to learn about the subject of Automation.

Bartee, Thomas C., **DIGITAL COMPUTER FUNDAMENTALS**, New York, McGraw-Hill Book Company, Inc., 1960. 342 pp.

As the title suggests, this book describes electronic computer principles. The subject matter can be easily digested by the reader having a very basic knowledge of electronics and some in algebra. The first two chapters offer a general introduction to the subject. The next three deal with number systems, computer circuitry, logical design, and Boolean Algebra. The last four chapters discuss in detail the major components of a computer. Chapters are closed with a set of questions and reference sources. A good book for the analyst who may want a firmer grip on computer hardware knowledge.

Baumes, Carl G., **ADMINISTRATION OF ELECTRONIC DATA PROCESSING**, Business Policy Study, No. 98, 460 Park Ave., N. Y. C. 27, N. Y., National Industrial Conference Board, Inc., 1961. 140 pp.

Based on two years of research among 124 companies, this excellent study contains 10 well-treated chapters as: 1. Gaining Background Knowledge, 3. Planning the Systems Studies, 5. Recommending a Course of Action, 6. Organizing the Data Processing Activity, and 8. Evaluating Performance and Progress. Of unusual interest is Chapter 10, "Other Administrative Problems", which deals with the nutty problem of effecting systems changes, especially the timing of systems changes and the assignment of responsibility for these changes.

Becker, Esther R. and Eugene F. Murphy, **THE OFFICE IN TRANSITION**, New York, N. Y.: Harper & Brothers, 1957. 190 pp.

Good "introduction" to Automation. Describes Punched Cards, Computers, Integrated Data Processing. Walks the reader "through" the preliminary steps required to prepare for Automation. Emphasizes need for comprehensive systems analysis before automating. Discusses "programming", accuracy checking techniques; design of forms for automation; the human relations aspects of automating.

Bell, William D., **A MANAGEMENT GUIDE TO ELECTRONIC COMPUTERS**, New York: McGraw-Hill Book Co., Inc., 1957. 391 pp.

A guide in non-technical language for the business executive on what a computer is and can do, the present state of the art and a realistic look at the future. Included are chapters on the various major computer components, programming, and computer feasibility study. A series of 11 case studies illustrate different applications in different companies.

Berkeley, Edmund C., **GIANT BRAINS**, New York: John Wiley & Sons, Inc., 1950. 270 pp.

This book was one of the first to appear following World War II which discussed in any detail, still palatable to the non-technical layman, the new electronic computer technology. Although after a decade this book has been somewhat outmoded by more modern developments, it can still serve as a good review of the basic fundamentals of data processing. For example, Chapter 4, "Counting Holes," can quickly refresh one's memory on punched card hardware principles. It is also a useful reference for reviewing the capabilities of early experimental computers as Harvard's Mark-I and the University of Pennsylvania's ENIAC.

Berkeley, Edmund C., and Linda L. Lovett, **GLOSSARY OF TERMS IN COMPUTERS AND DATA PROCESSING**, 815 Washington St., Newtonville 60, Mass.: Berkeley Enterprises, Inc., June, 1960. 90 pp.

Contains over 870 items pertinent to the field of Automatic Data Processing Systems. One of the most current glossaries presently available.

Berkeley, Edmund Callis and Lawrence Wainwright, **COMPUTERS — THEIR OPERATION AND APPLICATIONS**, New York: Reinhold Publishing Corporation, 1956. 366 pp.

Authors present basic information on automatic computers, both digital and analog. Eight sections:

1. Machines that Handle Information; 2. Automatic Digital Computing Machines; 3. Automatic Analog Computing Machines; 4. Other types of Automatic Computing Machines; 5. Miniature Computers and Their Use in Training; 6. Some Large-Scale Automatic Digital Computers; 7. Applications of Automatic Computing Machines; and, 8. Miscellaneous (including Bibliography and glossary).

Bittel, Lester R., Morley G. Helden, and Robert S. Rice, editors, **PRACTICAL AUTOMATION**, New York: McGraw-Hill Book Company, Inc., 1957. 376 pp.

A rather complete analysis of the various organizational problems associated with the installation of electronic data processing systems. The overtone of the book is that the problems are many and often complex, but never completely impossible to resolve. The entire Section 4, "Management of Automation" is excellent reading for systems analysts and managers. Here are given three interesting approaches of how to organize for computers. Worthwhile reading to learn more of the organizational impact of EDP.

Booth, Andrew D. and Kathleen H. V. Booth, **AUTOMATIC DIGITAL CALCULATORS**, (2nd ed.), London, Butterworths Scientific Publication, 1956. 261 pp.

Intended to serve as guide to theory of computers, and the concepts, language and literature of the field. Seventeen chapters, including coverage of computing system design, computer components, computer coding (incl. sub-routines), program design and computer applications. Also technical bibliographies.

Bowden, B. V., **FASTER THAN THOUGHT — A SYMPOSIUM ON DIGITAL COMPUTING MACHINES**, London: Sir Isaac Pitman & Sons, Ltd., 1953. 416 pp.

A symposium of papers by 24 British experts presenting an account of modern computing machines, their history, theory and design, and their applications to business and scientific research. The book consists of three parts. Part 1 covers the history and theory of computing machines; Part 2 covers electronic computers in Britain and the U. S.; and Part 3 covers electronic computer applications.

Bright, James R., **AUTOMATION AND MANAGEMENT**, Boston 63, Mass.: Harvard Business School, Division of Research, 1958. 280 pp.

Automation and Management is a comprehensive report of a field investigation of the managerial problems of automatic manufacturing, such as materials used in the manufacturing process, volume, complexity of the manufacturing process, and the gradual installation of the automatic equipment itself. Examined are the potentiality, impact, and limitation of automation to management in production areas only, excluding such aspects as data processing. Professor Bright consulted, in addition to current professional writing, top and operating management, staff specialists, and records of 13 United States factories identified in 1954 by experts as outstanding examples of automation.

This penetrating overview of management's responsibility for designing industrial automation programs gives insight also into the problems that may be encountered in data processing. For an understanding of what automation means in different industries, this book is required reading. Its content has many parallels for data processing.

Brown, R. Hunt, **OFFICE AUTOMATION — INTEGRATED AND ELECTRONIC DATA PROCESSING,** New York: Automation Consultants, Inc., 1955-1961.

A volume on ADP offering an updating service consisting of monthly newsletters with new pages containing revisions and descriptions of new equipment and applications. The treatment of the subject matter covering the entire field of automation is quite inconclusive. A standard reference manual recommended for the systems man's library.

Buckingham, Walter, **AUTOMATION, ITS IMPACT ON BUSINESS AND PEOPLE,** New York: Harper & Brothers, 1961. 196 pp.

Professor Buckingham has been a frequent expert witness before Congressional Committees studying the problems associated with Automation. Much of Dr. Buckingham's book is drawn from material presented before these Committee meetings. Here however it is easy to find and to use as the material has been carefully edited and placed in a logical sequence. Patently, the purpose of the book is, ". . . to explore and analyze the most important economic and social consequences of the new technology of automation." This book will make excellent reading for the systems analyst who wants a broad understanding of the development of both office and industrial automation.

BURROUGHS DATA PROCESSING GUIDE, 460 Sierra Madre Villa, Pasadena, California: Burroughs Corp., Electrodata Division, 1960.

Primarily, this manual serves, "to present a single, Burroughs approved, integrated set of standard operating procedures to serve as a primary tool in the successful installation and utilization of Burroughs Data Processing systems." This company-produced manual will give the systems man a good insight into one phase of "the software" provided by a small computer manufacturer.

Canning, Richard G., **ELECTRONIC DATA PROCESSING FOR BUSINESS AND INDUSTRY,** New York: John Wiley & Sons, Inc., 1956. 332 pp.

The book represents a non-technical discussion starting with management's initial interest in investigating EDP feasibility and ending with a proposed plan of action on installing EDP. Covered are EDP as a management tool, a summary of EDP machines, programming clerical operations, the systems study, design of EDP systems, role of Operations Research, equipment characteristics, and a reliability program. See also author's 1957 follow-up book *Electronic Data Processing for Business and Industry*.

Canning, Richard G., **INSTALLING ELECTRONIC DATA PROCESSING SYSTEMS,** New York: John Wiley & Sons., Inc., 1957. 193 pp.

The book covers what is involved in installing an EDP system *after* the equipment has been ordered, and covers the high-cost aspects as planning the installation program, programming installation, conversion to the EDP system, fitting EDP into the organization, selection and training of EDP personnel, and the early phases of operation. Many illustrations based on actual case studies are provided. The book as a whole represents a follow-up to the author's 1956 book, *Electronic Data Processing for Business and Industry*.

Carroll, Phil, **COST CONTROL THROUGH ELECTRONIC DATA PROCESSING,** 74 - 5th Avenue, N. Y. C., New York: Society for the Advancement of Management, 1958. 32 pp.

This monograph provides a non-technical coverage of the many management problems which lend themselves to the use of electronic data processing equipment. Mr. Carroll has done what seems to this reviewer to be an excellent job of placing in reasonable perspective the impressive capabilities of new electronic data processors. Writing in an interesting style, using many concise illustrations from his business experience, he warns against the pitfalls of the use of such equipment while at the same time pointing out the areas of management for which the equipment may be of great value.

Business managers, engineers, statisticians, accountants, and all who deal with quantitative data for business should find this monograph interesting and useful. For some it may point out areas of application of electronic data processing equipment which they have not yet explored. It may assist others in guarding against the pitfalls of misinformation or of expecting too much from this impressive tool.

Casey, Robert S., James W. Perry, Madeline M. Berry, and Allen Kent, editors, **PUNCHED CARDS,** New York: Reinhold Publishing Corp., 1958. 697 pp.

This second edition of a very complete authoritative book on electric accounting machines contains articles by experts in this field. Divided into five logically sequenced parts, it covers "Fundamental Machine Considerations" in Part I, "Practical Applications . . ." in Part II, ". . . Coding and Systems Design" in Part III, "Future Possibilities" in Part IV, and, an excellent bibliography on punched card equipment in Part V. One will also note in this book a distinct flavor of how

EAM methods may be used to implement Information Retrieval techniques.

Chapin, Ned, AN INTRODUCTION TO AUTOMATIC COMPUTERS, Toronto, Canada: D. Van Nostrand Co., 1959. 525 pp.

This book gathers in one volume much of the data relevant to electronic computers. Following a recent trend, the author deals with such subjects as the concept of computers, their background and development, installation costs and problems, operating costs, characteristics, and other matters. In short, much knowledge of a worthwhile nature is gathered.

Unfortunately, due to rapid developments certain sections are already outdated. This, however, is inevitable and for the next few years books on "Automatic Computers" will have a short life due to the introduction of new techniques and equipment. Chapters on basic principles, background and the summary of problems experienced by the pioneers in this field will have a continuing value, however.

Chapin, Ned, AUTOMATIC COMPUTERS: A SYSTEMS APPROACH FOR BUSINESS, Princeton, N. J.: D. Van Nostrand Co., Inc., 1957. 525 pp.

It is through books such as *Automatic Computers* that the mystery surrounding electronics and computers in business is gradually being dissipated. Mr. Chapin has presented the language and terms of business systems involving computers in a manner that can be understood easily by the uninitiated.

The 17 chapters cover the general areas of computers such as the Input, Output, Operation, Fundamentals, Cost, etc. In addition, there are chapters on the storage unit and programming. Each chapter concludes with some suggested reading material. Also some chapter have suggestions for further work. This tends to make the book adaptable as a text on Automation and Computers in business.

COMPUTER APPLICATIONS SERVICE, edited by Alan D. Meacham and Van B. Thompson, Detroit 26, Michigan: American Data Processing, Inc., 1962. Est. 300 pp. each volume.

Consists of two volumes, with each one having a collection of 50 applications of electronic computers, plus related material. Twelve computer manufacturers and 25 different computers are part of Volume I. Three ADP applications are primarily scientific . . . the rest business data processing. An attempt is made to keep a balance between bread-and-butter applications, and more advanced or sophisticated utilization of hardware.

COMPUTERS — KEY TO TOTAL SYSTEMS CONTROL, Proceedings of the Eastern Joint Computer Conference, Washington, D. C., December 12-14, 1961, Volume 20, New York: The Macmillan Co., 1961. 380 pp.

A publication of the American Federation of Information Processing Societies (AIEE, ACM, and IRE), this book contains the latest technical information on developments in the electronic computer field. Typical titles include: "Multilevel Programming for a Real-Time System," "A Simulation Model for Data Systems Analysis," "Card Random Access Memory (CRAM)", "Dataview: A General-Purpose Data Display System", "Communications for Computer Applications", and, "Chrysler Optical Processing Scanner". Most of the papers will have only a limited appeal to the systems analyst. But, one or two titles might be just the authoritative source of information an analyst may be seeking to back up his own imaginative concept of a new ADP system's design. Well worth skimming through for ideas.

Corvay, B., J. Gibbons, and D. E. Watts, BUSINESS EXPERIENCE WITH ELECTRONIC COMPUTERS, 2 Park Ave., N. Y. C., New York: Controllers Institute Research Foundation, Inc., 1960. 191 pp.

A research study reported by three directors of Management Advisory Services, Price Waterhouse & Co., this book has a significant place among the many fine studies published by the Controllers Institute Research Foundation. Its purpose is to present a synthesis of what has been learned so far from electronics data processing installations — "pioneered" electronic data processing installations. A hundred or so companies provide the raw data of experience from which valuable lessons are drawn.

This book is essential reading for all top management personnel of any firm large enough to support the possibility of EDP. It is certainly recommended reading for every Controller and for any systems man even remotely connected with EDP. As a collection of lessons learned to date on the management problems in connection with EDP installations, it would seem that the book belongs in every systems library.

Courtney, Peggy, editor, BUSINESS ELECTRONICS REFERENCE GUIDE, Volume 4, 2 Park Ave., N. Y. C. 16, New York: Controllership Foundation, Inc., 1958. 602 pp.

A monumental reference guide to electronic data processing has been prepared by the Controllers Institute of America. This reference work describes 383 company and governmental installations, including equipment and applications, and reports on 34 American and foreign digital computers commercially available for business applications.

Craig, Harold Farlow, ADMINISTERING A CONVERSION TO ELECTRONIC ACCOUNTING, Boston: Harvard University, 1955. 224 pp.

A Harvard Graduate School of Business Research Study on the administration of change in a large modern office, with special emphasis on the behavior of middle management personnel. Part 1 describes the office operation before and after conversion, the functions performed and the administrative problems during conversion. Part 2 covers administrative behavior during the conversion. Part 3 presents the author's own observations and conclusions.

DATA PROCESSING ANNUAL, Volume 3, Punched Card and Computer Applications and Reference Guide, Detroit 26, Michigan: Gille Associates, Inc., 1961. 320 pp.

Published by Gille Associates, Inc., now American Data Processing, Inc., this book is divided into three main sections: Special Features, Punched Card Applications, and Computer Applications. *Special Features* contains an article by Ray Marien on ADP Forms Design, several pages carrying half-page photos of the latest computers along with a description of them, and computer comparison charts. There is also a very good short annotated bibliography of 82 citations dealing with ADP, plus a listing of many of the articles on ADP which appeared in periodicals during 1960. *Punched Card Applications* encompasses 26 informative case studies on electric accounting machines which deal with such applications as interest calculations, billing, sales analysis, medical records, and tax billing. The third and final section, *Computer Applications* devotes itself to the use of electronic computers for 13 applications as engineering documentation, punched tape reports, municipal applications and supplier selection. Several other features serve to make this volume a very desirable addition to a systems man's library.

DATA PROCESSING BY ELECTRONICS, 67 Broad St., New York: Haskins & Sells, 1955. 113 pp.

This book, put out by a well known public accounting firm, aims to convey, to the interested reader who is not a specialist in ADP, a basic understanding of the operation and use of electronic data processing systems. One section gives an easy-to-understand illustration of what programming is. Write to Haskins & Sells for a free copy.

DATA PROCESSING EQUIPMENT ENCYCLOPEDIA, Electromechanical Devices, Volume I, Detroit 26, Michigan: Gille Associates, Inc., 1961. 384 pp.

Gille Associates, Inc., now American Data Processing, Inc., has compiled this authoritative volume to provide facts to the reader "with a need to know" with enough necssary facts to enable him to reduce equipment under consideration to a minimum number of models. Volume I includes electro-mechanical equipment that is usable in the preparation or semi-automatic handling of data. Typical hardware items included are: Accounting Machines, Addressing Machines, Bursters, Cardatype Machines, Data Transmitters, Document Readers, Mailing Inserters, Output Typewriters, Proof Inscribers, Tape Punches, Tag Readers, Tape Winders, Test Scoring Machines, and Transfer Posting Machines. With this research tool, the systems analyst and manager has "under one roof" the important specifications of a host of Source Data Automation devices.

DATA PROCESSING EQUIPMENT ENCYCLOPEDIA, Electronic Devices, Volume II, Detroit 26, Michigan: Gille Associates, Inc., 1961. 396 pp.

Until recently published by Gille Associates, Inc., American Data Processing, Inc., will now continue the updating of this valuable ADP research tool. Complete with specifications and photographs are most business data processing computers now extant. Included also are some computers of an historical interest, e.g., although still operating the BIZMAC, DATAmatic 1000. To be considered for inclusion in this volume an ADP system needs I/O, control, arithmetic units, and storage. Size may range from the LGP-30 or Bendix G-15 right up to the Philco 2000, Honeywell 800, IBM 7090, and further to STRETCH. Particularly valuable about this book is its inclusion of technical data on Magnetic Ink Character Recognition (MICR) and Optical Character Recognition (OCR) equipments.

DATA PROCESSING IN NAVY MANAGEMENT INFORMATION SYSTEMS, Washington 25, D. C.: Office of the Secretary, Dept. of Navy, April 16, 1959.

Divided into seven chapters, the Navy "Gray Book" on electronic data processing offers much in the way of sound advice which all systems analysts can benefit from. Noteworthy is the data processing plan of the Navy which attunes itself to six stages of five-year spans from 1940 to 1970. Nor should its comments on Human Relations be overlooked as the manual notes that, "Since most fear and uncertainty stem from a lack of knowledge about ADP, education is the solution." A letter to your Congressman may produce a copy for your own library.

DATA PROCESSING LIBRARY SERIES, edited by Alan D. Meacham and Van B. Thompson, Detroit 26, Michigan: American Data Processing, Inc., 1962. Est. 175 pp. each volume.

An ADP series of volumes on subjects as *Total Systems* (M. Ronayne and E. Haga), and *Information Retrieval Management* (L. Hattery and E. McCormick). Other volumes will deal with *Computer Management, Data Transmission,* and *Economics of Data Processing* to be released sometime in 1962. Through its contacts in private industry, campus, and government circles, the publisher has been able to enlist the support of experts in writing well-documented articles in their particular ADP specialties. A series to keep one eye peeled for.

DATA PROCESSING TODAY: A PROGRESS REPORT, AMA Management Report No. 46, 1515 Broadway, N. Y. C. 36, New York: Finance Division, American Management Association, 1960. 143 pp.

A good recap of progress in the use of computers in industry. Two of four sections deal with "Management and Data Processing" and "Advances in Data Processing Technology", and two more with applications. Items meriting attention by the systems man are found on pages 17 and 21, in an article by Milton M. Stone. Finally, there is very much to be gained from reading of the Chrysler Corporation application of data processing, led off by an interesting article by Gomer H. Redmond, Chrysler Manager of Corporate Systems and Procedures.

Dichter, Ernest, **WHY THEY DON'T BUY COMPUTERS,** a motivational research study conducted for **MODERN OFFICE PROCEDURES,** Cleveland, Ohio, September 9, 1960. 54 pp.

Dr. Dichter's study unearths many of the hidden reasons behind the hesitancy of potential users to employ computers. Of especial interest are chapters entitled, "Insistence on Rationality", "The Real Reasons for Hesitating", "How They Learn About Computers", and "The Real Decision Makers".

Diebold, John & Associates, **AUTOMATIC DATA PROCESSING SERVICE,** 6141 North Cicero Ave., Chicago 30, Illinois: Cudahy Publishing Co., 1956-1961.

This new service edited by John Diebold & Associates, a leading consultant in the automation field, is designed to provide its subscribers, from one source and in an integrated format, comprehensive, accurate and objectively appraised information on all aspects of the digital computer field.

This unique service is extremely ambitious in purpose and scope. Its subject matter covers operating manuals for equipment, news of new installations, book reviews, equipment evaluations and meeting notes to mention only a few of the topics treated.

Diebold, John, **AUTOMATION: THE ADVENT OF THE AUTOMATIC FACTORY,** Princeton, N. J., D. Van Nostrand Company, Inc., 1952. 181 pp.

One might say that this book has contributed greatly to the recognition by business and industry of the potential to be gained through the adoption of Automation techniques. The systems man will, after reading this book, gain a glimpse of the tremendous impact that Automation will have on our present business and industrial organizational structures. He should make it a point to read carefully the chapter entitled "Automatic Handling of Information".

Diebold, John, **AUTOMATION: ITS IMPACT ON BUSINESS AND LABOR,** Planning Document No. 106, A Special Committee Report, 1606 N. H. Ave., N.W., Washington 9, D. C.: National Planning Association, 1959. 64 pp. ($1.00)

Diebold writes that ". . . there is still a wide gap between engineering developments and business understanding of how the new equipment can best be used." Realizing the dilemma of management not exactly knowing how automation will affect it, Diebold tries to foresee the future economic and social impact of automation on business and labor. Key chapters are "The Social Consequences" and "The Search for Solutions".

DO YOU TALK "COMPUTERESE," edited by E. A. Murphy, Jr., Philadelphia, Pa.: Minneapolis-Honeywell Regulator Co., Industrial Div., 1960. 24 pp.

Honeywell tells "What's it all about" in an ADP glossary of 90 key words. Absolute address, binary scale, magnetic drum, multiple address code, off-line operation . . . all are explained in an easy-to-read and comprehend manner. Write to Honeywell for your copy.

Doss, M. P., editor, **INFORMATION PROCESSING EQUIPMENT,** New York: Reinhold Publishing Corp., 1955. 270 pp.

A thorough, yet compact, source book on data handling devices from the typewriter through the computer. Each chapter has been authored by a specialist in the area covered — areas such as Microcopying, Xerography, Letterpress, Audio Methods, Punched Cards, Lensless Copying with sensitized papers. Of particular value are the lengthy and complete bibliographies at the conclusion of each chapter. Pictures, diagrams and charts are liberally used.

Dreher, Carl, **AUTOMATION: WHAT IT IS, HOW IT WORKS, WHO CAN USE IT,** New York: W. W. Norton and Co., Inc., 1957. 128 pp.

A simple layman's introduction (with illustrations and cartoons) to automation and its industrial and social implications. Five chapters on: Sonner Than You Think, What Is It?, How It Got Here, The Machines, and Automation and The Boom.

Eckert, W. J. and Rebecca Jones, **FASTER FASTER,** New York: McGraw-Hill Book Co., Inc., 1955. 160 pp.

One might of the earlier books on electronic computers, it describes the development of the Naval Ordnance Research Calculator (NORC). Appendices give NORC characteristics, flow charts, operations, timing, and programming examples. As its subtitle suggests, the brief book is "A simple description of a giant electronic computer and the problems it solves."

EDP — THE FIRST TEN YEARS, New York: McKinsey and Co., Inc., 1961. 38 pp.

A series of 43 articles by McKinsey and Company staff members reviewing lessons of developments in order to guide management to a deeper understanding of the total business process. The articles are: 1. Data Processing in Transition (J. D. Gallagher and D. J. Axsmith); 2. Getting the Most Out of Your Computer (D. R. Daniel); 3. Overhauling Your Management — Information System in the EDP Age (R. F. Neuschel); and, 4. Computers, Models, and Business Management (W. C. Dalleck).

EDP IDEA FINDER, Data Processing Digest 1957-1959, 1140 S. Robertson Blvd., Los Angeles 35, Calif.: Canning, Sission and Associates, Inc., 1960. 656 pp. ($69.00)

Source document which gives digest of significant articles on all key developments in EDP from 1957 through 1959. Thoroughly indexed and cross referenced.

Einzig, Paul, **THE ECONOMIC CONSEQUENCES OF AUTOMATION,** London: Secker & Warburg, 1956. 218 pp.

The book deals with the technological and commercial aspects of automation as they affect economic consideration; the social aspects; as well as the economic consequences of automation.

ELECTRONIC DATA PROCESSING CONFERENCE, Selected Papers, May 14-15, 1959, University, Alabama; University of Alabama Extension News Bulletin, 1959. 38 pp.

After each annual conference on electronic data processing, a bulletin of this type is issued. This particular issue treats with such topics as "Profitable Utilization of Computers in Banking", "Electronic Data Processing and the Numerically Controlled Milling Machine", "Selecting and Training Personnel for Computer Work", and "Practical Experience with Routines and Sub-routines and Their Applications". The May 19-20, 1960, edition carries interesting articles as, "Selecting and Training People for Systems Modernization", and "Using Computers for Management Control".

ELECTRONIC DATA PROCESSING FOR GOVERNMENTS, 1313 East 60th St., Chicago 37, Illinois: Municipal Finance Officers Association of the U. S. and Canada. December 1, 1959. Special Bulletin 1959B. 22 pp.

Present articles by John E. Quinlan, "Opportunities for Systems Mechanization", and Henry P. Dowling, "Detroit's Experience with Electronic Data Processing". Both articles illustrate how municipal governments can use data processing for applications as Tax Accounting, Voter Registration, Licensing, Public Works, Utilities, etc. Good flow charts and form exhibits are in an appendix.

Even, Arthur D., **ENGINEERING DATA PROCESSING SYSTEMS DESIGN,** Princeton, N. J.: D. Van Nostrand Company, Inc., 1960. 282 pp.

This book contains a comprehensive coverage of mechanization possibilities for processing engineering drawings, engineering parts lists, and other engineering documentation. The author considers every aspect of an engineering department's data processing problems. Primary documents, basic records, and the approach necessary to design engineering system — with all of the ramifications involved — are thoroughly discussed. The author combines engineering, data processing, microfilm-

ing, and punched card handling into an integrated mechanized system.

Fahnestock, James D., **COMPUTERS AND HOW THEY WORK,** 1 Park Ave., N. Y. C. 16, New York, 1960. 288 pp.

Many systems men go deeply into electronic data processing problems without satisfying their curiosity as to what makes EDP equipment "tick". Generally this is because literature available to them on the subject is either over simplified or is heavy Einsteinian material.

Computers and How They Work is a presentation of technical principles about computers and periphery operations. It is in language that a non-electronics engineer can understand easily. It gets basic ideas across directly. Some 113 illustrations provide information about fundamental aspects of computer language, arithmetic programming, and circuitry; the means of communicating between men and the equipment; and the way in which a computer remembers. The book is not concerned with applications.

Although it is not vital that an EDP systems man be familiar with basic technical principles underlying EDP equipment, few will deny that added perspective afforded by such knowledge gives them more confidence and helps them do a better job. With this in mind, the book is recommended for persons who are involved in or who expect to be involved in EDP planning.

Fairbanks, Ralph W., **SUCCESSFUL OFFICE AUTOMATION,** Englewood Cliffs, N. J.: Prentice-Hall, Inc., 1956. 349 pp.

A comprehensive book covering both office systems work and application of automation to Integrated Data Processing. Included is coverage of modern office functions and paperwork problems and the relationship of the IDP concept to them; descriptions of the tools of office automation, including the various phases of systems planning, analysis, and design; cost comparison; reorganization; reporting to management; and conversion and installation; setting up a Methods Dept.; choosing consultants; human relations problems; and facts and fallacies on EDP.

Friedman, Burton Dean, **PUNCHED CARD PRIMER,** Public Administration Service, New York: American Book-Stratford Press, Inc., 1955. 77 pp.

The author states that the aim of the book is, "to introduce the reader to the basic facts of punched card life, and thereby to develop a general understanding of the equipment and its possibilities." IBM, Remington-Rand, and Samas-Underwood EAM systems are discussed. Chapter 7 describes in simple but educational terms the features of a punched card installation. The book is "required reading" for anyone planning an EAM installation.

Gotlieb, J. N. and P. Hume, **HIGH-SPEED DATA PROCESSING,** New York: McGraw-Hill Book Company, Inc., 1958. 338 pp.

The authors present some excellent points on critical EDP areas. The early history of computers beginning with Charles Babbage is reviewed. Coding, programming, and other computer skills are discussed. Interesting facts ar given on the number of clerical workers that can be replaced by a computer. The authors also favor the use of single functional computers in factories to do jobs rather than to rely on a large general-purpose computer capable of doing many separate jobs. A book full of perspicacious views and observations on EDP.

Grabbe, Eugene M., editor, **AUTOMATION IN BUSINESS AND INDUSTRY**, New York: John Wiley & Sons, Inc., 1957. 645 pp.

A series of lectures by 21 prominent engineers and scientists at the University of California in Spring, 1955 for the purpose of reviewing for engineers and managers the present status of developments and applications in the field of automation. Covers fundamentals of automation and description of automation systems applications, (including feedback control systems, instrumentation, analogue and digital computers and conversion between them, data processing, and manufacturing automation).

Grabbe, Eugene M., Simon Ramo, and Dean E. Wooldridge, **HANDBOOK OF AUTOMATION, COMPUTATION, AND CONTROL**, New York: John Wiley & Sons, Inc., 1958-59-60.

A three-volume series of comprehensive technical handbooks covering major phases of automation. Vol. 1 on *Control Fundamentals* stresses mathematics with sections on General Mathematics, Numerical Analysis, Operations Research, Information Theory, and Transmission and Feedback Control; Vol. 2 on *Computers and Data Processing* covers design and use of analage and digital computers; and, Vol. 3 on *Systems and Components* emphasizes systems engineering.

Gregory, Robert H. and Richard L. Van Horn, **AUTOMATIC DATA PROCESSING: PRINCIPLES AND PROCEDURES**, 431 Clay St., San Francisco 11, California: Wadsworth Publishing Co., 1960. 705 pp.

Every systems analyst should try either to have a personal copy of this book or be in a position to get one with a modicum of time and effort. Dr. Gregory and Mr. Van Horn began their tome while at M.I.T. It was originally developed for the U. S. Army Ordnance Corps and used extensively at their famous Ordnance Management Engineering Training Agency School at Rock Island, Illinois. The volume gives the reader a broad introduction to electronic computer systems in simple non-technical terms, as well as the fundamentals of equipment and systems environment. Each chapter is closed with excellent well-annotated references.

GUIDE FOR AUDITING AUTOMATIC DATA PROCESSING SYSTEMS, Auditor General, Comptroller, Department of the Air Force, Washington 25,

D. C.: U. S. Government Printing Office. Nov. 1961. 128 pp.

The latest of many excellent Air Force publications dealing with ADP. Designed as a handbook for the auditor (systems man too!) which can be used either as a textbook or general reference work. Specifically, its purpose is to provide the auditor with basic information on the general nature of automatic data processing systems and auditing their products, and to offer guidance in the approach to and conduct of these surveys and audits. Both EAM and EDP basics are reviewed. Write to the U. S. Superintendent, Washington 25, D. C. for a copy. A bargain for only 75¢!

HANDBOOK ON DATA PROCESSING METHODS, Part I, Provisional Edition. Prepared jointly by the Statistical Office of the United Nations, New York, and the Statistics Division, Food and Agriculture Organization of the United Nations, Rome, Italy, 1959. 111 pp. ($1.00)

This booklet explains in easy-to-read detail the fundamentals of data processing. Electric accounting machine and electronic computer methods are described. Of especial value is Chapter 3, which is an excellent outline of "The Elements of Planning and Operating a Punch Card Installation." Columbia University Press, 2960 Broadway, N. Y. C. 27, New York, is the U. S. distributor of this publication.

Hartkemeir, Harry Pelle, **PRINCIPLES OF PUNCH-CARD MACHINE OPERATION**, New York: Thomas Y. Cromwell Company, 1942. 269 pp.

This manual written by Dr. Hartkemeir provides, ". . . the beginning student with all the text and illustrative material necessary to a proper understanding of the fundamentals of the punch-card method." One caution should be observed in reading this manual. Although the manual will be a good way for punch-card students to comprehend electric accounting machine, the book is almost 20 years old. Since its publication, IBM-EAM hardware have had many special features added to them. This detracts from the manual only in a minor way, since for the beginner, his learning of fundamental principles should be of paramount importance.

Hattery, Lowell H., **EXECUTIVE CONTROL & DATA PROCESSING**, Washington D. C.: Anderson Kramer Associates, 1959. 92 pp.

Not a technical book about Electronic Data Processing, Dr. Hattery's latest contribution to the literature of management science, ". . . is intended to be a guide to the executive in meeting the challenge of using new data processing tools for more effective control." His analyses and conclusion make for fruitful reading, for the author writes from experience gained as Director of the Center for Technology and Administrative Studies, and as Head of the Annual Institute on Electronics in Management, both at the American University in Washington, D. C.

Executive Control & Data Processing is a concise, informative, and uncomplicated primer for the alert executive or systems man who must review old principles and learn new ones pertaining to reporting systems so that he can profitably utilize for his organization the kind and number of reports that EDP will generate.

Hattery, Lowell H. and George P. Bush, editors, **ELECTRONICS IN MANAGEMENT**, Washington, D. C.: The University Press, 1956. 207 pp.

The editors have compiled an interesting collection of papers written by a number of prominent figures who participated in one of the first Institutes on Electronics in Management held at the American University. Especially informative are "Tailored Electronic Data Processing Equipment", by F. D. Rigby, and "Management Impact of Electronic Systems", contributed by Dr. Hattery.

IMPACT OF AUTOMATION ON EMPLOYMENT, Hearings before the Subcommittee on Unemployment and the Impact of Automation of the Committee on Education and Labor, House of Representatives, 87 Congress, 1st Session. March and April, 1961. 793 pp.

An excellent Congressional document covering the effect of various types of Automation upon the worker. Those giving testimony before the Committee included, Solomon Barkin, James B. Carey, John Diebold, Arthur J. Goldberg, Seymour Wolfbein, David J. McDonald, Emerson P. Schmidt, and Paul A. Samuelson. Interesting testimony was Diebold's statement that:

> "The first trend in the automatic computers has been one that has been on continued accelerated scale and the nature of the machine has begun to get more diverse.
>
> "The second trend that makes up the automation picture is numerical control of machine tools.
>
> "The third factor in this development is the use of computers in the control of process plants, chemical plants, pure generating systems, and plants that have continuous processes as atomic energy."

Another interesting comment was that of R. Conrad Cooper of U. S. Steel who said that, ". . . the really tragic technological unemployment occurs, not in the companies making technological improvements, but in those that do not, thereby losing the ability to compete and sustain more and better jobs."

Good reading also are the comments of Howard Coughlin, President, Office Employees International Union, AFL-CIO, who sees office automation in a different light.

A single copy can usually be obtained through one's Congressman.

INFORMATION PROCESSING, Proceedings of the International Conference on Information Processing, UNESCO, 15-20 June, 1959, Paris, France.

United Nations, New York. 520 pp. ($25.00)

This document brings together the ideas of international experts on Automatic Data Processing equipments and techniques. Especially good chapters are Chapter I, Methods of Digital Computing; Chapter II, Common Symbolic Language for Computers; Chapter V. Logical Design of Computers; and Chapter VI, Computer Techniques of the Future. Dr. Howard H. Aiken, a pioneer in the field, contributes some interesting closing remarks on the conference.

INSTALLATION MANUAL — PHYSICAL PLANNING UNIT RECORD DATA PROCESSING EQUIPMENT, 112 East Post Road, White Plains, New York: International Business Machines Corp., February, 1961. 24 pp.

Points out the proper steps to prepare for installation of a punched card unit. Notes that physical planning should begin 6-12 months before operations and include attention to (1) Sufficient and suitable floor space, (2) Floor loading, (3) Electrical requirements, (4) Air conditioning for personnel, (5) Furniture, fixtures, and lighting, (6) Customer engineering service area, (7) Safety, and (8) Unit arrangement for efficient customer operation. A concise booklet of the main points to watch for during an EAM installation.

INSTRUMENTATION AND AUTOMATION, Hearings before the Subcommittee on Economic Stabilization of the Joint Economic Committee, Congress of the United States. 84th Congress. Second Session. December, 1956. 202 pp.

Early study on the role and relationship of instruments and automatic controllers to automation. Of particular interest is Albert F. Sperry's treatment of systems engineering and systems automation. A single copy usually can be obtained through your Congressman.

INTEGRATED DATA PROCESSING AND COMPUTERS; A Report of a Mission to the United States by a Group of European Experts, European Productivity Agency, Organization for European Economic Cooperation. Paris, France. November, 1960. 77 pp. ($1.75)

Between April and June 1960 a Mission of European experts visited the United States to learn about electronic data processing developments made to date in this country ". . . with the primary object of creating a greater awareness among management of the advantages to be gained from an appropriate degree of integration whenever data processing activities are being reviewed — especially, where the introduction of a computer is being considered." Very interesting chapters are those entitled, "Problems of Installing EDP", "Computer Service Centres", "Governments Role", and, "Summary of Conclusions and Recommendations". For a copy write to the OEEC Mission, 1346 Connecticut Ave., N.W., Washington 6, D. C.

INTEGRATED DATA PROCESSING AND COMPUTERS, Working Documents, 1961. 323 pp.

This volume supplements the Mission's main report and contains working papers used or prepared by the participants during their various visits to American data processing installations. Reports were prepared on plants and organizations as the Associated Grocers of New Hampshire, Inc., Service Bureau Corporation, Dennison Manufacturing Co., and the Chesapeake & Ohio Railway Co. Presentations made before the Europeans included ones by H. T. Engstrom, E. J. Cunningham, C. A. Phillips, C. Hammer, E. J. Mahoney, B. Mittman, L. Van Oosten, and P. Reveillion. Worth reviewing and remembering for future use, is the copy of the questionnaire used by the Mission for its investigation to be found in Part V of the appendix.

INTRODUCTION TO AUTOMATIC DATA PROCESSING, Washington 25, D. C.: Headquarters, Department of the Army. April, 1958. 88 pp.

Along with sister publications, "The Conduct of ADPS Feasibility Studies", No. 1-250-1, and "Program Planning Guide", No. 1-250-2, Army's Introduction to ADP, No. 1-250-3, discusses the subject matter in an interesting and informative manner. The text takes the reader from A to Z, in explaining to him the fundamentals of ADP. For systems analyst and manager, Chapter 2 provides fruitful reading with its careful review of the "Management Aspects of ADPS". More than enlightening is Section II on "Cost Consideration of ADPS". Write to your Congressman to see if he can get a copy of this Army publication for you.

INTRODUCTION TO IBM DATA PROCESSING SYSTEMS, 590 Madison Ave., N. Y. C. 22, New York: International Business Machines Corporation, June, 1960. 95 pp.

Although geared to one manufacturer's ADP hardware, this general information is a worthy addition to anyone's management library. It presents common fundamental concepts and operational principles as an aid in developing a basic knowledge of electronic computers. Designed for use in training programs. Write IBM for further details.

INVENTORY OF AUTOMATIC DATA PROCESSING (ADP) EQUIPMENT IN THE FEDERAL GOVERNMENT INCLUDING COSTS, CATEGORIES OF USE, AND PERSONNEL UTILIZATION, Bureau of the Budget, Executive Office of the President, Washington 25, D. C.: U. S. Government Printing Office, May, 1961. 127 pp.

Valuable as a quick reference to the location and kind of computer systems used in the Federal establishment. A comprehensive survey conducted by William A. Gill, Chairman, and members of the Inter-Agency Committee on Automatic Data Processing. Statistics include 531 computers (Main Frames) now in use for Fiscal Year, 1960, and 755 planned for the next Fiscal Year of 1961.

Irwin, Wayne C., **DIGITAL COMPUTER PRINCIPLES**, New York: D. Van Nostrand Co., Inc., 1960. 321 pp.

"This book is for the beginner. No previous acquaintance with computers, electronics or mathematics is necessary," writes the author. This is generally true of the book, but nevertheless, the reader cannot take his reading lightly. The discussion of Symbolic Logic and the Preparation of Computer Instructions requires an alert mind. The strength of the book lies in its lucid explanation of computer logic (especially of its foundation, Boolean Algebra) and of machine timing.

Jacobson, Howard Boone and Joseph S. Roucek, editors, **AUTOMATION AND SOCIETY**, New York: Philosophical Library, 1959. 553 pp.

In this book the combined resources of government, industry, and education provide a solid, well-balanced approach to what is often termed — in anticipation, awe, and sometimes fear — the "second industrial revolution". Essays of nearly three dozen thoughtful observers offer, in this book, a penetrating analysis of many facets of automation; its short past, long future, and effects on society.

For the reader who is more directly and actively engaged in this field, the book also offers extensive bibliographical material at the end of each chapter, an excellent 53-page dictionary of automation terminology, and 37 case histories of applications in U. S. and Canadian companies.

Jeenel, Joachim, **PROGRAMMING FOR DIGITAL COMPUTERS**, New York: McGraw-Hill Book Co., Inc., 1959. 517 pp.

An introductory text on programming for readers with no previous programming experience. Covers computer organization and components; addressing, sequencing, storage and input-output programs; problem preparation and planning; programming languages; and, operating, testing and checking. Also included is a series of nine appendices on specific techniques, a bibliography, and a glossary.

Jones, Gardner M., **ELECTRONICS IN BUSINESS**, East Lansing, Mich.: Bureau of Business and Economic Research, 20 Morrill Hall, Michigan State University, 1958. 106 pp.

The purpose of this short book is to assist those who are interested in the organizational consequences of electronic data processing. Machine descriptions and technicalities are kept to a minimum but there are many references for those who wish to delve further.

With the centralization of record keeping required for electronics and the building of a system around the computer, it has been found that the accounting, sales, production, personnel, and other departments must not operate as separate functions. "Compartmentalized training and thinking are not in accord with the way business operates."

Mr. Jones sets out several prerequisites for an educational background or re-education in an electronic era, e.g., higher mathematics, systmatic thinking, psychological and sociological sciences, economics, systems analysis, and others.

Kaufman, Felix, ELECTRONIC DATA PROCESSING AND AUDITING, New York: Ronald Press Co., 1961. 180 pp.

An excellent treatment of the effects of electronic data processing systems on accounting and auditing practices. It is addressed to all concerned with the control of electronic data processing systems in business and industry. It defines the elements in these systems, describes the way they are planned, and analyzes the electronic data processing arrangements for the typical basic accounting applications. Reliability of EDP systems, a variety of internal control systems, and the auditing requirements are discussed.

Klingman, Herbert F., ELECTRONICS IN BUSINESS, a Case Study in Planning, 2 Park Ave., N. Y. C. 16, New York: Controllership Foundation, Inc., January, 1956. 121 pp. ($4.00)

This booklet points out the trials and tribulations of planning for an electronic computer. Done well, the author points out the many obstacles that the Port of New York Authority had to overcome before finally selecting a computer capable of meeting agency job requirements.

Kozmetsky, George and Paul Kirsher, ELECTRONIC COMPUTERS AND MANAGEMENT CONTROL, New York: McGraw-Hill Book Co., Inc., 1956. 289 pp.

Written primarily for the business executive to explain new developments in and influence of EDP. Describes functions, components, operating methods and various applications of computers; administrative problems on their introduction; their influence on management planning and control; concepts of integrated business systems; and role of the executive in electronic system selection. Also four appendices on Language of Computer Programming, EDP Equipment and a Mathematical Model for an Integrated Data System.

Laubach, Peter B., COMPANY INVESTIGATIONS OF AUTOMATIC DATA PROCESSING, Boston, Mass.: Harvard University, Graduate School of Business Administration, 1957. 258 pp.

One of a series of studies by the Harvard Business School's data processing research project, discussing approaches by various companies on EDP feasibility studies. Three parts: 1. Introduction & Description of Automatic Data Processing Equipment; 2. Case Illustrations of the Over-all Approach to the Survey and Evaluation of Automatic Computers; and, 3. Some Aspects of the Survey and Evaluation of Automatic Data Processing Methods.

Levenson, J. H., editor, ELECTRONIC BUSINESS MACHINES, New York: Philosophical Library, 1960. 272 pp.

This volume is based upon a series of lectures delivered at Dundee Technical College by British and American experts about computers. The lectures have been rewritten and edited for publication so that businessmen, responsible for deciding about installing a computer, can find answers to three basic questions: (1) What are computers and how do they work? (2) What should be considered when reviewing the use of a computer? (3) What can computers do?

The book gives the uninitiated a broad picture about EDP with some detail about problems which must be faced in its use. The first seven chapters, while interesting, are of little direct value to an executive who must make the *yes* or *no* decision. They are of more value to subordinates who must prepare recommendations. The second section, highlighting problems and considerations, should be helpful to an executive. The section on equipment and applications, while interesting, is of less value to the man who makes the decision than the first two sections.

Levin, Howard S., OFFICE WORK AND AUTOMATION, New York: John Wiley & Sons, Inc., 1956. 196 pp.

This highly readable introduction to business automation ". . . Explores ways of obtaining more effective information." After introducing the subject, the author describes ". . . techniques by which information is gathered and made available for mechanized processing." Next, various types of computers and their application to office work are described, followed by explanations of "the fundamentals underlying computer feasibility and selection . . ." A description of scientific problem-solving techniques follows, emphasizing Operations Research. The volume concludes with a ". . . look at the combined effects of common language, computers, and operations research on the office."

Lybrand, Ross Bros. & Montgomery, SURVEY OF BENEFITS RESULTING FROM THE USE OF ELECTRONIC DATA PROCESSING EQUIPMENT; 2 Broadway, N. Y. C. 4, New York: 1959. 45 pp.

A May, 1959, survey report on the use of EDP equipment prepared by the Management Services Research and Consulting Division of Lybrand, Ross Bros. & Montgomery. The report presents findings on personnel displacement, improved management control, reduced expense due to faster billing, and improvement of competitive position. Also an appendix of 11 application case studies, nine on manufacturing companies, and one each on a railway and airline.

MACHINE FUNCTIONS, 590 Madison Ave., N. Y. C. 22, New York: International Business Machines, Inc., Form 224-8208-3, 1957. 31 pp.

Basic IBM reference for conventional electric accounting machines. Explains and illustrates in simplified form the functions of many EAM equipments employed in all types of accounting, statistical, and computational work. Sample card operations also depicted.

MANAGEMENT OF DATA PROCESSING EQUIP-MENT, A.F. MANUAL 171-9, Washington 25, D. C.: Statistical Services, Department of the Air Force, June 1, 1958.

This military government manual is probably the best of its kind. Put out by one of the biggest users of Automatic Data Processing hardware in the world, this manual reflects the experiences of the Air Force in this new field. Chapters cover in precise detail vital items as planning for ADP, its acquisition, ADP contractual matters, and procurement matters, preparation for and installation of ADP, its operation, and ADP reporting requirements. A copy may be obtained by writing directly to the Department of the Air Force or via one's Congressman.

MANAGEMENT'S ROLE IN ELECTRONIC DATA PROCESSING, Conference Board Reports No. 92, N. Y. C. 22, New York: National Industrial Conference Board, 1959. 64 pp.

Booklet discusses ADP in length, especially from the aspects of organizing for and implementing a computer application. Feasibility studies, application studies, ADP policy and ADP work force committees are covered thoroughly. Many examples of these facets of computer installation are shown from private industry.

MARK SENSING PRINCIPLES, 590 Madison Ave., N. Y. C. 22, New York: International Business Machines, Inc. 8 pp.

Requiring no more than 10 minutes reading, this little booklet explains in simple and clear terms the basic fundamentals of mark sensing input documents for electric accounting machine processing. Write IBM for a free copy.

McCracken, Daniel D., **DIGITAL COMPUTER PRO-GRAMMING,** New York: John Wiley & Sons, Inc., 1957. 253 pp.

A well-written book giving the basics of electronic computers . . . their operations and applications. An excellent text for classroom use. As the title infers, heavy emphasis is put on the principles of programming.

McCracken, Daniel D., Harold Weiss, and Tsai-Hwa Lee, **PROGRAMMING BUSINESS COMPUTERS,** New York: John Wiley & Sons, 1959. 510 pp.

This volume is directed to the reader who lacks an extensive background in mathematics but who is, or expects to be, involved in the application of electronic computers to business data processing problems. First, background information is supplied (nature of data processing, concept of the file, flow charting). Then basic computer coding techniques are described. Next, "advanced concepts" are covered (sorting estimating computer time, random access storage, etc.). The final two chapters deal with setting up computer applications and with accounting and auditing considerations.

Mellinger, Harry K., editor, **A GUIDE FOR BUSINESS SYSTEMS ANALYSIS,** Philco Corporation, Willow Grove, Pennsylvania, 1960. 34 pp.

An excellent practical guide to setting up a computer application based on actual first-hand experiences. It was developed by Mellinger and others at Middletown Air Material Area, Olmsted AFB, Penna., to survey manual and mechanized systems and procedures, select functional areas for application to electronic data processing equipment and conduct feasibility studies for the justification and acquisition of EDPE. Noteworthy sections are "Problem Definition: The Development of Objectives for the New System", "Planning the New System: The Creative Phase", and "Systems Design". A limited number of copies are available from Mellinger at his Philco business address.

Michael, Donald N., **CYBERNATION: THE SILENT CONQUEST,** A Report to the Center for the Study of Democratic Institutions, Santa Barbara, Calif.: The Fund for the Republic, Inc., January, 1962. 48 pp.

An exciting and thought-provoking study of the advantages, problems, and control of cybernation. (The author has coined the word *cybernation*, by equating it with both *automation* and *computers*). This booklet will bring the reader right up to date on some of the almost fantastic current applications of cybernation. It also forecasts what effect cybernation will have economically, socially, and technologically, upon our American Society in the next score of years. Of especial interest are the author's prognostications on page 5. The report will help the management and systems man to "be prepared" for these dynamic changes in our culture. Write to the Center, Box 4068, Santa Barbara, Calif., for a free copy.

MULTI-USE OF AUTOMATIC DATA PROCESSING SYSTEMS, Task Force Report to the Interagency Committee on Automatic Data Processing, Washington 25, D. C.: U. S. Bureau of the Budget, July, 1958. 46 pp. and Appendices.

This report presents an excellent analysis of ". . . the part-time and intermittent use of someone else's ADP facilities and services," in the Federal Government. The report contains information of universal value. Prepared under the direction of John R. Prouan, it is one of a series of excellent IAC/ADP task force reports on various significant facets of ADP in the Federal establishment. Information as to the availability of copies of this document, or others of this series should be directed to William A. Gill, Chairman of the IAC/ADP, Bureau of the Budget, Washington 25, D. C.

Murphy, John S., **BASICS OF DIGITAL COMPUTERS,** Three Volumes, 116 West 14th St., N. Y. C. 11, New York: John F. Rider Publisher, Inc., 1958. ($7.50)

These three volumes can provide to the beginner

in the field of electronic data processing an easy method of learning some of the fundamentals of computer logic and theory. The text is written rather lucidly and the illustrations are excellent. This should be read by systems analysts who have the desire to improve their comprehension of the "nuts and bolts" aspects of computer machinery.

Nett, Robert and Stanley A. Hetzler, **AN INTRO-DUCTION TO ELECTRONIC DATA PROCESSING,** Chicago, Ill.: The Free Press of Glencoe, 1959. 287 pp.

A thorough, highly readable guide for the neophyte, explaining what EDP is, and how it works. Describes analog and digital computers and how they work; computer language, programming; computer applications; personnel organization for an EDP program; and, training for EDP. Also contains an Appendix which dscribes several EDP systems (Burroughs, IBM, ECR, Rem Rand) as of 1959. An excellent "introduction" to EDP.

Neuschel, Richard F., **WHAT TOP MANAGEMENT NEEDS TO KNOW ABOUT ELECTRONIC DATA PROCESSING,** N. Y. C., New York: McKinsey & Co. (date unknown). 10 pp.

This recent tract on computer choice by management contains some information of definite value to the harried executive. It describes the three types of pressure that will be put on the executive, the only three possible justifications for an electronic computer system, four common mistakes to be avoided, and five guidelines to use to test the applicability of computers to everyday business jobs. An item worth reading by the busy executive who wants to avoid pitfalls.

NEW METHODS FOR KNOWING, 590 Madison Ave., N. Y. C. 22, New York: International Business Machines Corporation, Form No. 500-0002. 50 pp.

Printed in large type and cleverly illustrated, this IBM educational publication traces the growth of electric accounting machine development from the days of Dr. Hollerith's use of holed cards for the 1890 census, to its use as auxiliary equipment for electronic computers. Contains excellent photographs of various machines. Write IBM for a free copy.

NEW VIEWS ON AUTOMATION, Papers Submitted to the Subcommittee on Automation and Energy Resources. Joint Economic Committee. Congress of the United States, 86th Congress, 2nd Session. 1960. 604 pp.

Contains views of individual specialists in Government, industry, banking, and labor developments in automation. Of particular interest are papers on the automation of Bank Operating Procedure with an excellent section on developing account numbering systems for EAM-EDP. Contributors include: Walter Buckingham, Vannevar Bush,

John Diebold, James P. Mitchell, Ralph J. Cordiner, A. R. Zipf, and Walter P. Reuther. A single copy usually can be obtained through your Congressman.

OCCUPATIONS IN ELECTRONIC DATA PROCESSING SYSTEMS, Washington 25, D. C.: U. S. Employment Service, Department of Labor. January, 1959. 44 pp. ($0.25)

Although geared to those concerned with recruitment, training, and counseling of persons in this field of EDP, this booklet will help anyone who needs to know what such people do. Occupational descriptions are given for 13 ADP specialties, including ones as coding clerk, computing analyst, programmer, systems analyst, and tape librarian. Can be gotten from the Superintendent of Documents, Government Printing Office, Washington 25, D. C.

OFFICE AUTOMATION AND EMPLOYEE JOB SECURITY, Hearings before the Subcommittee on Census and Government Statistics of the Committee on Post Office and Civil Service, House of Representatives, 86th Congress, 2nd Session. March 2 and 4, 1960. 89 pp.

A very good resume of some of the problems met by Federal Government agencies in establishing ADP. Testimony of both government officials and union representatives is included. Most interesting is the detailed human relations approach taken by the U. S. Veterans Administration in introducing ADP to its personnel. A single copy can usually be obtained through one's Congressman.

Phillips, Charles A., **COBOL,** Report to Conference on Data Systems Languages, Including Revised Specications for a Common Business Oriented Language for Programming Electronic Digital Computers, Washington 25, D. C.: U. S. Department of Defense. June, 1961.

This report details the second product from joint meetings of user (private and public) and manufacturer representatives, called to develop a common machine language, basically in English, oriented toward business data processing problems, open-ended and independent of any make or model of data processing equipment. Charles A. Phillips, Dept. of Defense, chaired this study group. The initial report was published in April, 1960. Write for a copy to the Superintendent of Documents, Printing Office, Washington 25, D. C.

PLANNING FOR AUTOMATIC DATA PROCESSING, Commodity Stabilization Service Operating Procedure, Washington 25, D. C.: U. S. Department of Agriculture, 1960.

This *Planning* document for ADP along with its connected publications on *Charting and Diagramming Symbols and Standards,* and *Automatic Data Processing Machine Management* were prepared under the direction of Carl Barnes of CSS. The theme of these booklets is that, "the successful use of ADP equipment depends basically on careful and systematic preliminary planning, review and analysis and on thorough evaluations of different data processing systems and procedures." Systems development as well as installation operations techniques are covered carefully. Write to the CSS for information on getting a copy of these manuals.

POCKET GUIDE — SELF-CONTACTING WIRE COMPLEMENTS, 213 East Grand Ave., S. San Francisco, Calif.: PWI — Panels, Wires, Inc., 1961. 10 pp.

As noted on the cover of the booklet itself, it is, "a handy guide to size and quantity of wires making standard fixed or manual self-contacting wire complements." Systems officers, aiding in setting up an EAM installation, will find this a useful reference for the ordering of panel board wires. An essential complement to one's library on punched card references.

Postley, John A., COMPUTERS AND PEOPLE — BUSINESS ACTIVITY IN THE NEW WORLD OF DATA PROCESSING, New York: McGraw-Hill Book Co., 1960. 246 pp.

Author's general assessment of the impact of the digital computer on day-to-day activities of ordinary people in business. Nine chapters cover relationships of computers to business activities, existing devices, survey and selection, new operating concepts, decision making, hardware developments, role of the manufacturers, transition problems, and future developments and applications.

PROBLEM-PLANNING AIDS, Magnetic Drum Data Processing Machine Type 650, Form 22-6220-0, 590 Madison Ave., N. Y. C. 22, New York: International Business Machines Corporation. 18 pp.

The main value of this booklet is the way it explains and illustrates rather effectively how to plan the program a problem for processing on a basic computer. The technique of the block diagram is also clearly described.

PROCEEDINGS OF THE LIFE OFFICE AUTOMATION FORUM, 1959, New York: Life Office Management Association, 1959. 404 pp.

Conference considered several aspects of office automation as organizing for automation rental versus purchase, automatic programming, and feasibility study as applied to the insurance industry. Systems analysts, specialists as well as generalists, should also see the proceedings of the Annual Conferences of the LOMA organization, such as the one which took place in Washington, D. C. in September, 1957.

Pyre, Magnus, AUTOMATION: ITS PURPOSE AND FUTURE, New York: Philosophical Library, 1957.

An assessment of what automation is taking place, what its purpose is, its effects, and future developments. Thirteen chapters covering automation in industrial work, the electronic computers, uses of automation in engineering, chemistry, the Petro-leum industry, accounting, transportation, machine shops, food and catering industries, guided missiles, and in translation. Also an analysis of automation's sociological impact.

Reinfeld, Nyles V. and William R. Vogel, MATHEMATICAL PROGRAMMING, Englewood Cliffs, N. J.: Prentice-Hall, Inc., 1958. 247 pp.

The major objective of this book, according to the authors, is to bridge the gap between the techniques of mathematical programming and their application to practical business problems. Fundamental techniques are explained so that readers lacking an extensive mathematical background can absorb them. Examples are given of their application to common business problems. The whole emphasis is on a practical approach to mathematical programming sacrificing some of the preciseness of the theoretical approach. The problem of obtaining management acceptance of mp is thoroughly discussed.

REPORT OF THE UNITED STATES GOVERNMENT DELEGATES TO A MEETING OF THE INTERNATIONAL LABOR ORGANIZATION. The Fifth Session of the Advisory Committee on Salaried Employees and Professional Workers. Cologne, Germany. November 23, December 4, 1959. 74 pp.

This report is particularly important as it includes the observations and conslusions of an international study committee on "The Effects of Mechanization and Automation in Offices." Governmental, employer, and worker representatives participated together in this study. Write for a copy to the Government Printing Office, Washington 25, D. C.

REPORT ON THE USE OF ELECTRONIC DATA PROCESSING EQUIPMENT IN THE FEDERAL GOVERNMENT, Hearings before the Subcommittee on Census and Government Statistics of the Committee on Post Office and Civil Service, House of Representatives, 86th Congress, 2nd Session. August 31, 1960. 113 pp.

A comprehensive analysis of the use of electronic computers in the Federal establishment. Includes recommendations on how to plan for ADP, best deal with personnel, and use the hardware most effectively. The magnitude of the manpower problem includes an analysis of changes in personnel requirements, recruitment, training, and employee job security. Brief descriptions of selected applications are discussed. A single copy can usually be gotten through one's Congressman.

Richards, R. K., ARITHMETICAL OPERATIONS IN DIGITAL COMPUTERS, New York: D. Van Nostrand Co., 1956. 384 pp.

Keeping in consonance with its title, this book includes five chapters of interest on arithmetical operation and controls. Chapter 4 features binary addition and subtraction; Chapter 5 reviews binary multiplication and division; Chapters 8 and 9 with decimal operation; and, Chapter 11 with computer organization and control.

Say, M. G., A. C. D. Haley, and W. E. Scott, editors, **ANALOGUE AND DIGITAL COMPUTERS**, New York: Philosophical Library, Inc., 1960. 308 pp.

This book, written by a panel of British specialists, presents the basic material on the design and application of both analog and digital computers. It is designed primarily for newcomers to the field. An excellent book for those readers with an engineering bent.

Shultz, George P. and Thomas L. Whisler, editors, **MANAGEMENT ORGANIZATION AND THE COMPUTER**, Chicago, Ill.: University of Chicago, 1960. 257 pp.

Proceedings of 11 papers by 14 contributors presented at a seminar on management organization and computers sponsored by the Graduate School of Business, University of Chicago and the McKinsey Foundation in February, 1959. Four parts: 1. "Information Technology and Management Organization"; 2. "Technical Developments and Their Use by Management"; 3. "Organization: Concepts and Problems"; and 4. "Information Technology: Experience in Five Companies". Also a selected bibliography.

Smith, Charles V. L., **ELECTRONIC DIGITAL COMPUTERS**, New York: McGraw-Hill Book Co., Inc., 1959. 443 pp.

This book offers fine reading for the systems analyst who wants to go further than the generalist into "the insides" of a computer. The various computer components are all discussed somewhat in detail. This is a hardware-oriented book rather than a systems one.

SOURCE DATA AUTOMATION EQUIPMENT GUIDE, Navy Management Office, Data Processing Systems Division, Department of the Navy, Washington 25, D. C.: U. S. Government Printing Office, March, 1961. 92 pp.

This booklet covers the basic features of various equipments now on the market which can be used to capture data at the source in machine language, which, in turn, can be used to operate other machines automatically. Sections are devoted to machines as: Automatic Typing Equipment, Transaction Recording Equipment. Optical Scanning - Character Recognition Equipment, Punched Tag (Ticket) Equipment, Card Punches (Manual), Embossing Equipment, and Intercouplers.

Stevens, Mary Elizabeth, **AUTOMATIC CHARACTER RECOGNITION**, A State-of-Art-Report, Technical Note 112, National Bureau of Standards, Washington 25, D. C.: U. S. Department of Commerce, May, 1961. 168 pp.

A very complete technical report describing the latest developments in Automatic Character Recognition devices, including MICR and OCR ones. Study based upon data gathered in 1957 survey of these devices for the Air Force, Rome Air Development Center and updated for purpose of this report. Areas of applicability and possibilities for controlled solutions to automatic character reading problems are discussed. Consideration is also given to some commonly used methods for character recognition, the steps involved in a generalized recognition process, and comparative characteristics of certain representative character recognition systems.

Discussed also, as noted here in a descending order of importance, are major factors affecting the feasibility or the cost of automatic character recognition: (1) Quality of input; (2) Size and nature of the vocabulary of characters to be recognized; (3) Carrier handling requirements; (4) Reliability requirements; and, (5) Flexibility in making adjustments to meet changing requirements. The book is complete with good illustrations and the bibliography is excellent. An excellent source document for those in management seeking a more than general knowledge of the subject. Write to the office of Technical Services, U. S. Department of Commerce, Washington 25, D. C., on details for getting a copy.

UNIVAC EDUCATIONAL SERIES, 315 Park Ave., South, N. Y. C. 10, New York: Remington Rand UNIVAC, Division of Sperry Rand, 1959.

Written in plain language, the booklets that make up this very good *UNIVAC Educational Series* are:

(1) *How the Computing System Works For You.* This booklet gives the reader an excellent introduction into the basics of electronic computers. 36 pp.

(2) *Programming a New Profession For You!* This booklet explains the four basic phases of the programmers work: Analysis, Application, Flow Charting, and Coding. 28 pp.

(3) *An Annotated Bibliography.* This booklet contains an excellent selection of articles and books in the area of electronic computers. 54 pp.

UNIVAC'S REAL "MACOY," 315 Park Ave., New York 10, New York: Remington Rand UNIVAC, Division of Sperry Rand, 1960. 12 pp.

The value of this little booklet lies in the guidelines it shows are so important when installing an electronic computer. MAnagement COntrol for You maps out excellent aids for scheduling and controlling (1) Programming, (2) Personnel Recruitment, (3) Personnel Training, (4) Site Preparation, and, (5) Delivery and Installation phases of a computer implementation plan. Contact your local UNIVAC office for a free copy.

USE OF ELECTRONIC DATA PROCESSING EQUIPMENT, Hearing before the Subcommittee on Census and Government Statistics of the Committee on Post Office and Civil Service, House of Representatives, 86th Congress, 1st Session, June 5, 1959. 142 pp.

A highly valuable document as it contains reprints of two comprehensive surveys made on ADP in the Federal Government. One, made by the General Accounting Office, reviews present and planned ADP systems. The second, made by Harry Fite of Lester B. Knight & Associates for the Bureau of the Budget, reports on an intensive survey made of personnel problems of the govrnment in ADP. A single copy can usually be gotten through one's Congressman.

Vazsonyi, Andrew, **SCIENTIFIC PROGRAMMING IN BUSINESS AND INDUSTRY,** New York: John Wiley & Sons, Inc., 1958. 474 pp.

A book aimed at businessmen who want to become acquainted with mathematical techniques for solving managerial problems. Thirteen chapters in three parts: 1. The fundamentals (what mathematical programming is and concept of mathematical model); 2. Mathematical Programming; and, 3. Programming in Production and Inventory Control.

Von Neumann, John, **THE COMPUTER AND THE BRAIN,** New Haven: Yale University Press, 1958. 82 pp.

Interesting reading for the systems man who would like to know more about the logical theory of computers and their relationship to the brain. This field of study is called Cybernetics. Dr. Von Neumann, a mathematician and theorist, was one of the first men of science to realize the possibilities of those electronic computing devices. Unfortunately, this book is not quite complete as it was begun and partially finished by the author during a period of great illness which eventually caused his death.

Wallace, Edward L., **MANAGEMENT INFLUENCE ON THE DESIGN OF DATA PROCESSING SYSTEMS: A CASE STUDY,** Division of Research, Graduate School of Business Administration, Harvard University, Boston, 1961. 259 pp.

The uniqueness of this research book is that it actually discusses an ADP failure, albeit an EAM installation. The case study is that of the Bremfort Company in Massachusetts seeking a method of meeting the problems associated with a growing business, high operating costs, and large unnecessary inventories. According to the findings of the author, failure of the first attempt to solve these problems with EAM were attributed to (1) Insufficient cooperation in the development of procedures, (2) Incomplete planning of procedures and the use of machines, and (3) Technical inadequacies of the equipment.

The study falls into five parts: the introduction, description of the company and its planning methods, a previous attempt by the company to mechanize its data processing which failed, a description of the system now planned, methods employed in planning and expected results, and finally, a cri-

tique of the company's plan. Highly recommended for systems and management people alike.

Wallace, Frank, **APPRAISING THE ECONOMICS OF ELECTRONIC COMPUTERS,** New York: Controllership Foundation, Inc., 1956. 104 pp.

The purpose of this research report is to develop in the reader a "common-sense business appraisal of computers". That is, the reader should be made aware of the detailed cost studies that should precede the installation of any electronic computing system. Flow charting, volume studies, and cost determinations should be used to select activities for the introduction of this high-speed and expensive electronic hardware. Installation and operations costs are also included in this book.

Weber, Philip H., **DETERMINING SALARIES FOR COMPUTER PERSONNEL,** 600 West Jackson Blvd., Chicago 6, Illinois: Research Bureau of MANAGEMENT And BUSINESS AUTOMATION, 1960. 106 pp.

Essentially, what this booklet does is to take existing techniques for determining position grade, salary, duty, and responsibility levels within an organization, and apply them to the newly created Electronic Data Processing job requirements. The author relies heavily on the assignment of numerical values to job factors to determine their total score and ultimate relationship to other positions in the structural hierarchy. Statistical data from a 1960 survey of computer positions and salaries by the publisher is also included to serve as a sort of benchmark to the reader looking for facts he can compare to his own projected computer positions and salaries.

WHAT EVERY BUSINESSMAN SHOULD KNOW ABOUT ELECTRONIC BRAINS, 315 Park Ave., South, N. Y. C. 10, New York: Remington Rand UNIVAC, 1960. 21 pp.

"Lightheartedly written with a serious purpose," this ADP glossary explains key terms, the understanding of which is so important to those desiring to learn about this new management tool. Defines 43 terms as access time, buffers, coding, control section, random access, subroutine. Write to Rem-Rand for your copy.

Wiener, Norbert, **CYBERNETICS,** New York: John Wiley & Sons, Inc., 1948. 194 pp.

The writer notes in his introduction that, "We have decided to call the entire field of control and communiction theory, whether in the machine or in the animal, by the name of *Cybernetics* . . ." He goes on to write, "that the modern ultra-rapid computing machine was in principle an ideal central nervous system to an apparatus for automatic control . . ." In essence then, Dr. Wiener points out in his book the relationship between brain and computer, and how machine "feedback" of information might be used to cause the machine to take further action. Gives the systems thinker the theory behind automatic control electronic devices.

Wilmot, Enoll de Burgh, editor, **GLOSSARY OF TERMS USED IN AUTOMATIC DATA PROCESSING,** 109-119 Waterloo Road, London, S.E. 1, United Kingdom: Business Publications, Ltd., 1960. 39 pp. (est. $1.00)

This excellent English ADP publication offers immediate access to 1,200 definitions and abbreviations used in business and scientific information processing. A definite asset to any systems man's professional library.

WORLD OF NUMBERS, 590 Madison Ave., N. Y. C. 22, New York: International Business Machines, Inc., 1958. 18 pp.

Explains in brief and simple terms of the growth of mathematics from primitive times to our modern era. Also shows the close relationship between mathematics and the logic of electronic computers. Key sections are "The Story of Numbers", "From Numbers to Mathematics", "Mathematical Machines", "Organization of Digital Computers". Write IBM for a free copy.

Wrubel, Marshal H., **A PRIMER OF PROGRAMMING FOR DIGITAL COMPUTERS,** New York: McGraw-Hill Book Co., Inc., 1959. 230 pp.

An introductory book on what problems computers can solve and how they can be programmed, with use of an IBM 650 for illustrations. Two parts: 1. "Elementary Programming" covering introduction to computer concepts, components and programming, loops and branches, flow diagrams, subroutines and program libraries, testing and automatic programming (incl. Fortran and Transit) ; and, 2. "Advanced Programming" covering machine language instructions and SOAP. Also glossary of terms.

YES, NO — ONE, ZERO, Esso Standard Oil Company, New York, 1958. 15 pp.

Prepared by ESSO for use by schoolteachers, this booklet can be a ready tool for the systems man to quickly teach himself the basics of the binary system or as an aid in any ADP course he may be leading himself. Several practical problems are given to solve in binary. A reading list cites further references about numbering systems and computers. The development through the history of various numbering systems is also covered in capsule form. Even the page numbers are in binary! Write to Esso Standard, 15 West 51st St., N. Y. C. 19, N. Y. for a free copy.

II. Information Sciences

Acer, John W., **BUSINESS GAMES: A SIMULATION TECHNIQUE,** Bureau of Labor and Management, Iowa City, Ia.: State University of Iowa, 1960. 48 pp.

In keeping with modern times this publication describes background classification, and uses of business games followed by an examination of several pertinent areas of discussion. Concludes with an evaluation of business games at a teaching tool and a prediction to their future. Worth looking into.

A COMPREHENSIVE BIBLIOGRAPHY ON OPERATIONS RESEARCH, New York: John Wiley & Sons, Inc., 1958. 188 pp.

Prepared under the direction of Russell L. Ackoff, Operations Research Group, Case Institute of Technology, more than 3,000 references have been carefully listed. It saim is to offer an immediate reference aid to operation-researchers. References are current through 1957.

American Management Association, **OPERATIONS RESEARCH — A BASIC APPROACH,** Special Report No. 13, New York, 1956. 111 pp.

Eight papers by different authors adapted from AMA's Finance Division orientation seminar on "Operations Research: A Basic Approach", January and March, 1956. The papers cover an introduction to OR in industry and applications on allocation of resources, product distribution, multiplant scheduling, aircraft maintenance and use in an Engineering Laboratory. Also a chapter on new developments and applications.

Andlinger, Gerhard R., et al, **OPERATIONS RESEARCH — CHALLENGE TO MODERN MANAGEMENT,** Boston, Mass.: Harvard University, 1954. 125 pp.

A student report of the Graduate School of Business Administration, Harvard University, written from a business management viewpoint to aid management in evaluating the potential of Operations Research in specific situations. The report covers the why of OR, its historical development, industrial applications, OR as related to consultants and management's role, OR methodology, and a look at the future of OR.

AN INTRODUCTION TO OPERATIONS RESEARCH AND UNIVAC DATA AUTOMATION SYSTEMS, 315 Park Ave., N. Y. C. 10, New York: Remington Rand UNIVAC, Division of Sperry Rand, 1958. 22 pp.

A good way to begin learning about Operations Research is by reading this booklet. Written in plain language, the reader learns first about OR, and then of its close relationship to computers. A good bibliography is also included. Write to Remington Rand UNIVAC for a free copy.

Batchelor, James H., **OPERATIONS RESEARCH: AN ANNOTATED BIBLIOGRAPHY,** St. Louis, Md.: St. Louis University Press, 1959. 866 pp.

Features an imposing source of 4,195 referenced articles and books on Operations Research. A useful addition to the library of any organization.

Beveridge, W. I. B., **THE ART OF SCIENTIFIC INVESTIGATION**, New York: W. W. Norton Co., 1951. 171 pp.

This volume presents an analysis of the methods by which discoveries have been made, in order to deduce and state simply as many guiding principles of research as possible. Among subjects treated are experimentation, chance, hypothesis, difficulties, strategy and the attributes of the successful scientist. This book can be very useful to the business executive seeking to gain an insight and understanding into the research process.

Branbury, J., and J. Maitland, editors, **PROCEEDINGS OF THE SECOND INTERNATIONAL CONFERENCE ON OPERATIONAL RESEARCH**, New York: John Wiley & Sons, Inc., 1961. 810 pp.

Consists of the proceedings of the Second International Conference on Operational Research in Aix-en-Provence, 1960. Each paper is either in English or French, and a translated abstract appears at the end. Part I consists of the main themes of the plenary sessions, covering methodological aspects, computers and OR, measurement of human factors, new mathematical models and methods of programming and invited papers of production and inventory control. Part II contains papers on industrial applications in the steel, oil, atomic, and electric power, mining and transport industries and to local government and the military. Included are also summaries from various discussion groups.

Bross, Irwin, D. F., **DESIGN FOR DECISION**, New York: The MacMillan Co., 1953. 276 pp.

One of the earlier significant books in bringing home the questions of statistical aids to administrative decision making. It is easy to read. A sampling of chapter headings include: History of Decision, Nature of Decision, Prediction, Probability, Values, Rules for Action, Operating a Decision Maker, Sequential Decision, Measurement, and Design for Decision.

Brown, Robert G., **STATISTICAL FORECASTING FOR INVENTORY CONTROL**, New York: McGraw-Hill Book Co., 1959. 223 pp.

This book will serve as a very practical primer on designing an economical, effective inventory control system. It emphasizes better routine short range forecasting with suggestions for adapting a program to specific needs. Includes several of the latest techniques. Theoretical development is given with a minimum of symbolic notation, and the beginning of each chapter develops the concepts in non-technical terms suitable for management.

Chorfas, Dimitris N., **OPERATIONS RESEARCH FOR INDUSTRIAL MANAGEMENT**, New York: Reinhold Publishing Corp., 1958. 303 pp.

An advanced book on Operations Research concepts in the reading of which some familiarity with mathematics is necessary for full comprehension. The author covers experimental models for business, simulation, game theory, research on management analysis, linear programming, matrix analysis, and flow techniques, with considerable illustration of mathematical model applications of the above to industrial management problems.

Churchman, C. West, R. L. Ackoff, and E. L. Arnoff, editors, **INTRODUCTION TO OPERATIONS RESEARCH**, New York: John Wiley & Sons, Inc., 1957. 655 pp.

Traces the early development of Operations Research from a World War II military technique to a modern tool of management. Probably the basic American text on this subject. Contributors were lecturers at Case Institute of Technology.

Churchman, C. West and M. Verhulst, editors, **MANAGEMENT SCIENCES, MODELS, AND TECHNIQUES**, 1960. 2 volumes.

An excellent source reference for the systems analyst to familiarize himself more fully with the Management Sciences. Contains papers presented at the Sixth International Meeting of the Institute of Management Sciences held in Paris during 1959. Included are papers on management economics, organization theory, Management games, computer systems, behavioral sciences, simulation research, and measurements in management.

Croxton, F. E. and D. J. Cowden, **APPLIED GENERAL STATISTICS**, Englewood Cliffs, N. J.: Prentice-Hall, Inc., 2nd Edition, 1955. 843 pp.

This book was especially designed for the reader with no previous work in statistics and who has had only high school mathematics. It is a very complete study in basic statistics and has a rather "symbol vocabulary" at the beginning of each chapter. It provides extensive material on sampling, correlations, time series, analysis of variance, and confidence limits of arithmetic means and of proportions. It also provides exceptional materials in 21 appendices, including 33 demonstrations of formulas and relationships.

Deming, W. Edwards, **SAMPLE DESIGN IN BUSINESS RESEARCH**, New York: John Wiley & Sons, 1960. 517 pp.

A simplified presentation of statistical methods in business and industry. The author is a distinguished consultant who has brought forth methods that achieve measurably accurate results with a minimum of complex computation. Not for those uninitiated in the field of statistics, however.

Flagle, Charles D., William H. Huggins, and Robert H. Roy, **OPERATIONS RESEARCH AND SYSTEMS ENGINEERING**, Baltimore, Md.: The Johns Hopkins Press, 1960.

Includes a comprehensive collection of articles on various facets of OR. Its main value is its rather complete coverage of OR itself, plus background areas as statistics, symbolic logic, etc.

Excellent treatment is also given to various areas of systems engineering as EDP, simulation techniques, information theory, and human engineering. This book is probably best for the OR practitioner seeking a good reference source when he needs to brush up on a phase of OR he is not completely familiar with, rather than for the tyro systems analyst seeking to learn something about Operations Research.

Garvin, Walter W., **INTRODUCTION TO LINEAR PROGRAMMING**, New York: McGraw-Hill Book Co., 1960. 281 pp.

Slightly above a basic presentation for the rank amateur, this "introduction" fills a gap between the literature on this subject for the novice and for the specialists. It sets forth, in good style, the theory of linear program as an extremely useful tool to get useful answers to practical problems. Flexibility in application is stressed.

Gass, Saul I., **LINEAR PROGRAMMING**, New York: McGraw-Hill Book Co., 1958. 219 pp.

This volume served as the first formal text in Linear Programming. It offers a basic presentation of the theoretical, computational, and applied areas for the student, research analyst, and other technical personnel. The author explains what linear programming is, what problems it can solve, and how to implement its techniques. The presentation starts with the necessary basic fundamentals and includes the more important theoretical and computational procedures.

Greene, Jay R. and Roger L. Sisson, **DYNAMIC MANAGEMENT DECISION GAMES**, New York: John Wiley & Sons, Inc., 1959. 84 pp.

Authors introduce concept of use of business decision games in business administration education and executive-development programs. The 7 games in the book do not require the use of computers. The book contains an introduction, 3 chapters on the value of games, how to construct them and direct and modify them. The remaining 7 chapters cover games on materials, inventory, personnel assignment, retailing, production scheduling, industrial sales, top operating management, and market negotiation. Also a bibliography.

Hertz, David B., **THE THEORY AND PRACTICE OF INDUSTRIAL RESEARCH**, New York: McGraw-Hill Book Co., Inc., 1950. 385 pp.

The basic them of this book is that, "While the techniques for managing the productive capacities of machines and processes have become increasingly dependable and predictive, methods for managing research activity are perhaps little more effective than they were in Liebig's laboratory in 1825." Dr. Hertz writes in an area which, until recently, has had only a minimal amount of attention. He traces within his book the historical development of scientific research, its close association with industry since the last century, and the need to organize the research function more

effectively. He concludes that, "Management must arrive at a sound policy with regard to project selection, and research administration must objectively scrutinize proposals and the progress of its work." This book can be also used as an educational device for gradually getting a feeling for Operations Research Problems. The field of research administration itself is one in which systems analysis will eventually serve more fully.

Hildebrand, F. B., **INTRODUCTION TO NUMERICAL ANALYSIS**, New York: McGraw-Hill Book Co., Inc., 1956. 511 pp.

An introduction to the fundamental processes of numerical analysis. Ten chapters providing coverage of basic operations of computation, approximation, interpolation, numerical differentiation and integration, numerical solution of equations, smoothing of data, numerical summation of series, and numerical solution of differential equations in appendices, provides a bibliography and a directory of methods covered.

Holt, C. C., J. F. Muth, F. Modigliani, and H. A. Simon, **PLANNING PRODUCTION, INVENTORIES, AND WORK FORCE**, Englewood Cliffs, N. J.: Prentice-Hall, Inc., 1960. 433 pp.

A presentation of applied mathematical analysis to unsolved industrial decision problems which results in practical solutions. The authors highlight the savings in time and money that are avaliable to modern managers if they will but take the trouble to improve their decisions involving production, inventories, and employing by utilizing the newer mathematical techniques.

Luce, R. Duncan and Howard Raiffa, **GAMES AND DECISIONS — INTRODUCTION AND CRITICAL SURVEY**, New York: John Wiley & Sons, Inc., 1957. 509 pp.

A study of the Behavioral Models Project, Bureau of Applied Social Research, Columbia University, Book covers the central concepts and results of game theory and related decision-making models, including chapters supplemented by eight appendices of more technical topics arising in other parts of the book. Also an extensive bibliography.

March, J. G. and H. A. Simon, **ORGANIZATIONS**, New York: John Wiley & Sons, 1958. 212 pp.

A very heavy book which, however, stimulates thinking and jolts the mind out of its habitual thought patterns. It is too much of a pioneering work, though, to contribute much of anything tangible that the executive can put to work for himself right off. Dealing with a scientific viewpoint, it may be shocking to some in its dehumanization of an area that is normally overabundant with humanization. It tries to find something in past and present management knowledge which can serve as demonstrated truth. It has a rather difficult time as it probes psychology and sociology for scientific principles. The book systematically summarizes organizational theories available today, and the theories are presented as hypotheses to be tested. There are very few formulas presented simply because of the lack of scientific evidence available to translate into mathematics. A 36-page bibliography is included.

McDonald, John, **STRATEGY IN POKER, BUSINESS, AND WAR,** New York: W. W. Norton & Co., Inc., 1950. 128 pp.

This excellent little book, cleverly illustrated by Robert Osborn, offers a pleasant way of beginning one's indoctrination into the practice of Operations Research. Specifically, the book discusses the Theory of Games, or as the author writes, "Although based on the mathematical theory of games, this book is rather an interpretation of the theory of rendering it." This book will be especially valuable to the systems expert or the administrator, who wants to be informed about the latest management techniques and theories, but who may lack either the time or educational equipment to tackle the basic work on this subject, *Theory of Games and Economic Behavior*, by the late mathematician John Von Neumann, and the economist Oskar Morgenstern.

McKean, Roland N., **EFFICIENCY IN GOVERNMENT THROUGH SYSTEMS ANALYSIS,** New York: John Wiley & Sons, Inc., 1958. 336 pp.

How can a decision-maker determine the one best course of action from a series of alternatives during a particular moment? This is the general theme of the book. The author answers this question in his book by discussing in detail certain analytical methods available to the systems analyst seeking facts *for* the decision-maker. These methods have universal application, in both business and in government.

Expectant readers from the business world should not be misled by the book's title. Although the author mentions government and water-resources as part of the book's title, the contents discuss analytical methods which are universal in scope and application. Two government case studies of water resources serve only as props for the application of analytical methods.

For the skimmer, Chapter 6 sums up the basic principles discussed in the book. Chapters 1 to 5 deal with the development of these analytical methods and their basic theory. Chapters 7 to 13 deal with their general application.

McKinsey, J. C. C., **INTRODUCTION TO THE THEORY OF GAMES,** New York: McGraw-Hill Book Co., 1952. 371 pp.

This is on of the first books to treat the mathematical theory of games of strategy. As distinguished from games of chance, games of strategy involve conflict among individuals or groups capable of rational activity. This volume, then, goes past probability to deal with the new domain in which mathematics are applied to the more complex problem of intelligence and behavior. Requires no mathematics beyond calculus.

Metzger, Robert W., **ELEMENTARY MATHEMATICAL PROGRAMMING,** New York: John Wiley & Sons, Inc., 1958.

The objective of this book is to transmit the essential ideas of linear programming to people of limited mathematical background. This aim is remarkably well achieved, though the reader should not expect his tour through the book to be effortless. The job is possible for those of ordinary attainment but is *not* a snap. The methods used are arithmetical and algebraic and are well and clearly explained. A fair recollection of elementary algebra is required and the notation employed in some instances requires some mathematical sophistication for ready comprehension.

Miller, David W. and Martin K. Starr, **EXECUTIVE DECISIONS AND OPERATIONS RESEARCH,** Englewood Cliffs, N. J.: Prentice-Hall, Inc., 1960. 446 pp.

Authors present Operations Research relationship to executive responsibility in terms of basic decision theory foundations. Four parts: 1. The Executive and Decisions (stresses relationship of executives to decision-making); 2. O.R. and Decisions; 3. Decision-Problem Paradigms; and 4. The Executive and Operations Research. Also a bibliography.

Mode, Elmer B., **ELEMENTS OF STATISTICS,** Englewood Cliffs, N. J.: Prentice-Hall, Inc., 3rd Edition, 1961. 336 pp.

The third edition of this very reputable and reliable volume brings information on the subject right up to the latest minute. It provides a modern exposition of the concepts and methods of statistics, with emphasis on statistical inference. A systematic treatment of the testing of hypothesis is presented, beginning with coin tossing and the binomial case. General updating of the material includes a separate chapter on probability, less emphasis on computing, and far greater coverage of meaning and interpretation.

Morse, Philip M. and George E. Kimball, **METHODS OF OPERATIONS RESEARCH,** New York: Technology Press of MIT and John Wiley & Sons, Inc., 1952. 158 pp.

"Operations research is a scientific method of providing executive departments with a quantitative basis for decisions regarding the operations under their control," state the authors in their Introduction. One of the early American books on OR, it is fruitful reading from the aspect of learning about what the subject is, and its early history. Several concrete applications are used as examples. The chapter on "Organizational and Procedural Problems" advises on how to begin an OR group.

OPERATIONS RESEARCH, Conference Board Reports Number 82. N. Y. C. 22, New York: National Industrial Conference Board, 1957. 20 pp.

This book approaches Operations Research from

the point of view of how it can be successfully applied to resolving business-type problems. Good reading for the non-technical person who wants to know more about this new and somewhat esoteric tool of management.

OPERATIONS RESEARCH ANALYST, Announcement No. 193B, Washington 25, D. C.: U. S. Civil Service Commission, 1959. 6 pp.

This brochure describes the duties and responsibilities for operations research analysts in the Federal Government which may be of value elsewhere.

"Operations Research Analysts (Operations Analysts) work on the solution of operational problems requiring advanced techniques based on the scientific methods of the above specialized fields. More specifically, the work involves such matters as the following:

1. The application of scientific methods of research and investigation leading to the solution of complex operating problems;

2. The development and use of analytical models (in the manner customary with the basic sciences) to represent the operation in terms of mathematical symbols, thereby helping to identify and define the parameters of the operation;

3. The design and analysis of experimental operations for the purpose of attaining insight into the behavior of actual operations;

4. The evaluation of proposed actions or systems (for example, military strategy and tactics, weapon systems, logistics systems) as a basis for predicting the effect of different courses of action;

5. Simulation of operations through mathematical techniques and conceptual models (often involving high-speed computers) to determine the probable results of the operations under variable conditions and environments;

6. The recommendation of actions to be taken by the responsible executive to improve the operations of the organization under his control;

7. The development of new techniques for accomplishing Operations Research. The research is accomplished by teams of scientists whose backgrounds represent several scientific disciplines from the areas of specilization indicated at the beginning of this announcement."

Sasieni, Maurice, Arthur Yaspan, and Lawrence Friedman, **OPERATIONS RESEARCH: METHODS AND PROCEDURES**, 440 - 4th Ave., New York, New York: John Wiley & Sons, Inc., 1959. 316 pp.

This book is intended to fill the important need for a practical textbook on the mathematical techniques of operations research. As such, it contains illustrative problems and exercises based upon material which has been used in courses in Case Institute of Technology. While the book is written for a person with a knowledge of calculus, it contains much useful information even for one with only a background in high school algebra. The increasing application of mathematical techniques in the general and administrative area of a business makes it imperative that all systems and procedures analysts become familiar with operations research methods and procedures. For one who can diligently apply himself in learning a new subject, this book is an invaluable aid.

Senensieb, Norbert Louis, **THE ROLE OF OPERATIONS RESEARCH IN BUSINESS**, Detroit, Mich.: International Systems and Procedures Association, May, 1961. 29 pp.

An excellent short publication on OR which is thoroughly documented. It discusses the origins, characteristics, and techniques of Operations Research and relates them to OR's role in business. Contains a very good bibliography.

Vance, Stanley, **MANAGEMENT SIMULATION**, New York: McGraw-Hill Book Co., 1960. 102 pp.

A practical device for the development of an intelligent and skilled management is provided by this book. The significance of simulation in the learning process is discussed and highlighted. Through a relatively simple simulation device, this Game combines theory and practice, art and science. The emphasis is on top level management decision-making, as opposed to localized or functional analysis. All computations can be worked out manually and for once, the reader does not need the assistance of high speed computers.

Vazsonyi, Andrew, **SCIENTIFIC PROGRAMMING IN BUSINESS AND INDUSTRY**, New York: John Wiley & Sons, 1958.

This book comes closer than most towards clearly communicating the concepts of linear programming to the business executive of limited mathematical background. Paradoxically clear and sometimes upsetting in its seeming contradictions, it is not recommended as light weekend reading for the average Systems person. However, for those of mathematical bent, or for those looking for the clearest insight they can hope to gain into the concepts of programming, this book will serve well. Its three sections are termed: Fundamentals, Mathematical Programming, and Programming in inventory control. The author admits that Inventory Control is not part of Programming.

Von Neumann, John, and Oskar Morgenstern, **THEORY OF GAMES AND ECONOMIC BEHAVIOR**, Princeton, N. J.: Princeton University Press, 1944. 625 pp.

This book may present heavy-going for the systems analyst unskilled in mathematics, yet it should at least be skimmed, for it is the foundation for the Modern Day Use of Game Theory to resolve difficult problems. Abetted by the electronic computer capable of making micro-second computations, the Theory of Games has become an important pillar for Operations Research. A standard edition of the original book was published in 1947.

Williams, John D., **THE COMPLETE STRATEGYST**, New York: McGraw-Hill Book Co., 1954. 234 pp.

An easy-reading explanation of the theory of games and how it may be applied to problems involving conflict situations that resemble games. Light and humorous, the author introduces the theory without using anything higher than high school arithmetic. Many worked-out examples show how the theory may be applied to situations ranging from checker to card games to business problems and military strategy.

III. Information Storage and Retrieval

AN INTRODUCTION TO INFORMATION RETRIEVAL, 112 East Pound Road, White Plains, New York: Data Processing Division, International Business Machines, Inc., 1960. 16 pp.

A basic IBM document on this rapidly developing tool of management. Of especial interest to the systems man will be a paragraph on page 11 telling "How to Start an Information Retrieval System". Encoding and operating considerations are also discussed.

BASIC MICROFILM INDEXING AND FILING TECHNIQUES, Mount Prospect, Ill.: Charles Bruning, Co., Inc., 1959. 20 pp.

This booklet emphasizes that, "the most important key to any successful indexing and filing system is planning." It then discusses major methods of filing microfilm, roll indexing, and locating the record in file. From this booklet the reader will get at least the fundamentals of filing and indexing microfilm records.

CORPORATE RECORDS RETENTION, Volume 1, 2 Park Ave., N. Y. C. 16, New York: Controllership Foundation, Inc., 1958. 242 pp.

This book is the first in a series of three guides to be published by the Controllership Foundation, Inc., on records retention. The first volume covers the legal requirements of the United States Federal Government and its agencies relating to records retention and limitation periods for action. Specific schedules and limitation requirements can be easily located in the book, and are presented in a concise manner. There are 27 sections in the book, each of which covers excerpts from statutes and regulations bearing on record keeping requirements. The sections cover various categories and industries under broad titles such as Taxation, Labor, Banking, Aircraft, and Drug. It is an excellent source and guide for ascertaining the retention schedule of records without extensive research.

DOCUMENTATION, INDEXING, AND RETRIEVAL OF SCIENTIFIC INFORMATION, A study of Federal and Non-Federal Science Information Processing and Retrieval Programs, prepared by the staff of the Committee of Government Operations, U. S.

Senate, 86th Congress, 2nd Session, June 1960. 283 pp.

This particular Congressional document should be especially interesting to the person who must research for scientific information. Basically, the document explains the latest trends in the development of information-gathering techniques in the U.S.A. Information Retrieval programs of the Atomic Energy Commission, Central Intelligence Agency, National Science Foundation, and other federal agencies are included. Here is an aide which will update readers on the latest techniques for scientific information retrieval. Some of these methods will be useful in other fields as well. Write to your Congressman to obtain a copy.

Hattery, Lowell H. and Edward M. McCormick, editors, **INFORMATION RETRIEVAL MANAGEMENT**, Detroit 26, Mich.: American Data Processing, Inc., 1962. Est. 175 pp.

The editors have collected and compiled into a very useful book the most significant papers presented as speeches at the Fourth Institute on Information Storage and Retrieval, the American University, Washington, D. C., February, 1962. Leading IR authorities discussed operating and theoretical knowledge of the role of information retrieval in an organization; the relationship between information and data processing; economic evaluation and financing; IR as a basic tool in a management control system; the operation of an information center; selection and training of personnel; and, other related topics. A compendium of the latest and most expert thinking on this new management tool.

Mitchell, William E., **RECORDS RETENTION**, 314 Newcastle Road, Syracuse 4, N. Y.: Ellsworth Publishing Co., 1959. 48 pp.

In the introduction to this book, Mr. Mitchell states "the main objective of this publication is to acquaint the reader with practical measures that can be taken to dispose of old business records." He has met this objective, particularly through his schedules on state tax records, ICC regulations, statutes of limitation, and a recommended retention schedule. As with other authors on the subject, Mr. Mitchell does not attempt to answer all questions. He does provide a "new" approach, however, and one worthy of attention. His book is recommended as a good source of information and suggestions on retention scheduling. It may serve a challenge to experienced records managers, for Mr. Mitchell's viewpoints differ from those stated in other recent literature.

Odell, M. K. and E. P. Strong, **RECORDS MANAGEMENT AND FILING OPERATIONS**, New York: McGraw-Hill Book Co., 1947, 342 pp.

This book has been a standard reference on the subject for many years. Emphasis is on management and the importance of proper administration and control of all paper and card records for an organization. The book shows how to plan and manage files for quick service to users, how to index records, how to control incoming correspondence, how to prepare operating manuals, how to index foreign names, and how to maintain centralized control of all types of filing records. It is an indispensable reference aid to Systems Departments in large companies.

Shera, James H., editor, **ADVANCES IN DOCUMENTATION AND LIBRARY,** New York: Interscience Publishers, Inc., 1957.

A good entre' into the field of Information Retrieval. Contains a volume on Information Systems in Documentation, edited under the direction of Professor Shera by G. L. Peakes, Allen Kent, and H. W. Perry.

Tomeski, Edward A., Richard W. Westcott, and Mary Covington, editors, **THE CLARIFICATION, UNIFICATION AND INTEGRATION OF INFORMATION STORAGE AND RETRIEVAL,** New York: Management Dynamics, 1961. 94 pp.

A set of eight technical papers presented at a symposium held at the Biltmore, New York City on February 23, 1961.

The subjects are: 1. Automated Intelligence Systems — Some Basic Problems and Prerequisites for their solution (H. P. Luhn); 2. Developments in Machine Literature Searching (J. H. Shera); 3. The Library of Congress Looks at Mechanization of Information Retrieval — Some Recent Contributions (C. K. Schultz); 5. Research in Automatic Syntactic Analysis (V. E. Giuliano); 6. Information Retrieval by Digital Computer — Reality or Myth (A. Opler); 7. The Researcher and Information Storage and Retrieval (E. M. McCormick); and, 8. Automatic Indexing and Abstracting of Natural Languages (L. C. Ray).

Weres, Bertha M., **HOW TO FILE AND INDEX,** New York: Ronald Press Co., 1956. 306 pp.

Simplified, step by step approach to teaching the basics of filing. It explains the fundamental principles which are the key to all filing problems. It also covers thoroughly the important details of practical application to a particular business or department. Numerous illustrations and examples are provided to aid in the development of filing methods and procedures. A good aid to the training of Systems people.

IV. Supplementary Management References

American Management Association, **THE CHANGING DIMENSIONS OF OFFICE-MANAGEMENT — TECHNICAL AND MANAGERIAL TRENDS IN ADMINISTRATIVE OPERATIONS,** Management Report No. 41, New York, 1960. 159 pp.

A series of twenty-five papers presented by an equal number of authors at AMA's 1959 Annual Office Management Conference discuss individual subjects ranging from Automation to Operations Research. The papers are brief, accurate, and lucid, giving valuable indications of the new tools available for administrative operations, in a style that generalist and specialist will both appreciate.

Anshen, Melvin and George Leland, editors, **MANAGEMENT AND CORPORATIONS, 1985,** New York: McGraw-Hill Book Co., 1960. 253 pp.

At a symposium at the Carnegie Institute of Technology, fifteen distinguished leaders from business, law, education, the social sciences, religion, and philosophy contributed papers and participated in the discussions that form the contents of this book. The entire book reflects the principal theme of the symposium — the necessity for corporations and managers to adapt during the next quarter century to major changes in their environments. Problems concerning the future functions and relationships of business management are discussed. Systems people will be especially interested in chapters dealing with the requirements, skills, and attitudes of managers in their co-existence with the "thinking" machines of the 1980's. How will traditional business patterns be affected, particularly in the face of trends towards trans- and supra-national groupings?

A QUICK REFERENCE GUIDE TO IBM PUNCHED CARD DATA PROCESSING EQUIPMENT, 112 East Post Road, White Plains, N. Y.: International Business Machines, Inc., 1960. 14 pp.

As the title indicates, the purpose of this booklet is to provide a concise directory to IBM punched card machines. Only major characteristics are shown. Particularly informative are the definitions which describe the functions of individual pieces of equipment.

Beer, Stafford, **CYBERNETICS AND MANAGEMENT,** New York: John Wiley & Sons, 1959. 214 pp.

Presents the basic principles of the scientific study of the nature of control. Explains the main terms with a minimum of mathematics. Although it is unlikely that the book will be read and understood in the course of a weekend reading by the neophyte, it is nevertheless one of the more lucid treatments on the basic subject.

Cabell, R. W. and A. Phillips, **PROBLEMS IN BASIC OPERATIONS RESEARCH METHODS FOR MANAGEMENT,** New York: John Wiley & Sons, 1961. 110 pp.

This book presents a more complete understanding of the value of operations research by examining and discussing a wide selection of problems. There is an introduction to the subject, and discussion of problems in such areas as mathematical programming, inventory models, queing, Monte Carlo analysis, sequencing models, design of experiments, and analysis of variance.

Churchman, C. West, **PREDICTION AND OPTIMAL DECISION,** Englewood Cliffs, N. J.: Prentice-Hall, Inc., 1961. 394 pp.

This volume is concerned with the relationship

between problems of value and problems of fact. Specifically, it regards the question as to whether "science" can verify recommendations to managers, and if so, in what way. It discusses the extent to which the scientist can go in assisting the executive in making decisions. Illustrations are drawn from the social sciences, management sciences, and operations research. Technicalities have been kept minimal and are mostly in chapter appendices. Essential ideas are distilled from their technical content but kept intact.

COMPUTER USE REPORT (2nd Printing 1959), 8 pages, List Price $1.50, Member Price $0.75.

This publication gives specific figures on the use of electronic data processing equipment in three major categories. It clearly identifies the acceptance of EDP equipment in 14 named applications. Reasons, opinions, savings and computers used are statistically reported on applications accepted. Over a dozen reasons are listed on EDP equipment rejected on 14 applications as well as five stages at which rejection occurred. Figures from 20 different industries showing acceptance or rejection of EDP for use in the 14 applications are also included.

COMPUTING REVIEWS, Published bi-monthly, 14 East 69th St., N. Y. C. 21, New York: The Association for Computing Machinery.

Summed up, the magazine "aims to furnish computer-oriented persons in mathematics, engineering, the natural and social sciences, the humanities, and other areas with critical information about all current publications in any area of computer sciences."

DATA PROCESSING DIGEST, Published monthly, 1140 South Robertson Blvd., Los Angeles 35, California: Canning, Sisson, and Associates, Inc.

This digest covers articles on ADP and management sciences appearing in books and magazines. It also keeps the reader abreast of meetings in the field as well as the latest developments in training ADP'ers. Coverage includes foreign publications.

Evan, Arthur D., **ENGINEERING DATA PROCESSING SYSTEM DESIGN**, New York: D. Van Nostrand Co., 1960. 282 pp.

Presents the first comprehensive written coverage of mechanization possibilities in that area of the engineering department which deals with drawings, engineering parts lists, and allies documentation. It will serve as an authoritative guide in converting a manual system to a mechanized one. Further possibilities of automation through the use of electronic equipment is explored.

Gillespie, Cecil, **ACCOUNTING SYSTEMS, PROCEDURES, AND METHODS**, 2nd Edition, Englewood Cliffs, N. J.: Prentice-Hall, Inc., 1961. 641 pp.

Probably the most widely read book on accounting systems analysis and design. Explains thoroughly

how a survey is made and a new accounting system designed. After describing how the character of systems work is changing, the book goes on to demonstrate what (manufacturing) management gets from each of its procedures and how these procedures work in today's accounting. Up-to-date information on electronic data processing, punched card accounting, and cost accounting is included.

Knox, Frank M., **INTEGRATED COST CONTROL IN THE OFFICE**, NOMA Series in Office Management, New York: McGraw-Hill Book Co., Inc., 1958. 293 pp.

Well known for his work in all areas of forms management, the author in this book shows how the supervisor can apply recognized office work improvement techniques as forms, methods and procedures, clerical work measurement, work simplification, office automation, and records control to reach a fully integrated cost control system in an office environment. He also is careful to stress that the final success of any program rests on human relationships rather than on the application of specific techniques.

Lazarro, Victor, editor, **SYSTEMS & PROCEDURES, A HANDBOOK FOR BUSINESS AND INDUSTRY**, Englewood Cliffs, N. J.: Prentice-Hall, Inc., 1959. 464 pp.

Excellent source book with chapters by well-known practitioners in systems analysis, on concepts, charting, auditing, work simplification, work measurement, forms control, records management, budget, tab equipment, ADPS, research, and selecting and training of systems men. Contributors include: William A. Gill, Richard Pomeroy, Richard Neumaier, Gibbs Myers, William Buhl, David Hertz, and Elles Derby.

Malcom, Donald G. and Alan J. Rowe, editors, **MANAGEMENT CONTROL SYSTEMS**, 440 Fourth Ave., N. Y. C. 16, New York: John Wiley & Sons, Inc., 1960. 375 pp.

Prepared by the editors under the general direction of Lorimer F. McConnell, the modern-day book on systems is founded upon the symposium on management and control systems held at the Systems Development Corporation in Santa Monica, California in July, 1959. The book presents the latest thinking of experts researching in the theory of management control systems. Particular emphasis has been put upon the application of modern electronic computing techniques to present-day business applications. Participants in the symposium included Joseph E. Flanagan, Norman J. Ream, Robert H. Gregory, Alan O. Mann, Roger L. Sisson, R. Clay Sprowls, William W. Parsons, and M. O. Kappler.

Mann, Floyd C. and L. Richard Hoffman, **AUTOMATION AND THE WORKER: A STUDY OF SOCIAL CHANGE IN POWER PLANTS**, New York: Henry Holt and Company, 1960. 272 pp.

A highly informative study of the effect of automation on power plants carried out by the staff of the Survey Research Center of the University of Michigan. Its approach is perhaps a little more from the humanistic aspect of the human relations expert than from the organizational study approach of the systems analyst. But, it is superb reading for anyone desiring a comprehension of the human problems involved in Automation. Of especial value are the questionnaires used in the survey, found in the rear of the book. They can give the reader a good inkling to what problems he must face when installing Automation.

Milward, George E., editor, **ORGANIZATION AND METHODS**, New York: St. Martin's Press, Inc., 1959. 408 pp.

This is both an introduction into the field of systems and procedures (O & M) and a reference source for the veteran analyst. Included is a unique chart on the Field of Office Machinery, which shows diagrammatically the seven basic clerical operations and the machines existing to serve them. An all-purpose addition to systems literature which covers such S & P "basics" as: work simplification, forms (equipment & methods), office machinery, the assignment (survey techniques), office work measurement, the management of O & M work and organization.

Neuschel, Richard F., **MANAGEMENT BY SYSTEM**, New York: McGraw-Hill Book Co., Inc., 1960. 359 pp. ($7.50)

A comprehensive revision and updating of his early classic, "Streamlining Business Procedures". New chapters are included on the subjects of integrated management reporting systems, conducting computer feasibility studies, and IDP concepts and applications. The remining material has the role of procedures in mgt., organizing for procedures improvement, top-management approach to S & P, administering the S & P effort, etc. "Must" reading for anyone interested in becoming "a broad-gauged administrative analyst and problem solver".

Neuschel, Richard F., **STREAMLINING BUSINESS PROCEDURES**, New York: McGraw-Hill Book Co., 1950. 324 pp.

A "systems classic." Serves as an excellent "introduction" to, or "refresher" in, S & P as a discipline. Consists of two major parts: the first explains the role of "procedures research as a tool of top management" — describes the benefits of systems work, how an S & P program can be planned and carried out. The second section provides a comprehensive indoctrination in the "systems" approach to analysis and improvement, by taking the reader through the survey techniques, step by step: Planning the project, gathering and analyzing facts; developing and selling recommendations, installing the procedures, developing S & P manuals.

NONCONVENTIONAL TECHNICAL INFORMATION SYSTEMS IN CURRENT USE, No. 2, Washington 25,

D. C.: National Science Foundation, September, 1959. 66 pp.

This report describes technical information systems currently in operation which embody new principles for the organization of subject matter or employment of automatic equipment for storage and search. Three broad categories deal with systems that (1) store references, (2) store data, and (3) prepare indexes. A supplement issued in March, 1960, plus the basic document can be ordered from the U. S. Government Printing Office, Washington 25, D. C. for $0.25 and $0.30 respectively.

Optner, Stanford L., **SYSTEMS ANALYSIS FOR BUSINESS MANAGEMENT**, Englewood Cliffs, N. J.: Prentice-Hall, Inc., 1960. 268 pp.

A "must" for anyone seriously interested in S & P as a "scientific" discipline. The author proposes a "general systems theory", in terms understandable to any intelligent reader. Contains some useful "how-to" guides — e.g., checklists and outlines on setting up a systems assignment and conducting a feasibility study. An evaluation of several EDP systems, as of mid-1960, is also included. Exhaustive case studies, which provide stimulating "mental exercise," are included.

PAPERS DEVELOPED IN THE AREA OF SYSTEMS ANALYSIS, SP-1 to SP-167, Santa Monica, Calif.: Systems Development Corp., 1961.

A new non-profit organization developed to improve systems analysis techniques. Papers developed so far include "Space Analysis for Management", Richard M. Greene, Jr.; "A Bibliography on the Use of Simulation in Management Analysis", D. G. Malcolm; and "Modeling Considerations in Computer Simulation of Management Control Systems", Alan J. Rowe. Write to SDC for more details as to the availability of their publications to the general public.

PERT INSTRUCTION MANUAL AND SYSTEMS AND PROCEDURES FOR THE PROGRAM EVALUATION SYSTEM, Special Projects Office, Bureau of Naval Weapons, Department of the Navy, Washington 25, D. C.: U. S. Government Printing Office, 1960. ($0.15)

The United States Navy has come up with an unusual and highly advanced system for programming the progress of many of its scheduled production line items. First developed for the POLARIS submarine, the system called PERT, or *Program Evaluation Review Technique*, utilizes electronic data processing computers to assist the system to come up with estimates of the progress of a certain job. It is a management control tool that sizes up the reasonableness of plans and schedules, and figures progress and the possibilities for getting jobs done by deadline times. PERT uses TIME as a common factor to reflect three categories of denominators that affect success . . . TIME, resource applications, and required performance specifications. For further information about the reports issued to date by the Navy (8), contact the Superintendent of Documents, U. S. Government Printing Office.

Place, Irene, ADMINISTRATIVE SYSTEMS ANALYSIS, Ann Arbor, Mich.: Bureau of Business Research, School of Business Administration, University of Michigan, 1957. 83 pp.

Dr. Place has introduced into her book some very excellent material on what the systems and procedures profession is supposed to be. She describes what systems analysis is, shows how a systems department serves an organization, gives examples of some specifications for systems analyst job descriptions, and sets down in print the educational requirements for a successful systems man. Facts to support the conclusions found in this book were based on visitations to systems shops for interviews with systems practitioners. A good tool to be used by anyone planning to establish a systems organization.

Simon, Herbert A., MODELS OF MAN: SOCIAL AND RATIONAL, New York: John Wiley & Sons, 1957. 287 pp.

A series of "mathematical essays" designed to set forth a consistent body of theory of the rational and nonrational aspects of human behavior in a social setting. The essays are arranged in four groups: (1) essays concerned with *interpersonal influence* and the underlying concept of causation required for the operational definition of influence; (2) essays concerned with *interaction processes* in social groups; (3) essays concerned with *"the decision to belong"*; (4) essays concerned with the nature of *human rationality*, and the interaction of rational and nonrational in human decision-making. Not light reading.

Simon, Herbert A., THE NEW SCIENCE OF MANAGEMENT DECISION, New York: Harper & Brothers, 1961.

This excellent book provides "a terrain map of the revolution now being shaped by new instruments of management". The author, with remarkable clarity and unique insight, describes how new knowledge gained from automatic processes can be applied to unraveling significant mysteries of man's mind. The future business organization is pictured as a complex man-machine system in which men collaborate with computing machines in processing information and making decisions.

THE SYSTEMS MAN AND EDP, Detroit, Mich.: Systems and Procedures Association, 1st printing 1960, 8 pages, List Price $2.50, Member Price $1.25.

The booklet reports on the impact of the computer in the firms represented by SPA membership, and the effect of a computer installation on the individual systems and systems department. Figures record statistically percent of total period the systems man was associated with feasibility study, and percent of time spent after EDP system was in operation. Equipment manufacturers contacted and number of contacts made is tabulated by 15 EDP manufacturers.

Thurston, Philip H., SYSTEMS AND PROCEDURES RESPONSIBILITY, Boston, Mass.: Division of Research, Graduate School of Business Administration, Harvard University, 1959. 110 pp.

Dr. Thurston, "In developing his conclusions . . . has necessarily described and analyzed the beliefs entertained by both line and staff men (operators and specialists) regarding their part in procedures work." The main contribution of this book to management literature is its analysis of various methods of effecting change in an organization. The final approach of several possible ones found best was to use the ". . . technical ability of the systems analyst plus his broader view of systems combined with the operating knowledge of the supervisor . . ." A book that should be in every systems man's personal library.

Weik, Martin H., A THIRD SURVEY OF DOMESTIC ELECTRONIC DIGITAL COMPUTING SYSTEMS, Report No. 1115, Aberdeen Proving Ground, Md.: Ballistic Research Laboratories, Ordnance Corps, Department of the Army, March 1961. 1,131 pp.

This document is "a must" for any systems library. Included within this 2½" thick tome are detailed specifications, examples of applications, and other factual data about computing systems used within the Federal Government. If past practice is followed, a commercial copy may be made available to the general public through the Office of Technical Services, U. S. Department of Commerce, Washington 25, D. C.

Author Index